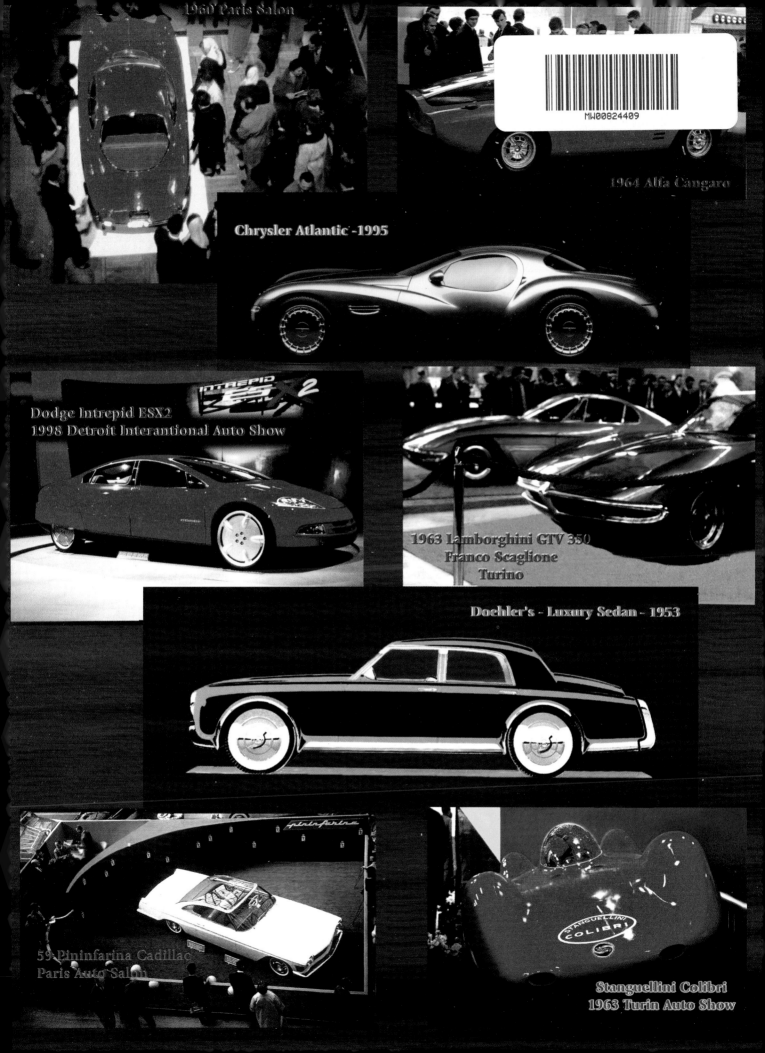

1960 Paris Salon

1964 Alfa Cangaro

Chrysler Atlantic - 1995

Dodge Intrepid ESX2
1998 Detroit Interantional Auto Show

INTREPID ESX2

1963 Lamborghini GTV 350
Franco Scaglione
Turino

Doehler's - Luxury Sedan - 1953

59 Pininfarina Cadillac
Paris Auto Salon

Stanguellini Colibri
1963 Turin Auto Show

Automobile
Design Techniques
AND DESIGN MODELING

**The Men
The Methods
And The Materials**

By Frederick E. Hoadley

Brougham -1890

Oldsmobile Proposal 1940 - Author

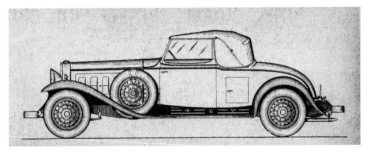

Locomobile Cabriolet - 1919

Horch V8:
1939 - Berlin Motor Show

Cadillac - 1930

Packard LeBaron Custom Phaeton - 1934

Mercedes - Benz T80 Record Car - 1939
Technische Hochschule, Stuttgart, Germany, 1962

Adler Sportwagen - 1935

Rust Heinz - 1938, Detroit Auto Show, 1976

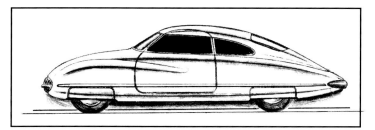

Aerocoupe 1950 - Robert H. Doehler

Grand Turismo 1954 - Author

Continental Proposal 1949 - Gil Spear

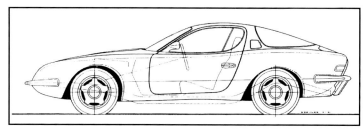

Avanti Coupe 1991 - Robert H Doehler

Chrysler K-310 Virgil M. Exner Sr.
S.A.E. Anual Meeting - 1952

Debonaire 1957 - Wesley P. Dahlberg

Mercedes-Benz W196 - 1954

Ford Contour - 1991

X-Turbo Coupe 1954 - Author

Maserati 3200 GT, 1999 - Giugiaro

Automobile Design Techniques and Design Modeling

The Men, The Methods and The Materials

Frederick E. Hoadley

Published by TAH Productions
Subsidiary of Hoadley Associates, Inc.
P.O. Box 2583, Dearborn, MI 48123, U.S.A.

TAH Productions

P.O. Box 2583
Dearborn, Michigan 48123
www.TAHProductions.com
www.HoadleyAssociatesInc.com

Editor-Timothy A. Hoadley
Assistant Editor-Jamie J. Becker

Printed By: Sheridan Books, Ann Arbor, Michigan

ISBN 0-9667673-0-6

PCIP
TL15.H63 1998   629.2'31
                      QB198-1529

Dedicated:

To -

Paul F. O'Neil

President, Chavant, Inc.

Who encouraged me to write this book, also

To -

the hundreds of unproclaimed Stylists, Design

Engineers, Design Modelers, and Fabrication

Craftsmen who contributed of their time and

talent to the appearance, line and form of

the motorcar, and

To -

all the suppliers who supported the design

profession and helped to change design dreams

into realities.

ACKNOWLEDGMENTS

This book has had input from a number of experienced designers, modelers, and skilled people in other professions. My indebtedness and thanks for the help and criticism from these friends and associates must be recognized.

David R. Crippen, has been most helpful with the historical section of the book. Martin Zane Skalski, recommended changes for improved presentation of the subject. Tom Beaubien, has supplied the West Coast resource list and has supported this effort in many other ways. Tom Stone, continues to aid me with working knowledge of the advanced CAD and computer 3-D modeling techniques. Jake Free, has contributed a considerable amount of processing information in the preparation of styling clay surface and the making of molds and casts. Thomas W. Quintal, has supplied information concerning materials and their uses. My brother, Howard W. Hoadley, technical writer, and author, edited the final draft and made recommendations for chapter content and format.

In addition, I have received information and advice concerning tools, fixtures and CMMs from Al Lamerson and his son, Ron Lamerson, Lamerson, U.S.A.; Gene Perry, Norton Equipment Corporation; Diane Hodges, Tarus Products Inc.; and Enzo Bruni, Brown & Sharp DEA.

Furthermore, information was recieved from Bob Lacovara, Composites Fabrication; Ray Kaligian, United States Gypsum Co.; and from Jack North, Chavant, Inc. Selected portions of this book (Automobile Design Techniques and Design Modeling) have been included in a pamphlet published by Jack North for use by Chavant.

The manuscript was reviewed by: Joseph J. Farrer, John Cline, and Stephen Stringer. A critical review of the draft was also made by Dennis F. Otto, Romeyn S. Hammond, Wesley P. Dahlberg, Joseph Papai and Samuel R. Wiley. Special appreciation goes to my long time friend Arthur B. Morrill, Jr., for editorial assistance and criticism of earlier drafts.

Acknowledgment in the review of the manuscript is also due: Michael Lamm, automotive writer, author, and publisher; Paul Shiloff, artist, sculptor, master modeler, and for twenty five years college level design modeling instructor; Gale L. Halderman, Ford Motor Company, for the Foreword to this book and to Jim and Cheryl Farrell, automotive writers and publishers.

Photographs came from many sources in addition to those from the authors personal collection and from the Hoadley Associates files. Ronald C. Hill, Industrial Design Department, and Diane Reed Semckem, Public Relations, supplied photographs from Art Center College of Design. Carl Olsen, Transportation Design, Center for Creative Studies, provided photographs from students in his department. I obtained photographs from the Archives of Henry Ford Museum and Greenfield Village, Ford Public Relations file, Auburn-Cord-Duesenberg Museum's published photographs, and historical photographs from the Oldsmobile History Center courtesy of Helen J. Earley. Other photographs came from Dennis Otto, Jake Free, Tom Stone, and Al and Ron Lamerson. In addition, there are reproductions from the Robert H. Doehler collection.

I received many important historical photographs from Floyd Joliet, GM photographic historian, through the good will of Charles Jordan, General Motors Design. Mary Maxwell, Ford Design Center, provided some very special photographs with the consent of Ford Design Chief, Jack Telnack. Also I received photographs from Jack Wildman and Brad Zribleman, with consideration from Chrysler Design.

My son, Timothy A. Hoadley, TAH Productions and Christian Television Network, WLPC, Channel 26, Detroit, Michigan, took many of the photographs, processed the pictures into a format useful for publication, and directed the publication of the book. Jamie Becker prepared the digital pages for electronic publishing and enhanced and corrected the photographs, drawings and charts and created the graphics art.

Finalizing plans for publishing and marketing was given support by Beverly D. Papai, The Farmington Community Library, Farmington Hills, Michigan.

And finally, the most appreciated thanks must go to my wife, Mary Louise Hoadley, for the continual word processing task of adding, changing, adding, changing, adding....to the eventual end.

Frederick E. Hoadley

PART THREE

ADDENDUM

SIDEBARS

Foreword

G. L. Halderman
Director
North American Design

Ford Motor Company
21175 Oakwood Boulevard
Dearborn, Michigan 48123

This book presents a comprehensive study of design modeling techniques; beginning with the early years, advancing to the procedures of today, and forecasting the expectations of tomorrow. Mr. Hoadley is eminently qualified to present his views regarding the design process, as he has been a major contributor to its evolution.

The process of design has changed considerably during the period covered in this book. The importance of the clay model and its ability to convert the designer's thoughts, ideas and sketches into three dimensional images is thoroughly discussed. Computers and clay surface milling machines have increased accuracy and shortened time required while eliminating the guesswork.

The use of Computer Aided Industrial Design Systems (CAID) will further expand the designers ability to evaluate proposals quickly and enable him to efficiently modify his designs.

As a designer with Ford Motor Company for forty years, I have had the opportunity to participate in the development of the first Mustang and I also contributed to the design of the Thunderbird, Ford, Mercury, Lincoln and Mark programs during these years. It has been my pleasure to observe first hand the many changes in the design process through these years and the reading of Fred Hoadley's book recalled to mind many fond memories.

I highly recommend this book to anyone interested in the design and model fabricating process.

G. L. Halderman

INTRODUCTION

Styling Clay Models

The year 1996 marked the centennial of the American automobile industry. One hundred years earlier, Charles Duryea and his brother Frank perfected their 'motorwagon' and built and sold a series of thirteen of these vehicles. This was the year after Charles Duryea won the first American automobile road race on a snowy Thanksgiving day in Chicago, Illinois. In this 54 mile road race, he beat European production automobiles and many other experimental American vehicles at an average speed of 8 miles per hour, including stops for repairs.

As other automobile companies entered the marketplace and the automobile became more dependable, greater emphasis was placed on appearance. Since early in this century, styling clay has played a major role in the surface design of automobile bodies. Styling clay models continue to play this important role because of the clay's inherent qualities not found in other materials. Neither can these three dimensional clay surface developments be replaced by computer generated visual interpretations. This includes holography, although it is three dimensional, it is an image and not easily adjusted or tuned as takes place on a styling clay model.

Styling clay is a very special material used in many areas of industrial design. Styling clay is not modeling clay, children's clay, plasteline, nor water clay or slip; it is a wax and oil based hard clay. It is shaped by hand when warm and soft, but must be carved with steel tools when cool and hard.

1896 Duryea - This is the only vehicle that remains from the original thirteen built and sold in 1896.

The term modeling is a popular term used in a wide range of applications. Design modeling or simply clay modeling is the process used in the development of industrial design models. It is sometimes referred to as sculpturing but that term really does not adequately apply to this process. Sculpturing is a part of the process but refers to the more artistic area of model development. Although design models may be constructed from various materials, this book is principally concerned with models constructed from styling clay. The task for their construction calls for not only skilled artisans but persons with artistic talent who understand line, form, highlight and proportion. It also requires persons who can read engineering drawings and surface drawings, and who can interpret a design sketch into a three-dimensional model. Today, a part of the design modeler's task includes operating computer aided industrial design (CAID) equipment and programs necessary to scan, process, and mill model surfaces.

1915 Studebaker Seven-Passenger Limousine. An early example of a closed passenger car.

1938 Lincoln Zephyr The first passenger automobile with a low grill.

Model Development

The influence of industrial design is well established and reaches into all areas of our lives. Using various two-dimensional presentation mediums, designers propose the design of articles through the creation of aesthetically pleasing line, form, style, color and functional ideas. In their development, many of these articles require the interpretation of proposals into three-dimensional models. The individual developing these models may be the designer or a person or persons working under the direction of the designer.

Styling clay is the principle construction material used to quickly translate many two-dimensional proposals into three-dimensional models. However, there are only a few design schools that teach modeling and normally it is taught only as a part of the school's design curriculum. Because of this, many design modelers learn the profession through on-the-job-training. Experience in allied arts and crafts, or other types of model building is also useful as a background when learning to sculpture design models from styling clay.

At the present time, more individuals and studios are using styling clay than ever before. Many more wish to use it but lack training and experience.

1963 Studebaker Avanti The first production automobile
designed to have the belt line rising toward the rear.

Why Design Models Are Needed

Computer specialists and companies developing new CAID systems have stated that their new systems will replace styling clay models. These statements are misleading. In an automobile design studio literally hundreds of sketches are made by designers in search of a new theme, or on variations of a theme, or on details. Many of these sketches may be further developed, evaluated, and tuned using one of the advanced CAID systems. Such full size

1992 General Motors Ultralite. A concept automobile of the future. EPA fuel economy - 45 city, 81 highway; 4 passengers, 110" wheelbase, 7.8 seconds 0 - 60 MPH, 135 MPH Top Speed.

studies do replace styling clay models, along with full size illustrations and tape drawings (or black board drawings), previously made for the same purpose. However, no matter how elaborate and photo realistic the CAID system is, three-dimensional models will always be required for final tuning and to sell a design. Also, several models are usually presented together and then modified and reshown with new proposals and competition vehicles.

Designers are usually artists and idea people who may not have the time, talent, or inclination to check and fine tune surface on a CAID system. This work is normally done by design modelers in three dimensions on a styling clay model. Designers may, however, develop a theme design through a CAID system with the aid of virtual reality (VR), high-definition television (HDTV) monitors or projection systems, or holograms. These systems are essentially presentation mediums and are used to 'blow up' sketches and develop ideas for a quick full size review by design and management personnel, and for market research. These systems, valuable for developing a design and for theme presentation purposes, do not lend themselves to true surface development without a considerable amount of engineering input.

Engineers who understand surface may not have the artistic sensitivity to tune a design. The end development might look engineered instead of styled. The task therefore reverts to the modeler. Although new programs permit modelers to utilize CAID systems in model development, I believe final surface tuning requires the eye and hand of a skilled modeler on the clay surface. Styling clay models will continue to provide three-dimensional surface definition.

History and Use Of Styling Clay

A history of the use of styling clay in the automobile industry, and men who developed automobile design techniques are covered in the next two chapters. The development of design systems, tools, and equipment for the construction of precision styling models are also covered.

This book is written as a text book for industrial design students and

1999 Ford Focus. A new direction for Ford's Small car.

for others wishing to design and build custom items of any kind requiring the use of styling clay. It is also directed to all persons interested in the development of automobile design, starting early in this century and continuing into the new millennium.

PART ONE

AUTOMOBILE DESIGN TECHNIQUES

CHAPTER 1 - Automobile Design Models

The largest market for styling clay has been the design development of automobile models commencing at the end of the 19th century. Styling clay has been used to develop many other industrial design products as well. Today it will be found in numerous design studios and model shops being used on a variety of projects from furniture to carnival rides, to sculpture works for malls, for motion picture props, various other vehicles, after market items, boats, toys, etc. For more information on autombile modeling see Yasusato Yamada, *Clay Modeling: Techniques for Giving Three-Dimensional Form to Idea*, Car Styling.

There follows a brief historical account of several men who have greatly advanced the art of automobile design.

This Willis P. Wagner design study was a proposal for a 1943 Ford. This full size clay model was developed by the author. The highlight run on polished clay is very interesting, December 1941. (Photograph: Ford Design Department)

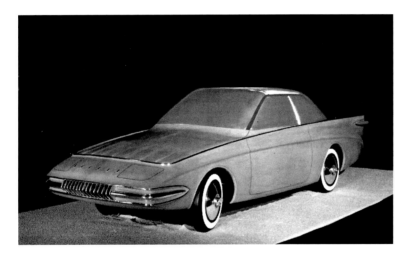

The Monaco, an advance concept three-eights scale clay model was designed by Wesley P. Dahlberg and the International Studio, 1957. (Photograph: Ford Design Center)

A one-fifth scale aero test clay model of the 1964 Ford Taunus 17M is seen here undergoing a smoke test by one of the wind tunnel operators, August 1962. (Photograph: Technische Hochschule, Stuttgart, Germany)

George J. Mercer

George J. Mercer was a body designer from the old school, that is, he started out in the horse-carriage business. Eventually these carriage makers all evolved into motor vehicle body builders. Generally, the same fundamental methods were used by designers in both businesses. One consideration that differed is that weight reduction in the horse-carriage, to help the horse, was of the utmost importance. Strength was the most important factor in body construction for motor vehicle use because of greater stress and strain on the body.

Carriage body design in the early days relied heavily on the artisans who made the parts and assemblies. These craftsmen had considerable knowledge about the materials they used and they had a lot of pride in their work. Body designers created the overall design, established the dimensions, and made the shop drawings.

Trade schools, had been established in the large cities of Europe and in New York City that taught carriage design. Some of these schools were supported by the trade itself. Trade schools had day and evening classes where, for a small fee, young men in the industry were able to learn the distinct art of carriage design.

At the beginning of the motor car business, the carriage trade was already quite successful, but there was a greater demand for automobile bodies. This caused the body shops to modify their methods to increase production. Where previously the carriage business was mostly single-order especially built work, motor car companies required bodies to be built in series. This greater demand for bodies and for new designs increased the position and importance of the body designers. Also, more drawings were necessary as well as closer coordination between body design and manufacturing. This increased work load required draftsmen and layout men to aid the body designers.

Draftsmen detailed the working drawings; they inked in the pencil lines, and where one view overlapped another view they used colored inks to distinguish them. Separate detail drawings were made for hardware, iron work, and die work. Wood framing was not detailed, instead the layout men made patterns and samples of all the pieces, chose the wood stock sizes, and numbered each part.

As the automobile industry grew and carriage shops became motor body shops, the body building industry experienced its most profitable and progressive period. More elaborate engineering and shop production methods, more information and detailed drawings, try out models, tools, metal stamping equipment, and volume production systems advanced far beyond what was ever possible in the carriage business.

George Mercer began his career during this period of tremendous change in personal transportation. Because of his long experience and special training, he became proficient and skillful in all areas of body design and construction. He was also competent as a writer and was sought after as a lecturer and teacher.

In September of 1920, the Society of Automotive Engineers, (S.A.E.) printed a copy of the paper Mercer had presented to the Metropolitan Section of S.A.E. The title of the paper was, "The Trend of Automobile Body Design". In this paper, Mercer gave a complete outline on automobile design, how it had developed out of the design of horse-carriages, and some thoughts on future design of automobiles.

Mercer explained that a design starts with sketches and one-tenth or one-twelfth scale drawings. These may be in pencil or in color but the aim is to show as much realism as possible so that those persons not familiar with drawings would be able to visualize the design. The next step was usually a full size blackboard drawing. This gave an impression of the design that was not possible in smaller drawings of the design. This was followed by a working drawing that was used to construct and tryout the body in actual service before going into production.

To accomplish this, the working drawing showed all of the pieces necessary to construct and assemble a body. Automobile bodies had wood framing with some structural pieces being cast aluminum. Surfaces on early bodies used wood paneling and later on these were replaced by steel or aluminum panels. One New Jersey company, J.M.Quinby & Co., perfected an all aluminum paneled closed body construction in 1903 that was used for several years. Moldings made from bronze were used to cover the edges of the metal panels. These were attached from the inside with machine screws that ran through the wood framing into drilled and tapped holes in the moldings.

Rothschild & Co. of New York brought out an overlapping panel construction for closed bodies in 1907. The upper quarter panel was hooked around a steel molding which was attached by machine screws through the wood framing. This upper body panel covered the edge of the lower body panel, thus making a clean transition. The upper panel was formed by hand to fit around windows and over the edge of the roof and was attached with nails. Aluminum castings were placed around the window openings to form a reveal and these were attached by machine screws from inside. There were no exposed moldings or attaching screws.

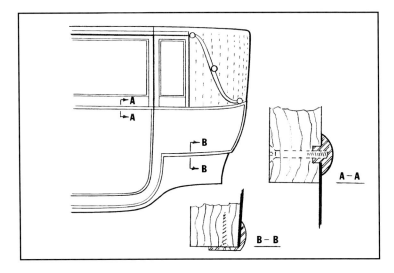

Quinby Construction (Re-drawn: Author)

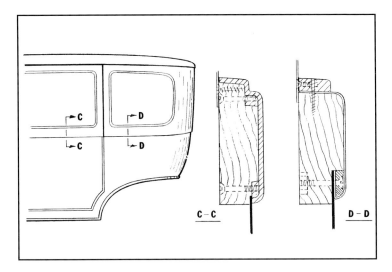

Rothchild Construction. (Re-drawn:Author)

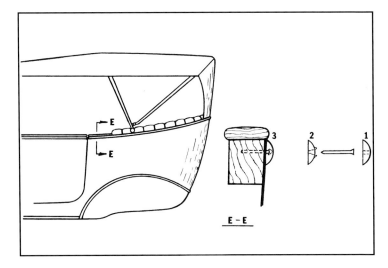

Panel Construction On Open Bodies. (Re-drawn:Author)

Panels on open bodies were attached and finished with aluminum moldings. These moldings had either tapered or punched holes. Nails were driven through the holes into the wood framing and the surface of the moldings around the nail heads was metal finished.

Because of all of the different materials, pieces, and assemblies, it was not possible to see whether a new design was satisfactory until the assembly work was completed and the body was painted, or at least had received the first coat of lead primer. Then if changes were in order, new drawings were made, and the body was disassembled. New framing, surfaces, and moldings were fabricated and the body was reassembled and refinished. This required a lot of time and work. To avoid this situation, a system for building clay models was developed.

To accomplish this, the body framing was set up as a sample body, but instead of installing formed steel panels, wood strips about one inch wide by one quarter inch thick were attached between the framing. A similar space was left between the wood strips and they were set back from the outer surfaces of the framing and the pillars. A clay composition containing wax was then applied over the wood strips, framing, and pillars and shaped with scrapers. After this surface was smoothed, the body was painted, set on a chassis, the fenders mounted, and the radiator and hood installed. Sometimes the radiator, hood, and fenders were modeled in the same way as the body.

The advantage of this system was that additional modeling clay could be added and the surface remodeled according to the designer's wish. These sample bodies were finished inside with trim and cushions to give the appearance of a completed automobile.

When the design was approved, plaster of Paris patterns were made from the surface. These were used in the foundry to make cast iron air-hammer forms. The clay would be removed, changes made to the framing as required, and the body was then covered with metal panels for a quickly built experimental automobile.

Mercer pointed out that a designer must use his artistic talent and experience as well as his engineering training in developing a pleasing appearance on bodies having curved surfaces. He should be able to develop his designs, using only the controlling dimensions and the general instructions as to the character of the design. It is also necessary that a designer's authority and freedom for accepting or making changes should be unquestioned. In addition, the designer instead of the engineer, should design the radiator shape, the engine hood, fenders, lamp supports, and tire carriers to create a harmony of the whole plan.

George Mercer wrote many articles and several books including *Motor Body Engineering*, *Motor Body Blue Print Technology*, and *Motor Body Designing Problems*.

Mercer was a body designer at the turn of this century. He later became a body design and engineering consultant for several companies. He was the first designer of automobiles who was able to articulate all facets of body design. He was also the first designer to write a treatise on the subject of automobile body design and construction, and give an historical account of its change and growth from carriage design.

George Mercer played an important and distinguished role in the development and training of automobile designers and body engineers.

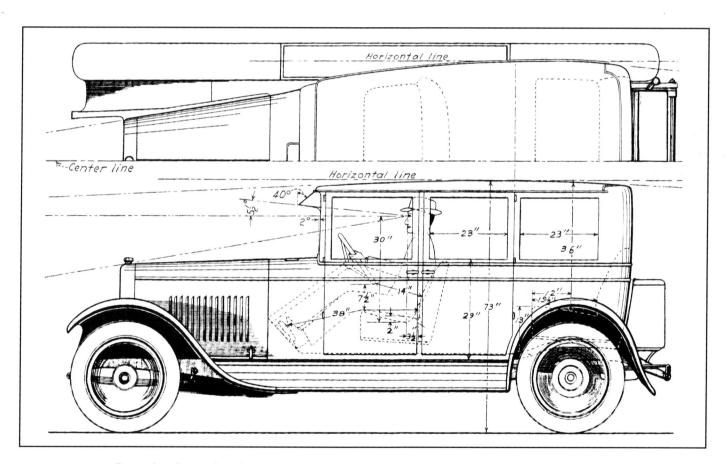

General outline and package dimensions for a 1926 five passenger sedan. (Re-drawn:Author)

Harley Earl

Harley Earl was born in Los Angeles and raised in Hollywood, California. He was the son of J. W. Earl who started the Earl Carriage Works, building various types of horse drawn wagons and carriages. Harley was the second of four boys and one girl born to Jacob and Abbie Earl.

Each June the Earl family would vacation and camp on a ranch in the mountains north of Los Angeles. It was on one of these vacations, as the story goes, that Harley Earl of GM Design fame made his first automobile clay models. It was 1910 and he was 16 years old. It had rained and the ground was wet. He dug clay from the edge of a stream and with help from his younger brother, Arthur, shaped the clay into various automobile body types.

The Earl Carriage Works started repairing and constructing automobile bodies and manufacturing windshields and other accessories. They began offering custom auto bodies and Harley Earl took an interest in design. The name of the company was changed to the Earl Automobile Works. His father sent him to Stanford University where he studied engineering and where he was involved in sports including rugby, track, and football. In one of the sport events his leg was injured when he was cleated and he had to leave school. He spent nearly a year recovering from this accident.

In June of 1917 Harley Earl married his high school sweetheart, Sue Carpenter. Also, his interest in the Earl Automobile Works began to grow and instead of returning to Stanford, he joined his father in the auto body business.

Harley Earl liked automobiles. He had grown up in the body business and learned to be a draftsman and a body designer from his father. When Jacob Earl became ill and was away from work for several months, Harley Earl learned to run the business. One of the first things he did was to make some special roadsters for the auto shows. In addition to customized bodies, he used brighter colors, innovative color combinations, and striping to distinguish his designs. People engaged in the motion picture industry had money and they liked these fancy show cars. By the time of the Los Angeles Auto Show in 1919, Harley Earl was well known as an automobile designer. In addition to showing clients renderings of custom bodies, he was also showing them full size clay models. So called wax models were common in custom body shops at that time and his carriage builders had become quite professional in building clay models. When Jacob Earl returned after six months, Harley Earl had about half a million dollars worth of special bodies under construction.

Prior to the use of modeling clay to build models, wood and sheet metal were used for mock-ups. Clay was much quicker to use, easily changed, and cleaner. The use of wood or sheet metal was relatively slow and could not be changed quickly. Body builders were using a modeling clay that was commonly called modeling wax. This material was made by the Chavant Company in New Jersey.

Don Lee had been a Cadillac dealer since 1906. By 1919 he had become the factory's West Coast distributor with retail outlets of his own in several major California cities. He was looking for an established custom body firm and bought the Earl Automobile Works and retained Harley Earl as chief designer and general manager. The Earl company, with 400-500 employees, had become one of the six largest builders of custom bodies in the United States. The name of the company was changed to the Don Lee Coach and Body Works.

By 1920, they were producing about three hundred custom bodies a year. The Don Lee Coach and Body Works had received national attention through exhibits in the Chicago and New York auto shows. Some bodies were being shipped overseas, some went to Cadillac dealers, and the Cadillac factory bought many of their bodies.

Earl also built custom coach work on European as well as American chassis. In addition to Cadillac this included Pierce Arrow, Packard, Marmon, Chandler, Crane-Simplex, Locomobile, Rolls Royce, Bentley, and Renault. His moving picture customers included: Mary Pickford, Douglas Fairbanks, Tom Mix, Wally Reid, Fatty Arbuckle, Viola Dana, Pauline Fredericks, Cecil B. deMille, and many other silent screen stars and executives.

When Harley Earl was at Stanford, he had a schoolmate from Los Angeles by the name of Andrew Baldwin. Andrew's father, Jimmy Baldwin, was the Chevrolet dealer in Los Angeles. In the winter of 1921-22, Andrew called Earl and invited him to meet and play golf with, whom he said, was one of Earl's competitors. He was introduced to Fred Fisher, the head of the famous Fisher Body Company that supplied bodies for all of the General Motor's automobile divisions. This of course was a good-natured jest because while Earl ran a custom body shop with about 500 employees, the Fisher brothers ran several body plants with many thousands of employees. Earl and Fred Fisher were partners on the golf course that day. They also played golf about every three days while Fisher was in California for a few weeks during that winter. This was repeated each winter for several years.

Fred Fisher's brother, Lawrence P. (Larry) Fisher, became general manager of Cadillac in 1925. He and Earl also became good friends. Cadillac was working on and engineering a second line of cars to be named LaSalle. Several proposals had already been made by other custom body shops. Fred Fisher recommended to Larry that Harley Earl should be permitted to try one. So Larry Fisher asked Don Lee to send Earl to Detroit as a consultant to propose

A town car designed by Harley Earl for the silent film comedian Roscoe (Fatty) Arbuckle and built by Don Lee Coach in the early 1920's. (Photograph: GM Design)

A special landaulet designed by Harley Earl in the early 1920's and built by Don Lee Coach in California. (Photograph: GM Design)

a design. Earl left California by train on January 6, 1926 to go to Detroit. For his design, Earl used the Hispano-Suiza, which he highly admired, as the theme for the LaSalle. Working with people from Fisher Body, it took about three months to complete four body styles in composite modeling clay and wood. These were presented to Alfred P. Sloan, Chairman of the Board, General Motors Corporation, and the various department heads. Earl's design was approved. After a full size wood mock-up was completed, Larry Fisher gave Earl a trip to Europe to see the Paris Automobile Show.

Earl returned to Los Angeles, but in the fall of 1926 he was called again by Larry Fisher and asked to style the 1928 Cadillacs. After that project was finished, he again returned to Los Angeles.

In May of 1927, Earl received a call from Sloan from his office in New York City. Fred and Larry Fisher were with him. Sloan was disturbed by the ungainly appearance, particularly of closed automobile bodies with their big wheels and high bodies and he wanted to set up a central design staff for General Motors. The introduction of the LaSalle in March 1927 had been a sensation and the Fisher brothers recommended Harley Earl for the job.

Mr. Sloan invited Earl to come to his New York office to discuss this idea and he accepted the invitation.

On June 23, 1927, Alfred P. Sloan made a proposal to the executive committee to establish a special department to be called the Art and Colour Section. Mr. Sloan invited Harley Earl to head this new department. To protect his new enterprise, Earl was assigned directly to Sloan. Harley Earl, his wife Sue, and their first son Billy moved to Detroit in the fall of 1927 and the Art and Colour Section was underway. Starting with just himself, Earl built up an organization of approximately 50 people by early 1928. Earl's staff used modeling clay in addition to sketches, renderings, and drawings to develop interior and exterior designs. He was also given the responsibility to develop colors, fabrics, and interior trim.

He built up the department from just a few people to what later became General Motors Design with 1400 employees. On September 3, 1940, Harley J. Earl was appointed Vice President of Design, General Motors Corporation. He designed automobiles for all U.S. divisions of General Motors as well as foreign subsidiaries. This included the German Opel, the English Vauxhall, and after World War II the first Holden in Australia. In addition,

Harley Earl sitting in the 1927 LaSalle which he designed for the Cadillac Motor Car Company, General Motors Corp. Lawrence P. Fisher, President of Cadillac, stands beside the LaSalle at the time of its press release. Notice the three tone color scheme. (Photograph: GM Design)

Alfred P. Sloan Jr., the administrative genius who built General Motors into a giant corporation. Sloan hired Harley Earl in 1927 and established the Art and Colour Section of General Motors. (Photograph: GM Design)

The dapper Harley Earl on his way to the 1927 Paris Automobile Show. Earl by this time had made his mark as a designer of fine automobiles in both California and Detroit. (Photograph: GM Design)

trucks, buses, and a line of industrial products and appliances were designed by his staff.

Prior to the establishment of the Art and Colour Section at General Motors, the engineers were usually the dominant design personalities. The chassis engineers designed, in addition to the chassis, the radiator shell, hood, cowl, fenders, running boards, headlights, taillights, and bumpers. Body engineers developed a body around these fixed parameters. Although industrial designers or stylists may have contributed to the development, the design was under the control of the engineers. In the Art and Colour Section, Earl designed complete unique forms, not just the body, unifying the various parts of an automobile from the standpoint of appearance and style.

Automobile bodies were built by either the automobile company itself or by separate body companies. Some of these body companies had custom body shops and designers. There were also many independent custom body shops such as Don Lee's that used a body builder's drawing and built special bodies on standard chassis. A body builder's chassis drawing provides all of the dimensions and information required to build custom coach bodies. Each of these custom body shops had their own designers or they bought their designs from independent designers. Custom designed automobiles were exhibited at the various salons and auto shows and sold through dealer sales offices. A body builders custom design might be installed on a chassis as a "one off" or produced in batches from perhaps 20 to 200 jobs per year.

The first all new car design coming out of the Art and Colour Section was a 1929 Buick. Earl created a body surface that rolled out approximately one inch at the belt line and ran from the hood all the way around the body. This roll replaced the popular moldings that previously had separated the lower body from the upper. Moldings by this time were stamped into the metal panels and were not applied to cover panel joints as they did originally in carriage design. This new design motif was minor compared to those much later when the body roll might extend a few inches. The instrument panel featured four black faced circular gauges in a row and was designed by Gordon Buehrig during his first employment in the Art and Colour Section. But the 1929 Buick was not well received. The public called it the "pregnant" Buick and sales were disappointing.

Earl complained that the production engineers had modified his design by pulling the side panels in at the bottom and adding several inches to the height of the body. This gave the car a "bulgy" look. So the 1929 Buick was changed to a more conservative design for 1930.

For 1933, General Motors car lines had several new innovations; bodies were larger and more rounded, a grill covered the radiator, the windshield visor was gone (in 1932), the body was lower so the step between the running board and the door sill was

The upper picture is a 1929 Buick 121 Four Door Close-coupled Sedan.(Photograph: GM Media Archives)

These two highly retouched photographs tell the story of the "pregnant" Buick. The 1929 Buick designed by Harley Earl and his Art & Colour Section replaced the conventional belt line moldings with a body roll. This roll started at the reshaped chrome radiator shell, ran back along the edge of the hood, and ran all the way around the body. Earl complained that the Buick engineers changed his design proposal by pulling the sides of the body in at the bottom and by adding several inches to the height. This gave the car a "bulgy" look, but the public called it the "pregnant" Buick. Earl replaced it in 1930 with an all new body for Buick that added a molding and a color applique or insert panel around the windows. This was reminiscent of his work on the 1927 LaSalle and "341" Cadillac, and his earlier work in California for Don Lee Coach and Body Works. The roll was still there but it was lowered and diminished.

The lower picture is a 1930 Buick Model 57 Four Door Sedan. (Photograph: GM Media Archives)

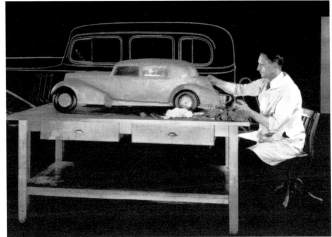

The 1933 Oldsmobile was the first production car to have pontoon type fenders. The fender shape was a convex form instead of having a sweeping ogee. It also had an attractive "V" shaped grill and horizontal hood louvers. This particular car had dual side mount wheels. (Photograph: Courtesy Oldsmobile History Center)

A design study model for Cadillac in the early 1930's. The blackboard drawing in the background represents a 1933 Pontiac. The design for this model seems to have been inspired by the 1932 Graham "Blue Streak". (Photograph: GM Design)

The 1933 Pontiac front end design was by Franklin Q. Hershey. He took a rather bland 1932 design and turned it into a very attractively styled car. He was also responsible for the Pontiac "Silver Streak" design that came out two years later on the 1935 model. (Photograph: GM Media Archives)

reduced, the back of the body was finished with a so called "beaver tail" that covered the fuel tank and the frame, etc., and the fenders had a skirt to cover the unsightly inner surfaces. Oldsmobile for 1933 was the first production car to have pontoon type fenders, that is a convex form instead of a sweeping ogee fender line which was customary. The Pontiac for 1933 was designed by Franklin Q. Hershey. It was a very attractive car with a Bentley style grill, bold hood louvers, and speed lines on the skirts of the fenders. Automobile styling at GM truly began with the 1933 cars.

In presenting his new designs to the Executive Committee for model year 1934, Earl displayed a fabulous new trend-setting design for the LaSalle. The tall, narrow grill and pontoon fenders were designed by Jules Agramonte and the biplane bumpers were designed by J.R. (Jack) Morgan. The committee was so fascinated with this fresh new style that it saved the LaSalle from extinction at that time. This however was the fate of the other lower priced second line of cars from the divisions except Pontiac. The lower priced line of cars from Oakland was the Pontiac but it out sold Oakland and it lived on. The demise of the Oakland coincided with that of the Marquette from Buick and the Viking from Oldsmobile. But Earl saved the LaSalle until 1941.

Earl created an all new enveloping body on a special sixteen cylinder Cadillac for the 1933-34 Chicago World's Fair, the Century of Progress Exposition. One of the features of this first GM show car, named the Aero-Dynamic Coupe, was a one piece steel roof. Until the middle of the 1930s, all sedan roofs were a composite construction of wood framing covered with padding and a layer of synthetic rubber material joined at the edges of the steel side panels with a small molding. The one-piece steel roof called the "Turret Top" was introduced on the all new 1935 General Motors cars.

The striking appearance of the 1934 LaSalle with its tall narrow grill and split bumpers is best displayed here in this 1934 LaSalle brochure cover. (Photograph: Cadillac Motor Car Company)

The 1934 LaSalle was chosen the Official 1934 Pace car for the Indianapolis 500 Mile Sweepstakes races. (Photograph: GM Design)

A one-eighth scale model of the 1934 LaSalle and a clay model of the hood ornament that was used on the LaSalle automobile. (Photograph: GM Design)

The special Cadillac V16 Aero-Dynamic Coupe designed by Harley Earl's Art and Colour Section for the 1933 Chicago Century of Progress World's Fair. This special design established the body style for General Motors for the mid 1930's. (Photograph: GM Design)

Following the direction of Earl's Century of Progress Aero-Dynamic Coupe, Fisher Body introduced the "Turret Top" on all of the new GM 1935 passenger car closed bodies. This steel roof required a new high-speed strip mill producing eighty-inch sheet steel, and a new giant press to stamp these very large panels. It was 1937 before the competition was able to follow with all steel roofs. (Illustration: Oldsmobile Division)

The Union Pacific GM diesel engine streamlined train designed by Harley Earl's Art and Colour Section, 1934. A Chrysler Air Flow stands next to the Union Pacific train. (Photograph: GM Design)

This was made possible when the steel industry perfected the modern high-speed strip mill supplying eighty-inch sheet steel. This also required an all new giant press used first by Fisher Body Division. The competition followed with steel roofs in 1937.

Earl was responsible for Union Pacific's streamlined trains in the mid 1930s that established a diesel locomotive design pattern still used today, also the Parade of Progress vehicles and shows.

The 1938 Cadillac 60 Special was another outstanding trend setting design that brought the torpedo body style into mass production. This style was first developed by Gordon Buehrig for Duesenberg. It is characterized by an extended rear deck that gives the impression of the lower body extending through and out beyond the back of the roof and back window. The 60 Special was designed by William L. (Bill) Mitchell under the watchful eye of Earl.

Harley Earl's experimental Buick Y-Job introduced in 1938 had many styling and engineering features that would be seen on future production cars.

For 1939 and 1940, General Motors brought about what I have always considered to be a coupe de theatre in automobile design. In 1939 General Motors introduced a very neat and beautifully detailed, conservative body style with a trunk that was formed in the body. Only a few years before specially built trunks were installed at the rear of sedan bodies. In 1935 trunks became a part of the body but as an appendage with a large fillet between the main body and the trunk. But while competition was busy following this boxy style, Harley Earl's design staff was working on something quite different. For 1940, General Motors brought out an all new body that followed the torpedo style of the Cadillac 60 Special but softer and more flowing. It was also much lower, wider, and longer than the 1939 sedans and was available on all car lines except Chevrolet. This body style set the pattern for all future sedan bodies. A variation of the 1940 soft body style has been used recently on the 1993 Infiniti J30 and the 1994 Lexus GS.

In the 1930's, General Motors traveled the United States with its Parade of Progress show. The special vans were designed by the Art and Colour Section of GM. (Photograph: GM Design)

The 1938 Cadillac 60 Special was designed by William L. (Bill) Mitchell following directions given him by Harley Earl. It has been said the 60 Special looked a lot like Earl's development for the 1929 Buick before Buick engineers changed it. The 1938 60 Special brought the torpedo body style, developed by Buehrig on the very expensive Duesenberg, to Cadillac a more affordable luxury car. Bill Mitchell rendered this illustration. (Photograph: GM Design)

Bill Mitchell posing with his face-lifted front end on the 1939 Cadillac 60 Special. The 'catwalk' grill theme, first introduced on the 1938 Lincoln Zephyr, was picked up in 1939 by several automobile companies including Cadillac. (Photograph: GM Design)

Harley Earl and his famous Buick Y-Job built in 1938. This was an experimental automobile used for testing innovative design and engineering ideas. (Photograph: GM Design)

Bill Mitchell joined GM Art and Colour Section in 1935 and headed the Cadillac studio from 1936 to 1954. When Harley Earl retired in 1958, Mitchell became Vice President of Design. He held that position until 1977 when he retired. (Photograph: GM Design)

During World War II, Earl completely altered his department and set up studios doing defense and military work. They did exploded view and production illustration drawings, made a thorough camouflage study, and developed unusual military weapons including the Wildcat tank that became a reality and was built by Buick.

After World War II, Earl introduced the tail-fin style that began with the rather elegant 1948 Cadillacs and concluded on the 1964 Cadillacs. But critics agree that the ultimate finned car was the 1959 Cadillac convertible. This was the extreme example of the overly ornate, pretentious, pompous style of American design.

The panoramic wrap around windshield introduced in 1954 on all GM car lines had the "A" pillar (windshield post) tilted forward and was a style trend Earl had been toying with for several years. It first appeared in production on the original Corvette. The 1953 Chevrolet Corvette was conceived by Earl as a show car for the New York Motorama. The following year it appeared in three forms: the Convertible Coupe with a removable hard top in addition to a soft top, the Nomad as a stylish station wagon, and the Corvair with a streamlined fast-back body style. However, it was Zora Arkus-Duntov that made the Corvette a sports car.

The Train of Tomorrow, designed by Charles Jordan, was Earl's idea to give airline glamor to train travel. This train was the first to have 'sky dome' cars. The styling work on the Euclid articulated tractor with its unique chartreuse color was also Jordan's design under Earl's direction.

A very clever trick was played on the automobile industry by Harley Earl and General Motors in 1939. An all new very conservative body style was introduced that year on larger models of Pontiac and Oldsmobile and on the smaller lines of Buick and Cadillac. It was the only body style available on the LaSalle. A full range of body types were available although not on each car line. There were coupes and convertible coupes, two-door and four-door sedans, and four-door convertible sedans. The design was neat and very well detailed. While competition followed this boxy style on their new designs, Harley Earl's design staff was developing something very different. In 1940 General Motors brought out a very attractive all new body style which was a reversal of the boxy conservative line introduced in 1939. This new body was lower, wider, and longer, it was a Torpedo style similar to the Cadillac 60 Special but softer and more flowing. This style switch caught competition by surprise. Shown here is a 1939 Oldsmobile Eight Series 80 Four-door Trunk Sedan and a 1940 Oldsmobile Series 90 Custom 8 Cruiser Touring Sedan. The first completely automatic transmission was introduced as an option on Oldsmobile in 1940 for a cost of $57. (Photographs: Courtesy Oldsmobile History Center)

Tail-fins first appeared in 1948 on Cadillacs. Shown here is the elegant 1948 Cadillac fast back coupe. This is one of Harley Earl's most beautiful and aesthetically correct automobile designs. The lines and forms were excellent from any angle. (Photographs: Author - 1950)

The 1959 Cadillac was the last Cadillac Earl was responsible for and the first for Charles Jordon as head of the Cadillac studio.The 1959 Cadillac represents American automobile design in its own glamour of bigness and illusory attractiveness, the period in history of the "Ugly American". Progress in design was stymied until the rude awakening of the gasoline crisis and environmental concerns. (Photograph: GM Design)

1964 was the last year for Cadillac tail fins. Looking at this car you think it's never going to end. (Photograph: Cadillac Division)

In 1954 GM installed Harley Earl's panoramic wrap around windshield on all car lines as shown here in this Oldsmobile 88 two-door sedan. This may be a finished engineering prototype. The photograph is one of a series of views taken for brochure illustrations. (Photograph: Courtesy Oldsmobile History Center)

For the 1954 Motorama, Harley Earl presented three different Corvettes: the Convertible Coupe without and with a removable hard top, the Corvair with a streamlined fast-back body style, and the Nomad as a stylish station wagon. (Photograph: GM Design)

Charles Jordon, with his lieutenants , critiques a tail lamp on what appears to be a GM show car. (Photograph: GM Design)

Charles Jordon was GM Vice President of Design, 1986-1993. (Photograph: GM Design)

Earl was also personally involved in establishing and setting up the traveling "Motorama" shows and in developing the many show cars for these events. These were yearly extravaganzas that started in New York City and subsequently shown at other major cities in the country.

Just to clarify one point, although Harley Earl was the first to establish a department devoted to the design of automobiles for mass production, he was not the first stylist or designer instead of an engineer to design a line of cars for an automobile company. J. Frank deCausse designed the famous line of Locomobiles in that company's Custom Department from 1914 to 1922. Herbert M. Dawley set up an art department for Pierce-Arrow in 1907. Also, Amos Northup designed the very conservative but clean Wills Sainte Claire in 1923.

Another designer, Alan H. Leamy designed the L-29 Cord. His attention to line, form, and color on the Cord (as well as the Auburn and Duesenberg automobiles) is highly acclaimed. However, his work on the Cord took place in 1928, one year after Earl established the Art and Colour Section.

During his career with General Motors, Earl and his organization dominated automobile design and set many of the styling trends. But most of all, he had the ability to know the direction to go and to choose the right designs for the time, and then to execute them to perfection. Some

we did not like because of their excesses but they could not be faulted because of the quality of design workmanship or of line or form.

Earl hired exceptional designers and illustrators for his organization, although he seldom did any drawing after the Art and Colour Section was established. Earl grew up learning carriage and body design, and using blackboard drawings. He understood elevations and sections, and he could lay down a "fair line". It can be seen through the many years of his General Motors products that Earl was a very capable design critic. He was a master at reading lines and form and choosing designs.

Harley Earl retired from General Motors in 1958 after building a permanent place for design in the automobile industry. Earl is remembered as the father of the automobile styling profession. It is interesting to note that many of the automobile designers of the 1930s and 40s had at sometime worked for Earl in his Art and Colour Section. He was the archetype for the position of Vice President of Design. He was quite tall, 6 feet 4 inches, with a domineering personality and he was always an immaculate and stylish dresser. Many of the leading designers who followed him copied his personal style, some even copied his authoritarian and acrimonious management practices.

The 1932 Graham "Blue Streak" surprised Harley Earl with its beautifully swept up "V" grill and skirted fenders. These new design ideas were picked up by Harley Earl's GM car lines in 1933. They also appeared in Ford, Hudson, Lincoln, Packard, and Willys. All of the other car lines added deep "V" grills and skirted fenders in 1934. The '32 Graham also included many advanced engine and chassis developments.

The Graham was styled by Amos Northup, it was lower, wider, and was a very graceful design. The "Blue Streak" was further enhanced by a beautiful light blue metallic paint color introduced with this model that made it a truly striking design. (Photograph: Pamela Chaffee, "Eyes on Classic Design", Edsel Ford Estate, 1996)

Because of a cooling problem, E.T.(Bob) Gregorie, head of the Ford Design Department, designed a new grill and made a mock-up on a test vehicle for the 1938 Lincoln Zephyr. This new grill design solved the cooling problem and started a low catwalk grill theme that affected all future automobile grill design. This photograph is one of a series taken for brochure illustrations. Note the dummy head lamp lens. (Photograph: Ford Public Relations)

The fresh look and clean design of the 1949 Ford took the automobile market by surprise. It brought back the sales volume lost by Ford in the late 30's and early 40's, and the 1949 Ford beat the 1949 Chevrolet by over 100,000 units. Credit for the spinner grill goes to Joe Oris and the full size development to Joe Oris and Elwood Engel. However, the theme model came from South Bend, Indiana.

Dick Caleal arranged to have a one quarter scale model developed and finished for George Walker who was the design consultant to Ford Motor Co. Caleal requested the aid of several designer and modeler friends who worked in Raymond Loewy's Studebaker Design Studio where he had recently been laid off. Credit for the design of the theme model of the 1949 Ford goes to Dick Caleal with support from designers Bob Bourke and Bob Koto, and modelers John Bird, John Lutz, Jr., and Joe Thompson. Bob Koto made the cast.

Caleal's model was presented to Ford management along with models from George Walker's team, and the model developed by Bob Gregorie and the Ford Design Department team. Caleal's model was chosen. (Photograph: Ford Public Relations)

Virgil M. Exner, Sr. designed the all new line of Chrysler products for 1957. The Plymouth shocked General Motors and especially Harley Earl. The larger Plymouth was 4 inches lower, 4 inches wider, and 11 inches longer than its previous model. This new large Plymouth became a final challenge for Harley Earl at GM.

The upper picture and the picture on the left show the 1957 Plymouth. The lower right picture is the modified 1958 Plymouth with real dual headlights. The 1958 Plymouth was the most pleasing front end design of this series from 1957-60.

The 1959 GM models were the last designs that Harley Earl was responsible for. Chevrolet introduced an all new "V" finned design that was 2 inches wider and 2 inches longer than the Plymouth. It ushered in the big "small car" that in time, along with the big cars of the other GM car lines, nearly sank General Motors Corporation. The large exterior dimensions gave a false impression of useful interior space. These cars also had ten inch thick doors, cavernous engine compartments, and two feet or more between the front of the bumper and the radiator. These cars did not handle well, they were heavy and cumbersome, they shook and rattled; but as usual, the rest of the U.S. auto industry followed General Motors. (Illustration: Chevrolet Division)

Ford, competing with Plymouth in 1957, was a more compatible and competitive product than Chevrolet. However, spy photos in late 1957 of the new 1959 Chevrolet shook Ford management out of its complacency. Ford scrapped their proposed new model and in record time developed an all new horizontal finned Ford for 1960. The studio named this new model the "Quicksilver". It was equal in size to the Chevrolet. (Illustration: Ford Division)

It took 20 years, the oil embargo, governmental emission standards, and a "different" Chairman of the Board, Rodger Smith, to reverse the "big car" death knell. Alfred P. Sloan built the General Motors giant, Rodger Smith's task was to turn around a failing corporation.

The 1980 Chevrolet Citation introduced the direction that passenger car design would follow to the turn of the century. It had front wheel drive, unit body construction, and a high performance four cylinder engine. It was a roomy five passenger sedan that was sporty to drive and produced amazing gasoline mileage. The Citation followed the successful design pattern that had been established in Europe and Japan and once again the U.S. auto industry followed General Motors. (Illustration: Chevrolet Division)

It must be remembered that Harley Earl was one of a handful of men including Charles F. Kettering, William S. Knudsen, Harlow H. Curtice, and Edward N. Cole, under the leadership of Alfred P. Sloan, who created the General Motors giant that eventually produced more than 50% of the automobiles in the United States.

Starting with just himself, Earl established a whole new transportation design field. He had a talent for choosing people for his design staff that made it the most formidable of all styling organizations. He also had a talent for choosing styling themes for GM car lines and for special projects that kept them in leadership positions. He was only caught short by four competitive designs:

the 1932 Graham "Blue Streak" with its handsome swept up grill and skirted fenders; the 1938 Lincoln Zephyr with the beautiful front end form and the low catwalk grill; the fresh new design of the 1949 Ford which caught Chevrolet completely off guard; and the 1957 Plymouth which had been lowered and lengthened several inches and was now a big car with a big car look.

Earl ruled GM Design for more than 30 years utilizing his own unique, very graphic vocabulary to explain his design ideas. He had a sharp eye and was always correcting the lines and forms of his designer's models. Harley Earl was very talented with a very unusual personality.

Alan H. Leamy

Alan H. Leamy was born in Arlington, Maryland and grew up in Columbus, Ohio. When he was a child, he contracted polio which resulted in his left leg being permanently impaired. As an adult, he required a leg brace and a cane for mobility. Leamy had a natural artistic talent and he loved to draw cars starting from his early childhood onward. After high school, he took a correspondence course in architecture and later he attended anatomy classes in Indianapolis, Indiana.

In New Jersey, Leamy designed houses and sold real estate but he continued to sketch automobiles. He was married to Agnes Garrett of Swarthmore, Pennsylvania in 1925 when he was 23 years old. He continued in the real estate business until 1927.

Leamy's father, also Alan, contacted a former colleague, Thomas Litle, Jr. and told him of his son's artistic talent and his love for cars. Litle had become chief engineer for Marmon Motor Company in Indianapolis, Indiana. He was pleased to give young Alan H. Leamy an opportunity at Marmon. So in March of 1927, Leamy commenced his automobile career.

Eventually Leamy became dissatisfied at Marmon because he felt American cars were too conservative and too far behind European automobiles. He liked bright colors and used pastels in his illustrations. He was eager for a more promising opportunity to express his automobile ideas. He learned about Errett Lobban Cord's development of a front wheel drive (FWD) passenger car and wrote to

Alan H. Leamy designed the L-29 Cord. The proportions and detail of this car were quite unique and beautiful. It was long and low because of its front wheel drive configuration. It had a straight eight cylinder engine with the transmission and differential positioned in front of the engine. The time and place of this photo is September, 1950, Watkins Glen Grand Prix. (Photograph: Author)

The L-29 Cord, designed in 1928 by Alan H. Leamy, was an all new car created by a stylist rather than an engineer. Photograph: Auburn-Cord-Duesenberg Museum, Auburn, Indiana)

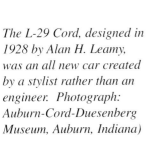

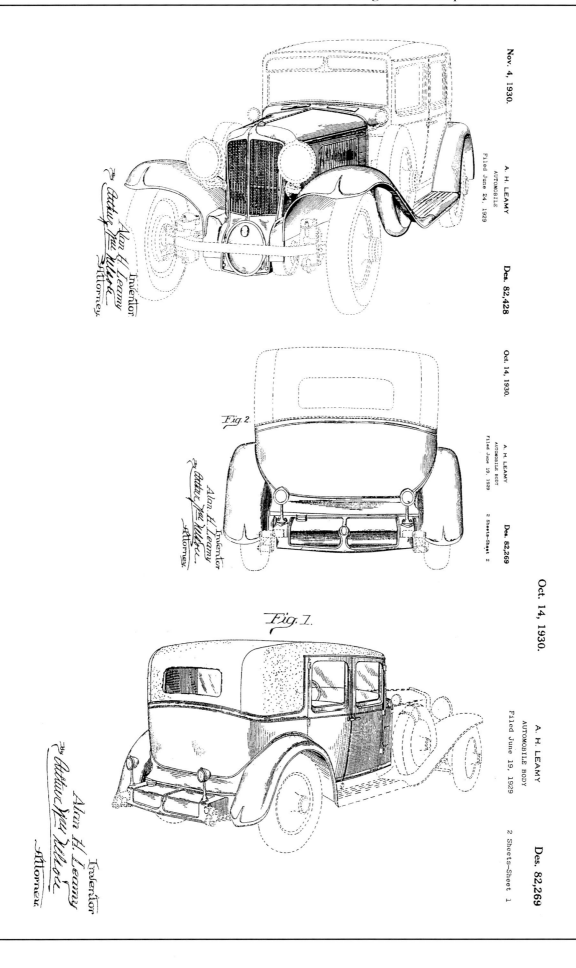

Nov. 4, 1930.

A. H. LEAMY

AUTOMOBILE

Filed June 24, 1929

Des. 82,428

Fig. 2.

Oct. 14, 1930.

A. H. LEAMY

AUTOMOBILE BODY

Filed June 19, 1929

Des. 82,269

2 Sheets-Sheet 2

Fig. 1.

Oct. 14, 1930.

A. H. LEAMY

AUTOMOBILE BODY

Filed June 19, 1929

Des. 82,269

2 Sheets-Sheet 1

Alan Leamy developed this elegant 1929 Auburn Victoria coupe body on a full size clay model. By this time, using clay models in automobile design was becoming a more common practice. (Photograph: Auburn-Cord-Duesenberg Museum)

him requesting a position with his company. In April of 1928, Leamy was directed to meet with Cornelius Willett vanRanst, chief of the FWD project at the Duesenberg factory in Indianapolis. Cord and vanRanst were so impressed with Leamy's sketches that he was named chief stylist of the front wheel drive project.

Alan H. Leamy was thus given the opportunity to design the L-29 Cord. He styled the grill, hood, body, fenders, lights, bumpers, etc., using the low vehicle height to establish a design motif that has been highly praised. The front wheel drive configuration greatly reduced the height of the body and hood. Until then it had been customary for automobile bodies to have flat floors and to be mounted on a frame above the drive line. Because there was no drive line to the rear wheels on the L-29 Cord, the height of the floor and the rest of the body and hood could be lowered.

The L-29 Cord is considered by many to be one of the best looking and most inspiring line of automobiles in the 1920s. Leamy also contributed to the design of the Model J-Duesenberg. Although both of these cars went into production and were introduced in New York City at the same time, Leamy only obtained a design patent on the L-29 Cord.

During the L-29 Cord project, Leamy was among an unusually talented group of automobile developers, engineers, and designers: Harry Miller, Leon Duray, Leo Goossen, Cornelius vanRanst, Herb Snow, and John Oswald.

Harry Miller was a highly successful constructor of race cars and the designer of the remarkable Miller race car engines. In 1925 Miller developed a front wheel drive race car following the principle of the fabulous J. Walter Christie machine that had been popular fifteen to twenty years earlier. However, instead of a transverse large

displacement V4 engine as on the Christie, Miller adopted his small displacement inline engine running fore and aft but turned around 180° with the power coming off of the front. Ahead of the engine was the clutch, transmission, and differential units. The brakes were inboard at the sides of the differential and power was delivered through Rzeppa constant-velocity universal joints and short drive shafts to the wheels. A deDion suspension using a tubular axle and quarter-elliptic springs joined the front wheels ahead of the drive train. The Miller FWD race car was very successful in 1926 and 1927. Because of the success and publicity that FWD race cars were receiving, E. L. Cord became fascinated with the idea of a FWD passenger automobile and bought Miller's FWD patent and consulting services. Prototype L-29 project vehicles were built in Miller's shop in Los Angeles.

Cornelius Willett vanRanst was another well known race car engineer who sometimes raced. He had also developed a successful FWD race car, the Detroit Special. He built and raced several of these cars. The Detroit Special was somewhat similar to the Miller FWD, however the transmission gear arrangement on the vanRanst car was a great improvement over the Miller system. Because of this improvement vanRanst was brought into the L-29 project. His transmission arrangement was used and he was made Project Engineer directing the entire program. His name is on all of the mechanical patents for the design of the L-29 Cord.

Leo Goossen had been Miller's development engineer but he designed the L-29 transmission under vanRanst using the Detroit Special gear arrangement. For the design of the rest of the drive line and suspension, he utilized the general layout of the Miller FWD system. Many standard parts from Auburn were incorporated into the design to comply with E. L. Cord's request.

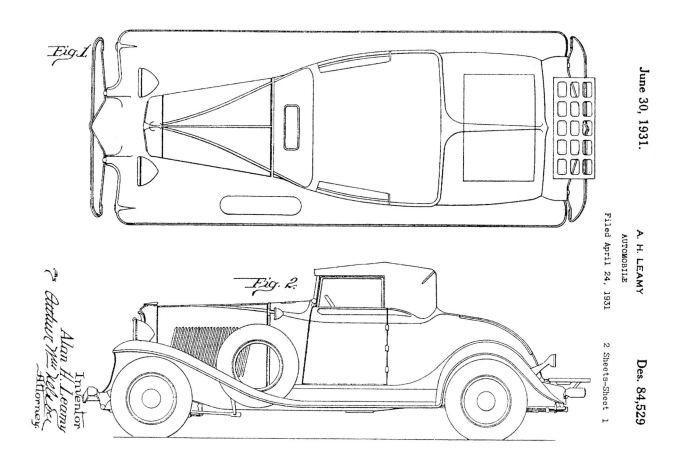

June 30, 1931.

A. H. LEAMY
AUTOMOBILE

Des. 84,529

Filed April 24, 1931

2 Sheets-Sheet 1

Fig.1

Fig. 2.

Inventor
Alan H. Leamy
By Arthur McNelson
Attorney.

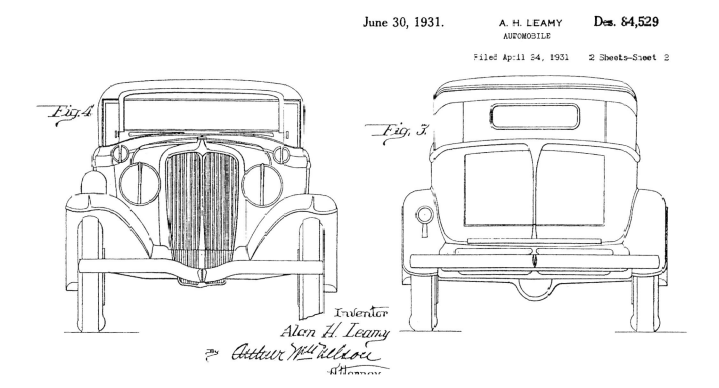

June 30, 1931.

A. H. LEAMY
AUTOMOBILE

Des. 84,529

Filed April 24, 1931   2 Sheets-Sheet 2

Fig.4

Fig. 3.

Inventor
Alan H. Leamy
By Arthur McNelson
Attorney

Alan H. Leamy in a 1931 Auburn 8-98 Speedster which he designed. This is in front of the administration building of the Auburn Automobile Company. (Photograph: Auburn-Cord-Duesenberg Museum, Auburn, Indiana)

The 1932 Model 12-165 Auburn V12 Salon Car was designed by Alan H. Leamy. This four door phaeton sedan represented the top line of Auburn luxury automobiles. It was in the medium price range and it had more luxury features and power than many Cadillac, Packard and Lincoln automobiles, but cost less. (Photograph: Auburn-Cord-Duesenberg Museum, Auburn, Indiana)

Herbert C. Snow was chief engineer for Auburn and Cord. He had held that position previously at both Velie and Winton automobile companies. Prior to that he had been an engineer at Willys-Overland and Peerless companies. To provide adequate torsional stiffness to the 137.5 inch wheelbase of the L-29 Cord, Snow incorporated what may have been the first use of an X-member brace to the central part of the Cord frame.

Leon Duray was a race car driver. He became a star-racer and campaigned on the board tracks all over the United States. He also raced at Indianapolis and in Europe. Duray had driven both the Miller FWD and the Detroit Special. It was from his recommendation that vanRanst was brought into the design team. Duray also aided in the development and testing of the L-29 prototypes and pre-production test vehicles.

John Oswald was the body engineer for the Cord organization. He did the body design work for the program, drafted the body layout drawings, and supervised body construction. He is credited with the development of the sweeping front fender line on the L-29 Cord (and the J-Duesenberg). The production fender line is somewhat different than seen on Leamy's illustrations and drawings. However, Oswald's developments were obviously a cooperative effort with Leamy. Oswald went on to become chief body engineer for Oldsmobile and later held that position at Ford in the early 1950s.

Leamy was also given responsibility for the design of the Auburn series of automobiles. Leamy may have had experience building clay models because he directed the construction of an Auburn full size clay model in the fall of 1928. He had a group of model makers build a wood form to the general shape of the Auburn and this form was then covered with clay. Templates were made from full size body drawings that he and Oswald had drafted. Leamy taught them how to make and use modeling tools. The model was completely finished and detailed. It was painted and striped and in pictures it looked like an actual automobile. Leamy also made small clay models and partial models to test design ideas.

It is possible that Leamy had seen clay models being constructed by one of the companies building bodies for Marmon automobiles when he was working for that company. Clay models were commonly used at this time to build up and finish sample bodies. This was the system explained by George J. Mercer in articles and in his book, "*Motor Body Engineering*", published in 1928. Leamy may have consulted Mercer or someone else who had been building clay models, and he possibly had Mercer's book.

The 8-98 Auburn was the next Leamy development. It was introduced in 1931 and became the best selling Auburn ever. For the Auburn, Leamy used the basic configuration of the high body and hood to develop a dramatic and powerful looking automobile. A speedster was added in the fall of 1931 and a V-12 was introduced in 1932. He also designed many custom bodies for Auburn and Cord.

In 1934, the state of the economy and the automobile industry was very poor due to the depression. Leamy left Auburn to work for the Fisher Body Company in Detroit, Michigan. He looked for another opportunity and found it a year later when Harley Earl promoted him to chief stylist of the LaSalle studio in the Art and Colour Section. Earl had a great admiration for Leamy's work.

Shortly after this promotion, Leamy suddenly died. The automobile industry saw a remarkably talented designer pass through the scene in a short eight years. He did not have time to build a name for himself, but his outstanding accomplishments live on. He was noted for his attention to details, for the strength and character of his designs, and his rendering technique using pastels and bright colors. Alan H. Leamy believed that the successful car must be designed as a unit. It is a tribute to his memory that the L-29 Cord, the 8-98 Auburn, the 12-165 Auburn, and the J-Duesenberg are among the most admired and sought after classic automobiles.

Joseph Thompson

One of the early automotive model makers who transferred his skills from wood to styling clay was Joseph Thompson. He was born in Kingsville, Ontario, Canada in 1887, about five years before the advent of the automobile in the United States. On a visit to Detroit in 1896, he saw his first horseless carriage chugging along the street. He was just nine years old but he fell in love with this new invention.

His boyhood was spent around lumber camps in Canada where he helped his family build their log cabin. By the time he was eight, he was making axe handles and selling them to the local lumberjacks. He began carving toy boats, sleighs, and wagons, and making full size furniture using only crude tools. An interested school teacher encouraged Joe by bringing him weekly magazines from Detroit telling about the new horseless carriages being built there.

After the equivalent of a fifth grade education, Joe left school and in 1904 at the age of 17, he moved to Detroit. Joe got his first job at the Shere Manufacturing Company as a brass polisher and buffer, working ten hours a day for seven dollars a week. Joe then moved on to the Wilson Carriage and Body Company where he learned to build seats, body frames and panels for Cadillacs. It was at this plant that he first met the Fisher brothers, Fred and Charles, with whom he later worked at the Fisher Body Company.

Over the next few years, Thompson was employed by several different automobile companies in various capacities. He learned all about the construction of the automobile and a lot about the auto industry.

Joe Thompson married Augusta Grosh in 1907. She worked at an auto trim shop and often had to pay their expenses when her husband was without a job.

Joe Thompson on the left is working with his students on a three eighth scale styling clay model. The Director of the Art Center College, Edward A. Adams, is second from the right. In the background is Andy Ragheb who later became a designer for Ford in Cologne, Germany and contributed to several Taunus programs. (PhotographFrom the Collection of Art Center College, Roland C. Hill)

Thompson's big opportunity came when he was hired into the pattern shop of the Fisher Body Company of General Motors. It was there that he began his involvement with clay. His long experience and skill as a wood model maker enabled him to quickly master the art of clay modeling. From there, Thompson began his association with Harley Earl working on some of the first models which were developed in clay in the Art and Colour Section of General Motors.

Thompson was not the first clay modeler in General Motors. That distinction should perhaps go to John Lutz, Sr., who began his career in Germany in a wood model making apprenticeship program. After completing his training, Lutz came to the United States and hired into General Motors. He worked his way up to become head of the pattern shop at the Fisher Body Company. Lutz was one of the first to help Harley Earl in the Art & Colour Section of General Motors.

When Thompson hired into Fisher Body, he worked under John Lutz, Sr. in the pattern shop. Lutz introduced Thompson to Harley Earl and to clay modeling. Lutz then taught Thompson the fundamentals of building models in clay.

In the late 1920s, Harley Earl asked Joe Thompson to investigate a harder modeling clay. Thompson worked with Joseph Marra, the Chavant company's owner, in developing the hard red styling clay.

After developing his skill in sculpturing models from styling clay, Joe Thompson worked for other design organizations in Detroit. He contributed to the development of Ford models, Hupmobile, Lincoln Zephyr, and many more of the new lines of automotive products coming out of Detroit during the late 1920s and the 1930s.

From 1941 to 1947, Raymond Loewy hired Thompson to head the model shop at the Studebaker Design Department in South Bend, Indiana. While there he developed models for the famous postwar Studebaker.

In 1947, the Thompsons moved to North Hollywood, California and Joe began his own business, Built Rite Models. He made scale models and mock-ups of everything from tractors to television sets. One of the most important clients he had was Walt Disney. Disney hired Joe to build the model cars for the "Autopia" for Disneyland.

Joe Thompson then received an offer to become an instructor at Art Center College of Design. He introduced some new concepts at Art Center that included day long classes and apprenticeship programs. He hired advanced students at his own Built Rite Model shop and gave them a chance to work on full scale models. He paid them a good hourly wage for their services while they were learning to use different materials and tools. Thompson was also responsible for sending numerous Art Center Transportation Department students to earn and learn in Detroit at the major auto companies in between school terms. Joe Thompson estimated that 2,000 of his past students became leading designers throughout the world.

To celebrate his ninetieth birthday in September 1977, Art Center College hosted a party with a large number of his friends, associates, and students. Tributes to Joe came from many of the industry's designers and culminated in the announcement that a permanent scholarship at the college was being endowed in Joe Thompson's name.

From the back woods of Ontario, Joseph Thompson progressed from shaping wood into ax handles for lumberjacks, to making patterns for Cadillacs; from sculpturing styling clay models for Harley Earl and Raymond Loewy, to teaching model making techniques and skills to future designers around the world. He progressed from simple wood toys and models to become a skilled pattern maker, and then when he had the opportunity, he learned to develop models in styling clay.

A similar scenario was played out in varying degrees by the contemporary model makers of Joe Thompson's time and by the hundreds of other modelers who have followed him in the art of design modeling.

Gordon M. Buehrig

Gordon Buehrig was born and raised in Mason City, Illinois. After graduating from high school in 1922, he entered Bradley Polytechnic in Peoria, Illinois taking a liberal arts course. When his chemistry instructor found sketches of automobiles on all of the pages of his chemistry notebook, he was expelled.

Buehrig then went to Chicago and while working for Yellow Cab driving taxis, he visited the custom body company of C. P. Kimball. He spoke with their designer, Clarence Wexelberg, who was also a body engineer and layout draftsman. When Wexelberg learned of Buehrig's interest in design and his problem at Bradley Polytechnic, he aided him in planning his education and career.

Gordon Buehrig returned to Bradley but instead of a liberal arts course, he enrolled in courses that included drafting, wood shop, metal shop and art.

Buehrig was hired by the Gotfredson Body Company in Wayne, Michigan in November, 1924. He first worked as an apprentice in the woodshop and after six months he was moved to engineering to become a body draftsman. Gotfredson built bodies for Jewett, Peerless, and Wills Sainte Claire.

In January 1926, Buehrig was hired as a draftsman at the newly established custom body company of Dietrich Incorporated in Detroit, Michigan. At that time Dietrich built bodies for Pierce-Arrow, Franklin, Packard and Lincoln.

In January 1927, Buehrig transferred to Packard Motor Company where he made drawings of body panels. He met Frederick J. Hooven there who gave him a book by Le Corbusier entitled *"Toward a New Architecture"* which helped him formulate much of his philosophy of design.

It was during this time that Harley Earl was establishing the Art and Colour Section at General Motors. Buehrig was interviewed by Earl and was hired as the fourth automobile designer in the new department. While there, he worked on the 1929 Buick program. The exterior design was developed on a full size clay model and it was Buehrig's first experience seeing an automobile sculptured in clay.

His contribution to the 1929 Buick was the design of the instrument panel.

From General Motors, Buehrig moved on to Stutz Motor Car Company in Indianapolis, Indiana in December 1928 and became the body designer for the company. While at Stutz, he designed the bodies for three Stutz Blackhawk speedsters entered in the 1929 LeMans 24 hour race.

Buehrig left Stutz and was hired by Harold T. Ames, Vice President of Duesenberg, Incorporated in the summer of 1929 as chief body designer. He was 25 years old.

Duesenberg was first located in Indianapolis, but later the design office moved to Auburn, Indiana. Duesenberg is known as the most prestigious automobile built in the United States. He designed many special bodies and special new features and designs for interiors as well as the exterior. A few of his outstanding designs are the Beverly Berline, the Derham Tourster, the Torpedo Phaeton, the Brunn Town Car, the Twenty Grand and the Rollston Convertible Torpedo Victoria.

Gordon Buehrig is seen here in 1930 working on body designs for Duesenberg at the Duesenberg plant in Indianapolis, Indiana. (Photograph: Auburn-Cord-Duesenberg Museum, Auburn, Indiana)

During his time at Auburn, Cord, and Duesenberg, Gordon Buehrig designed many famous automobile bodies. A fine example is this Duesenberg Convertible Torpedo Victoria built by Rollston. (Photograph: Auburn-Cord-Duesenberg Museum, Auburn, Indiana)

Perhaps the most famous Buehrig Duesenberg is this SJ four-door sedan built by Rollston for the 1933 Chicago World's Fair exhibit. It was tagged the Arlington Sedan by the company but quickly became the "Twenty Grand" when it was displayed with the $20,000 price tag. (Photograph: Auburn-Cord-Duesenberg Museum, Auburn, Indiana)

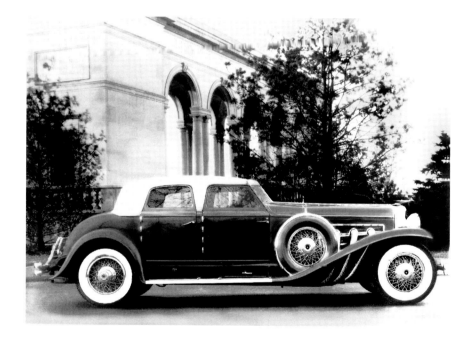

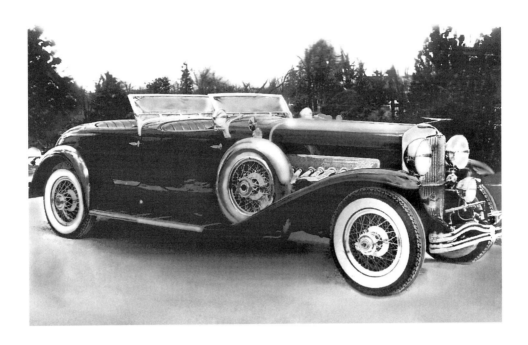

These pictures show Buehrig's design drawing and the completed Duesenberg Torpedo Phaeton built by Brunn. Original rough sketches were submitted by a young man, Mark Lawrence, who lived in Washington, D.C. He wished to have a Duesenberg built to his design. His ideas inspired one of the company's greatest models.
(Photograph: Auburn-Cord-Duesenberg Museum, Auburn, Indiana)

This photograph is of a 1932 Duesenberg LaGrande, Dual Cowl Phaeton "Sweep Panel". The body for this series was designed by Gordon Buehrig. (Photograph: Auburn-Cord-Duesenberg Museum, Auburn, Indiana)

In the midst of the depression, automobile sales were down and Buehrig returned to General Motors Art and Colour Section. This was in the Spring of 1933. Because of slow work, Harley Earl set up a design contest among his designers. There were five team leaders in the design staff and each leader was the chief designer for a team of two or three other designers or apprentices. The five team leaders, in addition to Buehrig, were Frank Hershey, Jack Morgan, Jules Agramonte, and Tom Hibbard. The prize for the winning team was an all expense paid trip to Chicago for several days to attend the World's Fair, called A Century of Progress Exposition.

The contest specified a four-door sedan developed on a one-quarter scale model. In an unofficial judging by all of the designer contestants, not including their own team's model, Buehrig's design came in first. But his design was too radical for the actual contest judges, which included the heads of the various General Motors Divisions. Jack Morgan's team went to Chicago.

Buehrig's design was quite unusual. It had two radiators located between the hood and the front fenders. This was ostensibly to block out direct air to the engine compartment to aid in maintaining a clean engine.

In the Fall of 1933, Ames called Buehrig back to design a small Duesenberg. He made a sketch for Ames based on his rejected contest design at General Motors. Ames gave his approval after Buehrig built a one-eighth scale model. This project was done in complete secrecy from other designers at the plant.

The engine turning on the instrument panel of this 1932 Duesenberg LaGrande, Dual Cowl Phaeton is a mark of Gordon Buehrig's design. (Photograph: Auburn-Cord-Duesenberg Museum, Auburn, Indiana)

The small Duesenberg was based on a design Gordon Buehrig had proposed for a contest organized by Harley Earl when Buehrig was at the GM Art and Colour Section. Although many of the design elements of the small Duesenberg were used on the award winning Cord 810, the Duesenberg did not possess the magic of the Cord. (Photographs: Auburn-Cord-Duesenberg Museum)

Oct. 2, 1934.   G. M. BUEHRIG   Des. 93,451

AUTOMOBILE

Filed May 17, 1934   3 Sheets-Sheet 1

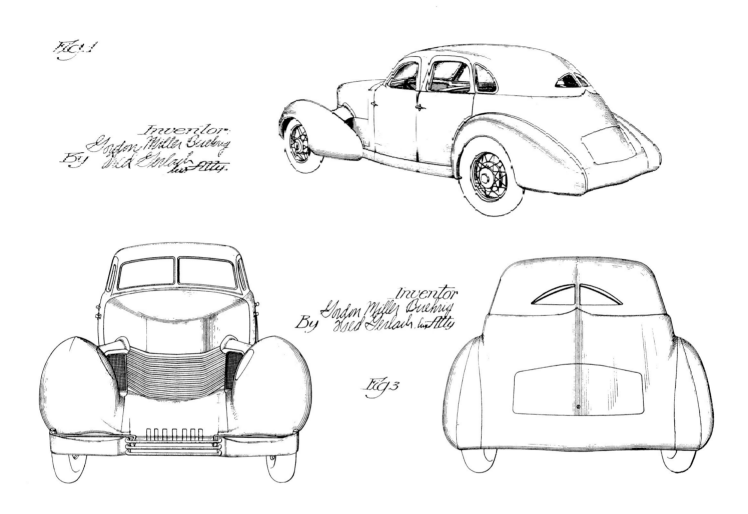

Fig.1

Inventor:
Gordon Miller Buehrig
By Fred Gerlach, his Atty.

Inventor
Gordon Miller Buehrig
By Fred Gerlach, his Atty.

Fig.3

Fig.4

Inventor
Gordon Miller Buehrig
By Fred Gerlach, his Atty.

The 1935 Auburn 851 Super-charged Speedster was a sensation at the Auto Shows. Gordon Buehrig developed this by updating and reworking left over 1933 Auburn Speedster bodies and adapting them to the 1935 Auburn chassis. The folding top disappeared below a panel behind the seat.
Seen here is a 1936, Auburn 852 Speedster. Each Super-charged Speedster carried a plate on the instrument panel certifying a maximum speed of over one hundred miles per hour. The Speedsters had super-charged straight eight L head engines developing 150 horse power. (Photograph: Auburn-Cord-Duesenberg Museum, Auburn, Indiana)

The Cord 810 automobile was more advanced in concept, design, and engineering than any other automobile at that time. (Photograph: Auburn-Cord-Duesenberg Museum, Auburn, Indiana)

Gordon Buehrig designed what he called a "no nonsense" instrument panel for the Cord 810. The aircraft influenced, engine turned panel with round instruments and toggle switches was very unusual and attractive. The radio speaker was in the header as were the individual windshield wiper switches. The finger control Bendix gear shift lever was mounted on a steering column stock. Headlamp cranks were located at the bottom of the instrument panel near the door on either side. (Photograph: Auburn-Cord-Duesenberg Museum, Auburn, Indiana)

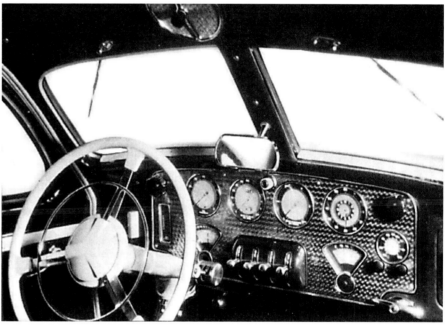

The idea for a small Duesenberg came from Cadillac. The LaSalle, first introduced in 1927 and styled by Harley Earl, was a separate line of automobiles built by the Cadillac Motor Car Company of General Motors. It had a V-8 engine like Cadillac but it was a more advanced engine design and it had a shorter stroke, giving it less piston displacement. Otherwise, the LaSalle was still a large car, only slightly smaller than the Cadillac, but it was more stylish. However, for 1934 LaSalle used the chassis and engine block from the Oldsmobile. This engine was a straight eight but for the LaSalle cast iron pistons were replaced by aluminum pistons and there were other detail changes. This was a much smaller LaSalle than the previous model and it had an all new trend setting style. For 1934, the Cadillac-LaSalle sales doubled.

The small Duesenberg was based on the Auburn straight eight, thus it followed the idea of the 1934 LaSalle. An orthographic three-view drawing was made from Buehrig's one-eighth scale model and a prototype was built by Weymann Body Company in Indianapolis, Indiana. An Auburn chassis was modified by Augie Duesenberg to receive the body. The prototype was finished and was very interesting, but it did not capture the unique design feeling of Buehrig's sketch.

The program for the small Duesenberg was dropped when the Auburn, all new for 1934, was not liked by the dealers nor the public and Buehrig was called on to redesign the Auburn for a mid-year 1935 introduction. His Auburn face-lift was well accepted but to have something more sensational for the Automobile Shows, Buehrig designed the Auburn 851 Super-charged Speedster. The Speedster stole the shows and received much publicity. It became highly sought after as a collectors car. Many copies of the Speedster have been built and sold through the years since then.

Shortly after this, Buehrig was assigned to design a

View of the Auburn Automobile Design Department, September 1935. Gordon Buehrig can be seen in the center background working on a proposed Gentlemen's Roadster for Auburn. The styling bridge, pointing, and measuring system designed and developed by Buehrig is being used on the Roadster model. (Photograph: Auburn-Cord-Duesenberg Museum, Auburn, Indiana)

This is one of several photographs Dale Cosper took of the one quarter scale Cord styling clay model. Four photographs of the model were presented at the Cord Corporation in Chicago on July 8, 1935. From these photographs the Board of Directors gave a go ahead for the Cord 810 project. (Photograph: Auburn-Cord-Duesenberg Museum, Auburn, Indiana)

new front drive Cord with a new drive line configuration and an ideal package layout. While the design theme for the Cord had some similarity to the smaller Duesenberg, the proportions and workout was quite different. The whole vehicle was much lower and it had a step down floor between the door sills since there was no drive line to interfere. It also had a short V-8 engine with the transmission ahead of the differential. The original L-29 Cord was also front wheel drive, but it had a long straight eight engine with the differential and front wheels ahead of the transmission.

Gordon Buehrig's background is not unusual for the early industrial design period but it is quite interesting and worthwhile reviewing. His training, experience, and talent was the background for his many achievements. The 1936 Cord 810 which he designed is one of the all time outstanding designs. In 1951, the Museum of Modern Art of New York City called the Model 810 Cord one of the eight finest automobile designs ever. Very interesting also

are the details surrounding the Cord's development which are unique for the time and very important.

First of all, the design was developed in styling clay on a one-quarter scale model. Second, Buehrig originated the styling bridge and pointer system. This system provided several measuring and pointing capabilities. These include setting points into the model, obtaining accurate dimensions off the model's surface for developing a surface draft, and transferring points from one side of the model to the other to duplicate the surface. The bridge traveled on rails on either side of the model and was always orthogonal to the set up on any station where it was positioned along the length of the model. Next, short pieces of wooden dowel rods were used to set all critical dimension points (hard points) into the clay surface of the model. The model was roughed-in with templates made from an orthographic scale drawing using the hard points as minimum reference points. The design was developed, cleaned up, polished and completed.

A one quarter scale replica of the Cord 810 model can be seen in the Auburn-Cord-Duesenberg Museum, Auburn, Indiana. The model is shown with a reproduction of Gordon Buehrig's original styling bridge, bridge pointer, and table rail arrangement. Note the bored holes through the bridge side supports and top cross member. The pointer can be seen locating a point on the right hand side of the roof. The bridge arrangement and the various model replicas were constructed by museum members. (Photograph: T. A. Hoadley)

The Cord 810 design is as fascinating and inspiring to me today as it was 62 years ago when advertisements for the new Cord 810 first appeared in the Saturday Evening Post and other magazines. Most of the design elements came from Buehrig's ill- fated small Duesenberg, yet the Cord possesses a mystique that just does not appear in the Duesenberg. This is due in part to front wheel drive and unit construction which permitted the Cord to be about eight inches lower. But the appearance difference is greater than the package difference.

I believe the design success of the Cord 810 was due to its team development. The team designers and modelers were: Paul Peter Rueter Von Lorenzen, Dale Cosper, Vincent Gardner, and Richard H. Robinson. Lorenzen was a design illustrator, Cosper and Robinson were body draftsmen and modelers, Vince Gardner was a talented designer, modeler, and craftsman who later on was involved in the design of many other automobiles. This team, led by Gordon Buehrig, created the design of this award winning Cord 810. In contrast, the small Duesenberg was developed as a secret one-man project.

Although the Cord program had not yet been approved, Gordon Buehrig took a well deserved vacation and married Betty Whitten in December 1934. They drove to Florida in an Auburn four-door convertible sedan.

One of the more interesting aspects of this program, was that the Cord design was not sold to management by a styling studio review. Instead, the design was sold to the Board of Directors through the use of photographs taken from the finished one-quarter scale clay model. The Board met in Chicago, Illinois instead of Auburn, Indiana and had not seen the model. The photographs were taken at a low angle and with a focal length lens that gave the model the appearance of being full size. Dale Cosper took the photographs and processed them on a Sunday evening and they were rushed to Chicago on Monday morning for review by the Board.

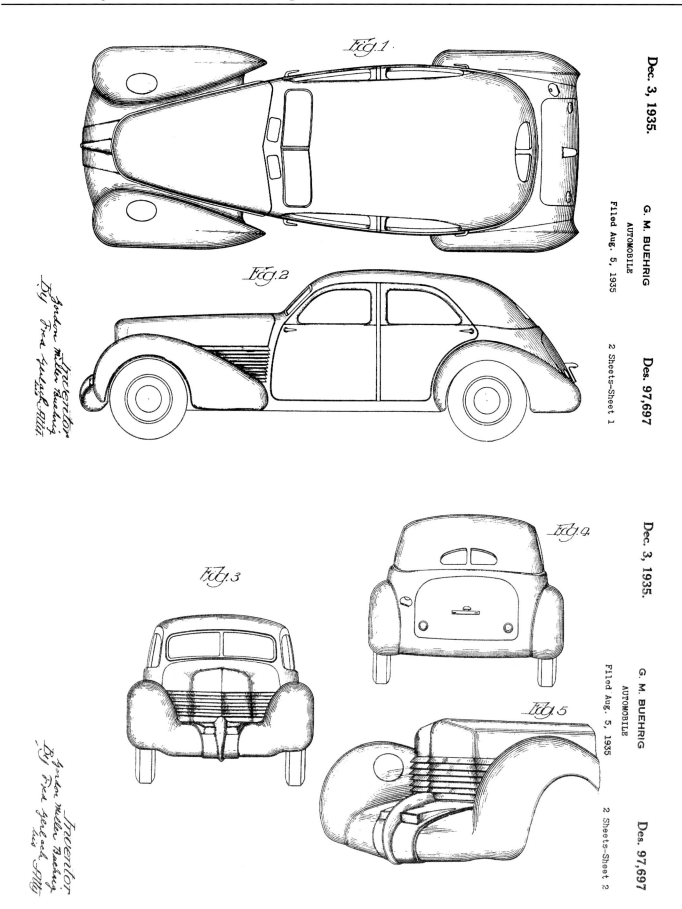

Fig.1

Fig.2

Fig.3

Fig.4

Fig.5

Dec. 3, 1935.

G. M. BUEHRIG

AUTOMOBILE

Filed Aug. 5, 1935

Des. 97,697

2 Sheets-Sheet 1

Dec. 3, 1935.

G. M. BUEHRIG

AUTOMOBILE

Filed Aug. 5, 1935

Des. 97,697

2 Sheets-Sheet 2

Standing beside this Cord 810 automobile in the Henry Ford Museum, Dearborn, Michigan, are from right to left, Gordon Buehrig, Mrs. Buehrig, and Arthur B. Morrill, Jr., 1985. Mr. Morrill edited the manuscript of this book. (Photograph: From the Collection of Henry Ford Museum and Greenfield Village)

Because of Buehrig's background, he had a strong hand in the chassis development and the engineering of the body. The program was completed in a very short time, on a very low budget but adequate time had not been allotted for tooling and testing. The vehicle was in production for only two years. Never-the-less, the Cord 810 made automobile design history and had a great influence on contemporary design.

Buehrig, next became chief designer for the Budd Body Company in Detroit. He designed a styling studio for Budd, had it constructed, and hired a staff of designers and modelers. He developed a concept for a small inexpensive passenger car. If produced, it might have been good competition for the Volkswagen after World War II. He also developed a very attractive small cab-over-engine truck and several other automobile designs.

During this time at Budd, Buehrig produced a 16mm movie entitled, *"The Development of an Automobile Design Model"*. Although it is a silent film, it has captions that explain how to build a 1/4 scale wood armature, apply the clay, and tool the clay to a finished model. The film then

shows how to make a plaster negative and a positive plaster cast of the model. The film is only twelve minutes long but is quite informative. This movie film can be seen at the Auburn-Cord-Duesenberg Museum, Auburn, Indiana.

Buehrig then moved back to Auburn, Indiana and established an industrial design office in association with John Reinhart. They did design work for White Truck and for the King Seeley Company.

When World War II started, Buehrig hired into Consolidated Aircraft in San Diego, California as a draftsman. He also worked for Goodyear in Akron, Ohio tooling the F4U1 Corsair aircraft. During this time he took a trigonometry course and due to that training along with his experience in body drafting, he was able to solve many complicated layout problems. These were problems common in body engineering such as drawings of parts that had to be rotated and redrawn in many different planes for tooling purposes.

After World War II he worked for Raymond Loewy

This picture brings out the magic of the 1937 Cord 812 Supercharged Phaeton. The time and place is September 1954, Watkins Glen Grand Prix. In a road test published in 1937, the Supercharged Cord exceeded 100 MPH and accelerated from 0-60 MPH in 13.2 seconds. The article is very positive for the exceedingly quiet, high speed, good ride and handling of this exceptional front wheel drive automobile. (Photograph: Ron Sheward)

The 1930s saw the greatest advance in automobile design. On the left is a 1929 Ford Model A Sport Coupe and on the right is a 1937 Cord 812 Supercharged Beverly Sedan. Although these two cars were designed only a few years apart, the difference is quite remarkable. On the far left is my father, Harry W. Hoadley, next to him is Jock Garden (owner of the Cord and oil man from Kansas), in the center is my uncle, Wilber Hoadley, and on the far right is the author at age 16. My brother Howard, the owner of the Model A, had just returned to Findlay, Ohio from Los Angeles where he attended Art Center School, March, 1938. (Photograph: Howard W. Hoadley).

on the postwar Studebaker. He then developed a very unusual automobile, the Tasco. On this vehicle he originated and patented the T-top roof which later became a highly desirable option on other production vehicles.

In August 1949, Buehrig hired into Ford Motor Company and held several managerial positions. He was responsible for many design engineering developments. The first Ford hardtop, the 1951 Ford Victoria, and the first all steel Ford Station Wagon were developed under his direction.

Buehrig became Chief Body Engineer for the Lincoln Continental Mark II program in 1952, and was responsible for many of its features. William Clay Ford initiated and led this program and John Reinhart was the Chief Stylist. The Ford Motor Company top management desired to have the most prestigious American car. The Continental Mark II was designed and engineered toward this goal. It was to have been equal in quality and finish to the English built Rolls Royce. But that level of dedication and perfection was not to be found in the craftsmanship available in the American labor market.

However, two advances in design and safety were derived from the development of the Continental Mark II. One was a thin "A" pillar which eliminated the blind spot caused by the wide pillars of other contemporary automobiles. The other was a strong deep frame that was moved outboard of the floor. This repositioning of the frame permitted the Mark II to be lowered three inches in overall height without reducing the inside headroom. This frame design was the prototype for future automobile frames because of the wide low package and new improved proportions. Safety was improved because the outboard location of the frame resisted side impact and it lowered the center of gravity.

Buehrig completed his stay at Ford by doing basic research on plastic bodies. He retired from Ford Motor Company in 1965 after 16 years with the company.

Gordon Buehrig patented the removable hardtop T-top in 1948 while developing the ill-fated Tasco sporty car. He obtained a second patent on this device in 1951. He also installed it on a 1955 Thunderbird removable hard top. The Thunderbird T-top was demonstrated to executives at Ford, Fisher Body, GM Design, Chrysler, American Motors, and the Golde Company of Germany. No interest was shown for the idea.

In 1967, Corvette introduced the T-top on their hard top, (it was installed later on many other models). This came as a great surprise and shock to Buehrig. His patent had not expired so this was clearly an infringement on the patent. He hired a lawyer, met with a representative of General Motors, and accepted their offer for a settlement.

After his retirement from Ford, Buehrig was invited to teach a course in plastics to students at the Art Center College of Design in Pasadena, California. Gordon Buehrig completed his career as a college professor teaching design students from his broad background of technical design experience.

Top view of the 1/4 scale Tasco Sporty Car, designed by Gordon Buehrig.

Eugene T. Gregorie

E. T. "Bob" Gregorie was raised on Long Island, New York and attended private schools. He was always interested in boats and yachts but he was also interested in automobiles. When Gregorie was growing up, he was around many famous cars that his father owned including: a 1910 chain drive Mercedes, a French Delage and Amilcar, a Simplex, Pierce-Arrows and Franklins. He owned a small Citroen at the time he went to Detroit.

After he was out of school, he got a job with Bill Fleming at the Elco Works, Bayonne, New Jersey as a marine draftsman and worked there for a year and a half. Next he worked for Cox & Stevens (later Gibbs & Cox) in New York, one of the top naval architectural concerns. He worked under Phil Rhodes and Dan Cox, renown marine designers. This training provided him with a fine foundation in marine design and naval architecture.

Gregorie could see a wider scope for his interests in cars, so he started drawing some interesting body designs. In 1928 he obtained a position with Rolls-Royce Brewster in Long Island City sketching automobile designs and drafting.

Early in the Fall of 1929, Gregorie decided to go to Detroit. On the way he stopped at Franklin, in Syracuse, New York and at Pierce-Arrow in Buffalo, New York. On this trip he met Ray Dietrich who advised him to try Harley Earl's new Art and Colour Section at General Motors. On the last leg of his journey he took the D&C line boat from Buffalo and arrived in Detroit on his 21st birthday.

Like many other young designers, Gregorie hired into GM's Art and Colour Section and worked there for a short time. However after the stock market crash, he was laid off. Looking for something to do he visited the Cox & Stevens office in Detroit and found an old friend, Bill Ferman there. Ferman was happy to see Gregorie because he needed help on a large yacht (126 foot) that was being built for W. C. Rands, founder of Motor Products Company. Working on the plans for this yacht kept him busy until mid-Summer 1930. Before going back to Long Island, Gregorie contacted Henry Crecelius of the Ford Motor Company. Crecelius had worked for Brewster previously but now was chief body engineer for Lincoln Motor Company, Division of Ford Motor Company.

Eugene T. (Bob) Gregorie with the 1941 Ford in the Ford Design Department, Engineering Laboratory, Dearborn, Michigan. Gregorie is responsible for the clean classic designs of the Ford Motor Company products from the middle 1930's through the 1940's. (Photograph: From the Collection of Henry Ford Museum and Greenfield Village)

The famous English Ford Model Y, began production in August 1932. It was designed by Gregorie and was the lowest priced four-wheeled car in its class. Some parts of this car remained in production until 1962.

The styling theme for this car became the theme for the 1933-34 domestic Ford and the seven passenger Lincoln Town Car for 1934. (Photograph: Autocar)

The 1933 Ford was scaled up from the English Ford Model Y. There is also an obvious similarity to the 1933-34 seven passenger Lincoln Town Car. (Photograph: Ford Public Relations)

Gregorie designed a sports car for Edsel Ford using a modified 1934 Ford V8 chassis. It had an underslung rear axle and redesigned front suspension to greatly reduce the height of the frame. The design featured cycle fenders all around, molded in driving lights, and an open cockpit. (Photograph: From the Collection of Henry Ford Museum and Greenfield Village)

The beautiful 1938 Lincoln Zephyr was designed by Eugene T. "Bob" Gregorie. The Museum of Modern Art, New York praised the 1938 Lincoln Zephyr as one of four of "the most satisfactory" American automobile designs. The vehicle shown here is a prototype and is being photographed for advertising art purposes. Notice the dummy headlamps. (Photograph: Public Relations, Ford Motor Company)

Gregorie returned home and skippered a yacht that summer and went to South Carolina with his family in the fall. In December he received a telegram from Henry Crecelius asking him to come to work for Ford at the Engineering Laboratory in Dearborn, Michigan.

Gregorie started working for Crecelius under Edsel Ford in January 1931 making design sketches for Lincoln cars, Lincoln bodies, and custom bodies. In 1932 Edsel Ford asked Gregorie to redesign the small Dagenham English Ford. When this was completed, Edsel ordered the design of the new English Ford scaled up to a larger package size for the 1933-34 American Ford. This work was done by Clare Kramer, in the drafting section. When this larger version of Gregorie's English Ford design was completed, Edsel asked Gregorie how he liked it. Gregorie said, "Fine", and then Edsel asked, "Do you recognize it?" and Gregorie said, "Yes". Gregorie was not directly involved with the scaled up 1933-34 American Ford except that it came from his design of the new English Ford.

During this period, Gregorie designed and supervised the construction of a boat tailed speedster that was built for Edsel Ford using a modified 1932 Ford V8 chassis. He also developed a sports car with a special chassis based on the 1934 Ford. It had an underslung rear axle and redesigned front suspension to greatly reduce the height of the frame. This idea was used on the early Jensen Ford when Edsel arranged for it to be built in England. The Jensen production series was built on the 1935 and later Ford chassis which was lower and did not require an underslung axle. The Jensen was built until 1939 when the second World War started.

Another one of Bob Gregorie's early tasks for Edsel was to modify and redevelop the front sheet metal and grill during the design phase of the 1936 Lincoln Zephyr. The Zephyr was designed by John Tjaarda at the Briggs Body Company but Edsel did not like the sloping (VW Beetle type) hood on the original mock-up. Gregorie did the redevelopment work at Briggs with Briggs design people.

Gregorie established the Ford Design Department in 1935 and designed the 1938 Fords and the expanded model range and face-lifting on the 1938 Lincoln Zephyr. The front end sheet metal form and the low grill of the 1938 Zephyr is still one of the most beautiful of all time. The low grill theme revolutionized grill design for virtually every American automobile.

For 1939 Gregorie designed the all new Mercurys, restyled the Fords, did a minor face-lifting on the Zephyr, revamped the entire Ford truck line and developed a bus. In 1940 an all new Zephyr was introduced, the Ford and Mercury lines were refined, and an unusually clean Ford sedan delivery was introduced. Most important of all, Gregorie designed the original Lincoln Continental.

All of the above designs were developed under the guiding hand and influence of Edsel Ford. This clean contemporary line of vehicles ranks as one of the highest statements of design in automobile history. This was an amazing feat especially when one considers the fact that these products were developed with a small design staff of only 18 people under the direction of Gregorie and the influence and good taste of Edsel Ford.

The clean aero design of the 1940 Lincoln Zephyr by Bob Gregorie differs in a refined and unique way from the more stylized automobiles from other marques of the period. (Photograph: Public Relations, Ford Motor Company)

This is the original styling clay model of the 1940 Lincoln Zephyr. The model has been painted and the bright moldings on the body side and the hood have been finished with aluminum foil. Bumpers are mounted on separate stands.

Note the excellent modeling and beautifully painted finish. Note also the clay cracks due to the lack of structural stability of the model. Side window surface has been finished with thin plastic sheet material.

The 1940 model year was the first year that sealed beam head lamps were required by government regulation. (Photographs: Ford Design Department)

Edsel Ford was the only child of Henry and Clara Bryant Ford. Edsel was president of the Ford Motor Company from 1919 until his untimely death in 1943.

In 1922, Ford purchased the Lincoln Motor Company from Henry and Wilfred Leland, (Henry Leland also developed the Cadillac). Edsel was given much more control over the Lincoln by his father, Henry Ford, than he was ever permitted to have over the Model T Ford.

Edsel was a true gentleman and he was always fashionably dressed. He had a good mechanical background and had been trained to run the Ford Motor Co. The elegant classic Lincolns of the 1920s and 30s were the result of Edsel's

Edsel Ford was the only heir to Henry and Clara Bryant Ford and was president of the Ford Motor Company from 1918 until his untimely death in 1943. Edsel's influence on the beautiful classic Lincolns and the clean design of the Ford products in the 1930's and early 1940's, is quite evident. (Photograph: From the Collection of Henry Ford Museum and Greenfield Village, Dearborn, Michigan)

influence. The beautiful clean appearance of the Fords, Mercurys and the various Lincolns from early 1930s to 1940 was due in part to his exceptional good taste in design. This was in contrast to some of the rather overly styled designs coming from General Motors.

According to Gregorie, "Edsel knew what he wanted and he knew when something looked right. He was able to control design because he was an excellent critic."

During the 1920s and 30s, when Lincoln was one of the most prestigious automobiles, Edsel Ford would select ten or twelve designs each year from sketches submitted by each custom body company. He would criticize these designs and request modifications when he felt they were necessary. A series of bodies would then be ordered for Lincolns from designs submitted by these companies. Bodies in white (unfinished bodies) would be shipped in and would be painted, trimmed, and assembled to Lincoln chassis according to customer wishes. A certain number of body designs each year become standard catalog models.

The body companies who built custom bodies for Lincoln included: Dietrich, Willoughby, Brunn, LeBaron, Waterhouse, Locke, Judkins, Holbook, and Derham.

The automobile marque for which Gregorie is most noted is the highly esteemed classic Lincoln Continental, (the product line was later redesignated as the Lincoln Mark). This design started as a special vehicle for Edsel Ford. Gregorie had worked with Edsel on other specials including the Jensen Ford, built in England from Ford parts and sold in limited numbers.

In the fall of 1938, Edsel discussed his wish to have another special-built car. Edsel's idea was to build it from Ford parts in limited numbers. But to interrupt the Ford production line to build a series of special cars was impossible. It was Gregorie's idea to use the Lincoln Zephyr instead of the Ford. Gregorie sketched the design of a low convertible automobile configuration over a side elevation outline of a 1939 Lincoln Zephyr. Edsel liked the sketch and authorized a further development. Gregorie directd a modeler, Gene Adams, to construct a one tenth scale model using a scale modeling bridge set up. When Edsel saw the completed model, he wanted one built. This was in November 1938. The model was turned over to Martin Regiko, the head body draftsman, and a paper draft was made and given to the Lincoln plant.

This 1931 Lincoln Dual Cowl Phaeton Series was part of the custom line of bodies ordered by Lincoln Motor Company. It is a model K with a V8 engine and built on the 145 inch chassis. (Photograph: Public Relations, Ford Motor Company)

LeBaron built this 1932 Lincoln convertible on the KB, 145 inch chassis. It had the new V12 engine. (Photograph: Public Relations, Ford Motor Company)

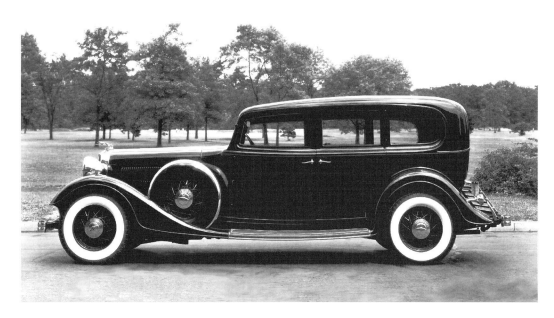

The seven passenger Lincoln Town Car for 1934 was built by Lincoln Motor Company and installed on the KB, 145 inch chassis. The 1933-34 domestic Ford had a style distinctly similar to this automobile. (Photograph: Public Relations, Ford Motor Company)

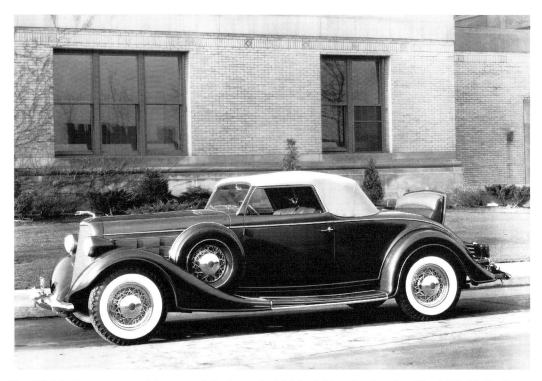

The 1935 LeBaron convertible coupe is built on the 136 inch Lincoln chassis. The 1935-36 Ford roadster and cabriolet were designed to imitate the style of this Lincoln. (Photograph: Public Relations, Ford Motor Company)

This Dietrich bodied 1932 Lincoln is mounted on the 145 inch KB chassis. It is a study in refined elegance. This photograph was taken at the back of the Edsel Ford Estate. (Photograph: Public Relations, Ford Motor Company)

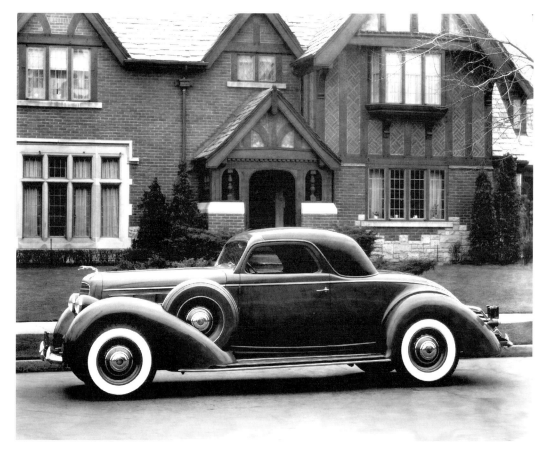

In 1936 the Lincoln style turned modern. This LeBaron two passenger coupe is mounted on the 145 inch chassis. Custom bodies were ordered in series after Edsel Ford had critiqued and approved design proposals submitted by the custom body companies. (Photograph: Public Relations, Ford Motor Company)

Photograph of the original one tenth scale model of the 1939 Lincoln Continental prototype. The design was Bob Gregorie's and the model was developed by Gene (Bud) Adams. (Photo: Ford Design)

A prototype was built from a modified 1939 Lincoln Zephyr. It was finished in Eagle Gray and shipped to Edsel's winter home in Florida on March 1, 1939. The car received a lot of attention around the Ford estate and in the Palm Beach area. Edsel telephoned Gregorie to proceed with limited production plans because he could sell 1000 copies right there in Florida.

The first production Continentals were built from 1940 Lincoln Zephyr parts that had modified exterior sheet metal surfaces. So the production Continentals were somewhat different in appearance than the two original prototypes built from 1939 Zephyr parts. The first production Continental was completed on December 13, 1939.

As indicated above, the first Continental model was developed in styling clay on a one tenth scale modeling bridge set up. It is very interesting to note the similarity of this to Gordon Buehrig's development of the Cord 810 on a one quarter scale modeling bridge set up. Like the Cord, the scale model of the Continental went directly to a surface draft and the draft to the prototype shop.

An exhibition concerning the aesthetics of motorcar design was presented at the Museum of Modern Art, New York City in the autumn of 1951. One of eight automobiles chosen primarily for their excellence as works of art was the 1941 Lincoln Continental. As mentioned earlier, Gordon Buehrig's Cord 810 design was also included in the eight automobiles.

Also significant and of considerable importance to this book, is that Gregorie was responsible for the development of a series of full size styling bridges. Willys P. Wagner, a staff designer and engineer under Gregorie, designed the bridges and supervised their

construction and installation in the department. These bridges were used to develop the full scale styling clay models starting with the line of 1938 Ford Motor Company products. The use of this styling bridge made improved model accuracy possible. The bridge provided a system for controlling points at one tenth inch intervals orthogonally anywhere on the surface of the model. These features made possible the bridge offset pointing system and a method for recording surface data in a note book. It was a portable assembly; the bridge rails could be moved and set up on any open floor area. These bridges were constructed at the Ford Rouge Plant, Tool and Die Shop.

The idea for the bridge offset pointing system came from Gregorie's training and experience in naval architecture where all hull forms are set up as a table of offsets. An offset is a measurement of distance to a given point on a surface from a given reference line or plane on a given station or section. Rather than making templates from the surface of a model and tracing them off on a drawing, measurements from the surface would be recorded as offsets in a note book. Offsets rather than templates were also used to set points into rough clay for developing surface. A book of offsets of a model could be sent to body drafting, the pattern shop, or the model shop. A surface layout drawing would be made from the offset sheets.

The importance of the offset pointing system and the ability to have a complete body surface recorded in an offset book should be noted here. This system provided many advantages to the Design Department. It also presaged the use of coordinate measuring machines and computer systems in recording surface data for use in product design and engineering. Present systems for scanning surface data also record offset points relative to fixed points or planes; however, scanned surface data (offsets) that is retrieved and kept is recorded on a disk instead of in a note book.

The Lincoln Continental was a born "classic" design. Its lines and form are as refreshing today as they were in 1940. If you compare the production Continental with the original clay model, you will see that the windshield and door were moved forward, the front fender was shortened, and the belt line above the rear fender was raised. This photograph was taken at the front entrance of the Edsel Ford home. (Photograph: Public Relations, Ford Motor Company)

Gregorie is also credited with the use of aluminum foil to represent bright metal parts such as grills, moldings, handles, etc. One day while eating a Hershey bar, he took the aluminum foil that the chocolate bar was wrapped in and laid it on the slicked surface of a clay molding. He smoothed out the foil and it looked like a plated surface. Rolls of special soft foil were then ordered to be used for this purpose.

Before Edsel Ford's death in 1943, Gregorie designed the 1941 and 1942 domestic company products and the 1941 German built Ford Taunus. After Edsel's death, Gregorie continued on at Ford Motor Company to design the post World War II Mercury, Lincoln and Lincoln Cosmopolitan, the French built Ford Vedette, a new line of Ford trucks, and a post war Ford bus.

Gregorie retired to the St. Augustine area of Florida in 1947 and returned to boat designing and yachting.

The Ford Motor Co. Design Department, Dearborn, Michigan as it looked in March, 1939. There are several full size modeling bridge work areas. In the center background are the surface layout tables where body engineers support the design model work. In the right background a black board drawing is underway.
(Photograph: From the Collection of Henry Ford Museum and Greenfield Village)

A painted one quarter scale styling clay model of the 1948 Ford truck developed by the author under the direction of Bob Gregorie and designer Eric Ramstrum. The full size development followed closely the one quarter scale model. The 3-ton truck design went directly into a full size surface layout. (Photograph: Ford Design)

The full size development is very similar to the scale model. (Photograph: Ford Motor Company Brochure)

This one quarter scale model of the post war cab-over Ford truck has a cab that is cast in plaster. The hood, fenders, step, and front end design was developed in clay by the author in 1945. The cab-over development went first into a full size model and then into surface layout. There were several changes made for the production truck shown below.   (Photo: Ford Design)

The 1948 Ford Bus was designed by Eric Ramstorm and the 1/10th scale design model was developed by the author in 1945. (Photo: Ford Motor Company)

F- Series Trucks were first produced in 1948. This 1/2 ton pickup was scaled down from the 3-ton design. (Photo: Ford Motor Company)

CHAPTER 2 - Design Systems

Surface Development Systems

As noted in the previous chapter, George C. Mercer was a widely known designer, body engineer, and automotive writer early in this century. Mercer had considerable knowledge and a long experience in body design from the horse carriage to the automobile. Mercer provided a great amount of insight into automobile body design and engineering.

Mercer found that the credit for creating a system for developing curved surfaces of the sides, back, and top of horse carriages to produce an harmonious effect and be theoretically correct, belongs to the French. The horse carriage was known as the French rule of body design. For many years, Paris was the learning center for young carriage draftsmen who wished to become proficient body designers. Dupont was the proprietor of a trade journal called Le Guide de Carrossier. Brice Thomas, a young man who had worked in a carriage shop and later worked in a shipyard, conceived the idea of applying geometry to carriage bodies in a manner similar to that by which it was applied to shipbuilding. He suggested this to Dupont and, between Dupont and Thomas, the system of body designing was developed.

Two-dimensional surface development, originated by the French, still applies. It is based upon orthographic projections of the item being designed. Each view of the drawing is laid out in a geometric grid. Side, front, and rear elevations, and top plan views in product design and transportation design drawings show design lines, orthogonal section lines, and lines through critical areas of the object being developed.

The advanced "Unisurf" system discussed later in this chapter, was developed by Dr. Pierre E. Bezier in the 1960s. This system extends the geometric grid to a patch structure that can be manipulated mathematically.

With the proper computer, software, and monitor, two-dimensional images can be viewed in perspective in a grid or patch form, or in color as a shaded object, and further developed through 3-D computer modeling. The image can also be projected full size onto a large screen. Using holography, the image can be viewed in three dimensions but it would not be easily modified and it would still be only an image. However, to develop these images correctly in a three dimensional model, stable armatures, fixtures, and positioning systems are required in addition to accurate measuring and marking (scanning and milling) equipment.

Model Measuring Systems

The two basic systems for measuring models in a point to point mode are:

1.   A movable single upright column or portable angle, having machined surfaces from which a pointer or scale can be used to measure to the surface of a model, in an orthogonal manner. Using a second column or angle and a machined portable cross bar, measurements to the surface from above and to the front and rear of a model can be taken.

2.   A bridge moving on tracks and having two upright columns joined together by a structural cross member and having a movable machined cross bar, forms a continuous machined work surface around a model. This permits scales or pointers to be used to measure from the bridge to the surface of a model on either side, or from above, or to the front or rear of a model in an orthogonal manner.

Either one of these systems can be used for taking or setting points and for making or setting templates.

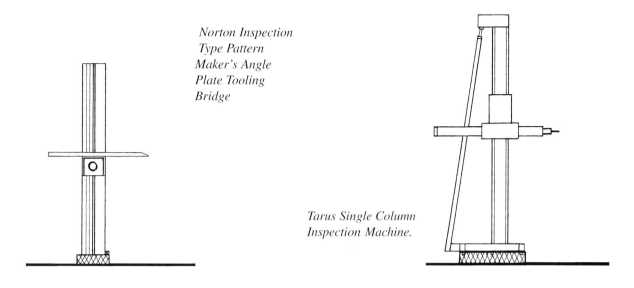

Norton Inspection Type Pattern Maker's Angle Plate Tooling Bridge

Tarus Single Column Inspection Machine.

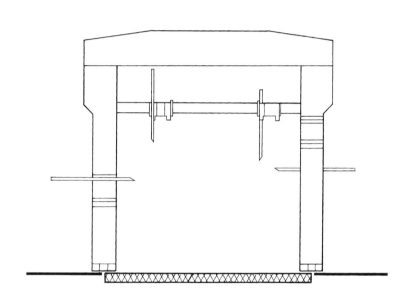

Lamerson Point Scanning Bridge.

The use of angles is the classic system for controlling the fabrication of parts and the construction of assemblies. A surface plate, angle, scale, and height gauge have been essential tools used when inspecting parts. An angle can be found on every tool maker's bench and on every pattern or model maker's work table or surface plate. Angles are still one of the most useful tools used by design modelers.

A sophisticated angle system for styling clay models was developed by Fred Norton in the mid 1940s. This system has been further improved by Gene Perry and continues to be built by Norton Equipment Corporation, Blissfield, Michigan.

The first styling bridge and pointing system was developed by Gordon Buehrig in 1934 for the development of one-quarter scale clay models at the Auburn, Cord, and Duesenberg design office in Auburn, Indiana.

Bob Gregorie developed the first full size styling bridges and offset pointing system in 1936. These bridges were first used for the styling clay model development of the 1938 line of Ford, Mercury, and Lincoln Zephyr automobiles.

The current styling bridge was designed by U.D. (Al) Lamerson, and Ron Lamerson, Al's son. It is being built and sold by Lamerson U.S.A., Oak Park, Michigan. This bridge is highly refined and very accurate. It's precision equals that of a coordinate measuring machine. Scanning and milling heads can be installed on this bridge.

To engineer a new design requires a surface development of the model. A model may be built-up using advance information from a package drawing or data from a computer study. An accurate development of surface is necessary to complete the many details required for tooling and manufacturing. The production body engineering task is two-fold, it encompasses the design and engineering of the structure including all functional items therein, and the development and recording of the entire outside surface. Body engineers should be able to develop surface. Engineers specializing in surface development need the technical training available in surface layout courses. Starting early in this century, special courses have been offered to engineers covering both body construction and surface development.Early efforts at surface development were based on systems that had evolved in Europe from boat hull and carriage design. With advancements in automobile design and tooling, more complete drafts were required. Also, body designs were becoming more elaborate with more emphasis being placed on appearance. These early surface development systems had a great number of short comings. Models were not accurate, templates were not exact, and surface drafts had irregularities and hollows.

One of the more well known and popular courses in surface development was offered by Edgard C. DeSmet. His course was entitled "Surface Design and Planography". DeSmet's planographic layout systems resolved these surface irregularities and provided engineers, modelers, and designers a level of confidence in the final draft not possible before. The DeSmet course is still being taught by E.D.S. Alumni.

Another engineer, Harold Philpot, taught a specialized course in body construction that included the development and operation of the many functional body parts and assemblies. This course was very valuable to the engineer on the job who had to solve the seemingly endless body design problems. A surface development course similar to DeSmet's was also offered by others including the Ford Trade School. This course was taught by J. J. Harrington and was available to engineers at Ford Motor Company. Body engineering courses are taught at many engineering schools and colleges. When rigid styling clay model frames and exact positioning systems became available, many of the surface development problems went away. Computer programs now have software that emulate the surface development principles contained in the courses taught by DeSmet and others. Exact scanning and milling capabilities are now combined with stable model surface. Surface development irregularities and hollows that are present occasionally today, are possibly due to the computer designers lack of three dimensional surface development techniques and problems. Information for this outline was provided by Robert J. Todd, Resident Body Engineer, Ford Design Center, Retired.

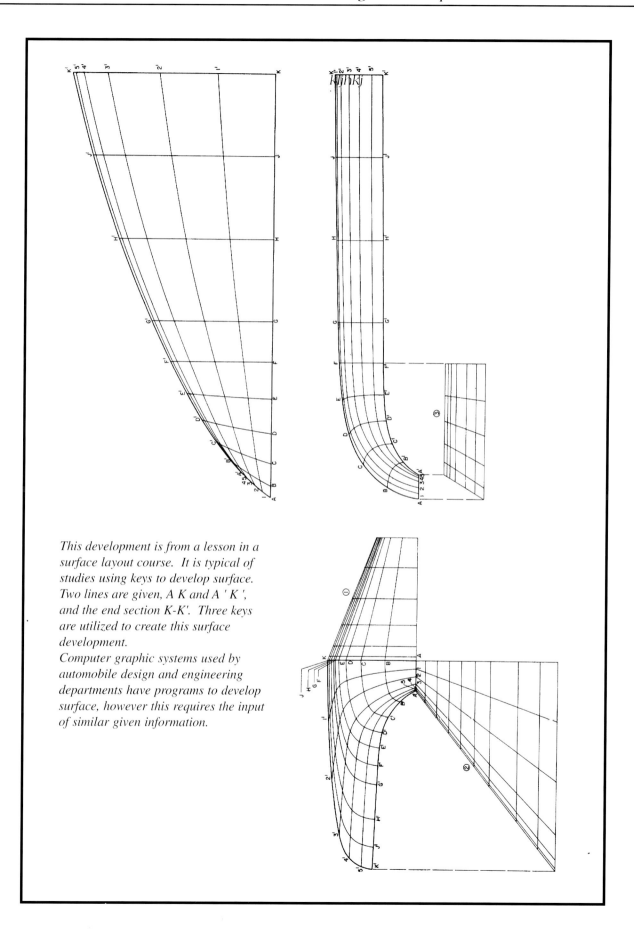

This development is from a lesson in a surface layout course. It is typical of studies using keys to develop surface. Two lines are given, A K and A ' K ', and the end section K-K'. Three keys are utilized to create this surface development.

Computer graphic systems used by automobile design and engineering departments have programs to develop surface, however this requires the input of similar given information.

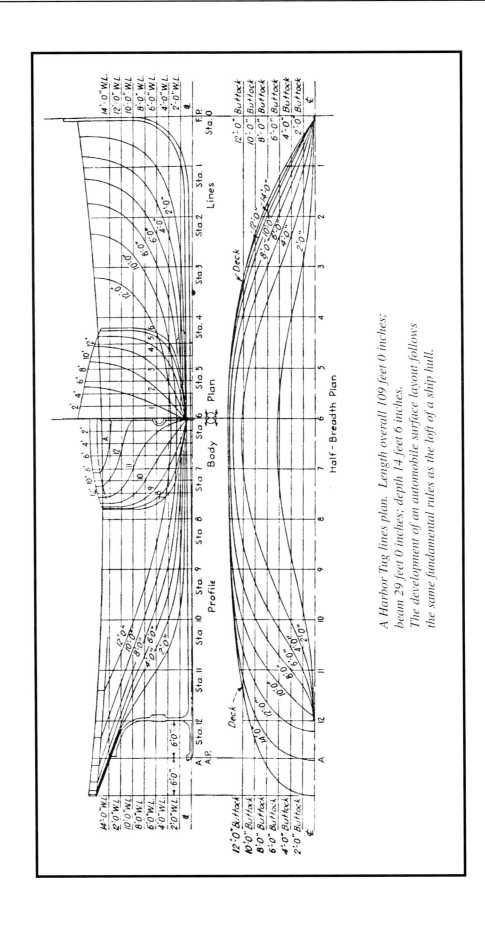

A Harbor Tug lines plan. Length overall 109 feet 0 inches; beam 29 feet 0 inches; depth 14 feet 6 inches. The development of an automobile surface layout follows the same fundamental rules as the loft of a ship hull.

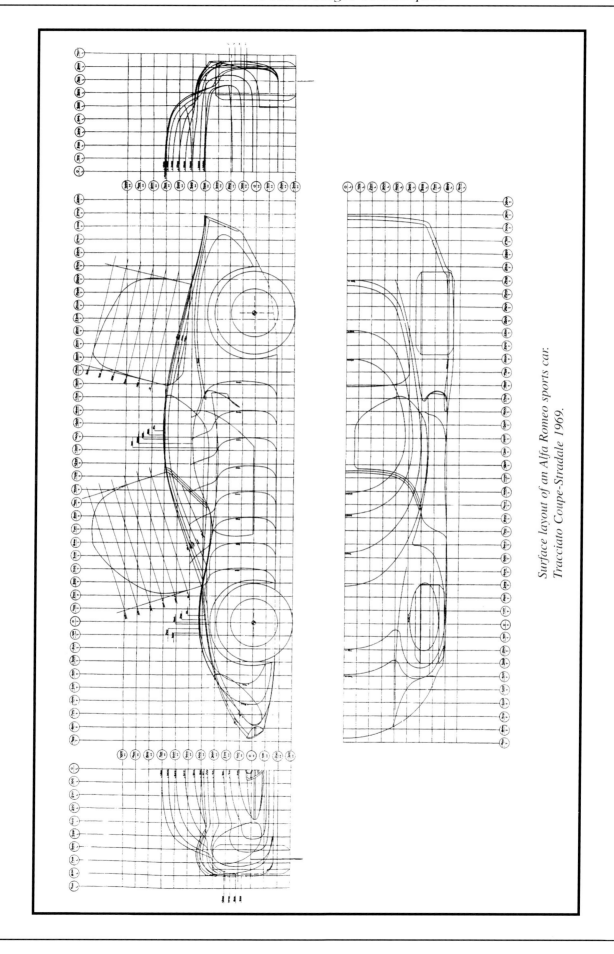

Surface layout of an Alfa Romeo sports car:
Tracciato Coupe-Stradale 1969.

Design Modeling Equipment

As dimensional control of models improved with the use of new bridges and other measuring systems, it became apparent that modeling armatures and related equipment were quite inadequate. Development of new modeling equipment and systems began in the Design Office, Ford of Germany. These developments originated from studies made by Rainier Kersting, Supervisor of Fabrication, supported by Heinz Baer and Dietrich Tenner, Supervisors of Interior and Exterior modeling. This was during my assignment to Cologne, Germany from 1958 to 1967 and was part of my responsibility.

Two new Progressive type modeling bridges, constructed by Schiess A.G., Dusseldorf, Germany, were installed in an enlarged studio area in Cologne in 1960. These bridges ran on long tracks so that each line had three separate work stations. To locate the models, each work station had four turned steel stands that screwed into machined cross members which were aligned to the bridge tracks and flush with surface plates. Full size exterior modeling armatures or bucks were set up and fixed with tapered pins to these stands. The tapered pins, attached to the frame of each armature, assured accurate positioning and repositioning of the design models.

Special axles were developed so that when models were not positioned in the work stations they would be standing on their own wheels and tires and could be wheeled about this way.

Many interior models were developed on surface tables. When the small Schiess modeling bridge became available in 1964, styling clay models of instrument panels, seats, and consoles as well as scale wind tunnel models were dimensionally controlled by this bridge. However, one bridge could not handle all of the work, so normal table modeling continued to supplement the bridge.

In 1966, plans for the new Design Center for Ford of Germany were finalized and the design for the all new full size bridge was completed. This bridge, engineered and constructed by Schiess, provided design model accuracy not possible previously.

In 1967, when I returned to Ford Design Center in Dearborn, Michigan, very little had changed other than the addition of many more people in the design modeling work force. There was an attempt to overcome equipment handicaps by adding manpower. Timing schedules were not being met because of inaccuracy and difficulty in working with the poor equipment. Much rechecking and reworking of models was necessary. There was no way to maintain sufficiently accurate dimensional control of models nor to obtain accurate data from finished models.

This was a very frustrating situation for design modelers, since they were not able to perform at the level of their skill and talent. It was obvious that other modeling methods were necessary to improve modeling efficiency and dimensional control of models.

Accurate dimensional control of design models requires:

1. Stable armature construction.

2. Exact armature (model) positioning and repositioning.

3. A method for precise measuring of models.

The advent of Coordinate Measuring Machines and plans to scan and mill clay model surface greatly exacerbated this situation. It was impossible to correctly align or maintain any model, interior or exterior, to the degree of accuracy modern methods now required. Because of poor dimensional control of clay surface, data taken from models in the form of cardboard templates and points required extensive resurfacing when drafted. It was necessary to remodel redeveloped two-dimensional surface drafts for final model prove out. But remodeling resulted in the same problem as before: no way to correctly dimension the model and no way to correctly check surface.

Automotive engineering and tooling is an exacting business, requiring long timing schedules. It was essential to correct this impossible situation that existed in design model development to improve timing in the Design Center.

Interior Modeling Systems

First of all, in 1968, I established the Modeling Systems Unit to develop and engineer the necessary equipment. The Modeling Systems staff came from the design modeling work force. These men were experienced modelers with backgrounds that included engineering, tooling, model shop training, and drafting. They understood the problems and we worked together to solve them. The Modeling Systems Unit was supervised by Nicholas Waskul.

For interior design we developed a complete modular system. Three-piece units were designed for interior bucks. They were constructed from aluminum tubing, I-beam sections, and plates that were welded together and normalized. They were machined in areas where mating occurred and where armatures attached. Armatures that attached to these bucks were all located by pins. These three units consisted of an instrument panel buck, a front seat roll up, and a rear seat and package tray roll up. These were fitted with modeling armatures that allowed model development either in the bucks or on table fixtures. Door armatures included the correct hinging. The three-piece interior bucks could be rolled (on casters) together, pinned, locked, and leveled. Fiberglass skin could be installed so the appearance of a complete vehicle, interior and exterior, resulted.

Blackboard models (the complete interior side of a vehicle) were built up on armatures attached to precision fixtures mounted on surface tables. Instrument panel armatures could be built up on surface table fixtures and moved to an instrument panel buck for work or presentation.

Modeling armatures were not constructed to close tolerances but once they were positioned onto a modeling fixture and their locating pins were locked in place, they became stable and precisely positioned.

These fixtures, tables, interior bucks and armatures were all modular. They could be interchanged from one model to another, from one car line to another, and from one year to another. Efficiency and timing were greatly improved, and unit cost was greatly reduced.

This instrument panel buck is constructed from welded aluminum tubing, channel, and plate material. It is normalized and machined. A separate work platform is constructed and finished and locks into place with expanding pins on the base of the instrument panel buck. Note the adjustable leveling feet. Locator sockets on the lower cross member and pins on the side of the base are for locking in the seat roll up buck. A small fork lift truck with a tilting pickup, lifts and transports styling clay instrument panel models, 1970. (Photograph: Ford Design Center)

A door armature frame is mounted on hinges that are in the proper hinge lines, 1970. (Photograph: Ford Design Center)

The seat roll up buck is constructed similar to the instrument panel buck. It has leveling feet, locators, and locking "C" washers. To accommodate four door models, "B" pillar structures are attached to the seat roll up bucks, 1970. (Photograph: Ford Design Center)

The rear seat and package tray roll up buck completes the set. A two door armature frame is attached to the left side of the buck, 1970. (Photograph: Ford Design Center)

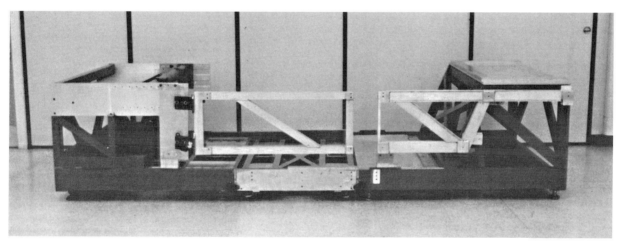

The three interior buck structures leveled and clamped together. They form a two door configuration, 1970. (Photograph: Ford Design Center)

An instrument panel and door model during design development. A windshield has been installed along with floor surface and door sills. The seat roll up is attached, 1985. (Photograph: Ford Design Center)

The three interior bucks are completed with finished models. Fiberglass exterior surface has been installed to complete the picture. The clay instrument panel has been painted. Gene Urbisce, James Hart, and LaMarr Ferguson are pulling the units together, 1970. (Photograph: Ford Design Center)

Another view showing these three bucks being slid together forming a single interior presentation model. All design items can be easily removed so the bucks can be used for other car lines and programs, 1970. (Photograph: Ford Design Center)

A design model of an instrument panel is developed on a steel table and fixture by Fred Twork. The modeling armature with the instrument panel model is removable and portable and can be set in an instrument panel buck or any other instrument panel fixture. This is from 1969. (Photo: Ford Design Center)

Exterior Modeling Systems

Previously on exterior models, clay was laid up over soft styrofoam that was built up over a plywood subsurface. The plywood was laid over wood bulkheads attached to steel outriggers that were welded to a steel I-beam frame. The clay surface was a long way away from the steel frame thus causing a very unstable condition. Also, the foam was usually not built up close enough to the model surface thus requiring several inches of clay to be added. It was not uncommon for a clay model to weigh twice as much as the vehicle it represented. The excess weight was a destabilizing force in itself.

In addition to this, after a presentation, it was not possible to reset a model into the same position in which it had been set originally. A positioning device did not exist and the surface was always moving.

These conditions caused the clay to crack and constant model repair was required.

To solve these problems, the heavy wood and steel armature was replaced with an aluminum framework. Over this, polyurethane foam blocks were both bolted and bonded to the frame and bonded to each other. This was a more stable and rigid foam. The foam was preshaped to within two inches of the model's surface. When built up with clay, these models weighed no more than the vehicles they represented.

A positioning system with stands and pins was developed and installed. This was similar in concept to the one in Cologne, Germany except that on this new system the pins could be screwed up or down for height adjustment of the armature. Stands were threaded into surface plates or floor plates depending on the type of bridge that a studio had. Any model could be set up in any studio simply by setting it down on the stands.

Adjustable axles were attached to the armature to control wheelbase and tread. These axles were also adjustable vertically to allow for correct vehicle load height. With the weight of the model on the axles, tires had their correct deflection and wheels had their correct relationship to the model. Models stood on their own wheels and axles except when they were in a work station on stands.

A static load test of an armature was made to determine actual frame stiffness. Eight thousand pounds of clay in boxes was distributed over the armature. This was three to four times more clay than was expected to be used on a model. Total deflection in the center of the frame was only 0.040 of an inch. When five hundred pounds of clay was added at the front or rear of the armature, several times during the test, the difference was negligible, only 0.001 of an inch at the ends of the armature.

The first of these developments was completed in 1970. By 1973 when the DEA Coordinate Measuring Machine was fully operational, all new exterior and interior models were built on the new fixture/armature systems. Locator stands were installed on the surface plate of the DEA Alpha machine and locator pins were fixed to all exterior models and all fixture tables for interior models. Models and tables were simply dropped onto the stands and positioning of the models for scanning or milling was automatic.

To clarify a point, only a part of design model development uses numerical control. However, there were considerable savings due to the use of numerical control in model development, but these savings were made possible by improved model accuracy. In a study conducted by the controller's office and released in February 1977, projected modeling savings relating directly to these new modeling systems and the use of numerical systems amounted to the equivalent of 52.7 people and $1,590,000.00.

Prove out hours (the hours required to redevelop surface drafts for final model prove out) accounted for half of the above savings. But to put this in a better perspective, prove out hours from 1973, when the new equipment and systems were operational, compared to 1969, when design of this equipment first started, resulted in a reduction of 65% for exterior and 68% for interior.

Due to these new systems and equipment, there was a significant increase in creative modeling work while conversely, many menial tasks, as well as several lost time tasks were eliminated. Direct labor hours indicated a considerable increase in developmental creative modeling. The amount of clay used for each direct labor hour (actual) increased from 0.56 pounds per direct man hour in 1970 to 0.75 pounds in 1973. This represented a 34% increase in creative modeling work.

There were many other developments that were all aimed toward maintaining the integrity of the models. One of these was the improvement of the workability and crack resistance of the styling clay. Working with Paul O'Neil, the President of Chavant, Incorporated, we developed a test and evaluation procedure for styling clay samples. The result was an improved clay for our models.

These developments were all for Ford Design Center; however, design studios of other companies were having the same problems. As time passed, many of these concepts were adapted by other companies but modified to meet their particular requirements.

Four highly skilled and competent craftsmen and artists from Dearborn supported the development of the 1961 German Ford Taunus 17M. From left to right are: Modeling Supervisor John Snider, Designer Bill Wheeler, and Master Modelers Mitchell Rukat and Gilbert Treweek. In the background of this picture can be seen the beginning of the 1961 prove out model. This was before any of the modeling armature improvements had been incorporated. Only a skin coat of clay had been rubbed in over the armature. The ends of the dowels that stand up over the hood area, indicate the thickness of clay necessary to develop the hood surface, September, 1958. (Photograph: Design Office, Ford Werke A.G., West Germany)

The first full size model positioning system was installed on the line of bridge work stations in the Ford Design Office, Cologne, Germany.

An H-beam was a part of the structure that supported the bridge rails and surface plates. This H-beam had been accurately bored and threaded to accept the model locator stands. The stands were 250mm tall and had 50mm risers for additional height.

The locator pins were tapered for easy positioning. Pins were available in different lengths for modeling buck height adjustment. Each pin was attached to a threaded plate.

To set up a model, the modeling buck or frame was positioned over four locator pin and plate assemblies that had been set into four locator stands. The locator pin plates were then welded to the frame. From then on, the model need only be set down on the stands to be correctly positioned. (This system was developed in 1963 although this photograph was taken in January of 1967 before the author returned to Dearborn. Photograph: Design Office, Ford Werke A.G., West Germany)

The exterior frames and interior bucks were all studied in one quarter scale models. Structures were assembled from dimensioned hollow wood tubes. Assemblies were glued and tested for rigidity and strength. Seen here is designer Robert Kirkpatrick and the author, 1970. (Photograph: Ford Design Center)

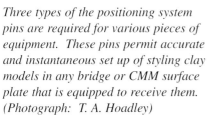

Three types of the positioning system pins are required for various pieces of equipment. These pins permit accurate and instantaneous set up of styling clay models in any bridge or CMM surface plate that is equipped to receive them. (Photograph: T. A. Hoadley)

Two welders put finishing touches on an aluminum frame. These stable substructures weigh only half as much as the steel-and-wood armatures formerly used to support clay models. Several sizes of armatures are used to accommodate the various vehicle sizes, January, 1971. (Photograph: Ford Design Center)

The under carriage of an exterior modeling frame showing the sliding armature, the positioning system, and the adjustable axle assembly. (Photograph: Ford Design Center)

During a static load test at the Ford Motor Company Design Center, an aluminum armature is stacked with 62-pound boxes of clay totaling 8,360 pounds . Dial indicators around the frame determine stress or deflection in the framework. Total deflection in the center of the frame was only 0.040 of an inch. The test also measures the armature's lifting mechanism under load, January, 1971. (Photograph: Ford Design Center)

A precision drilling fixture and positioning jig was fabricated and used to drill and tap surface plates and install floor plates. In addition, surface plates at all independent supplier locations were prepared for the model positioning system. This system is used for both clay and composite material models, 1971. (Photograph: Ford Design Center)

With the aid of four locator pins, millwrights move an aluminum armature into position in a portable modeling bridge. In contrast to the previous method of hand-adjusting armatures on pedestals and jacks, which took anywhere from 20 minutes to two hours, precise positioning of the framework with the locator pins takes only three minutes. These pins, and the four metal plates attached to the floor, permit more precise modeling and measurement because the framework is always level and in the same relative position within the bridge, 1971. (Photograph: Ford Design Center)

The first full size styling clay model built up on the new exterior modeling frame. The model stands on locators that are positioned and attached to the bridge surface plate, February 1971. Notice the "see thru" roof armature. Glass or plexiglass windows will be mounted in the model. The work is lead by master modeler Paul Gonzalaz, who is at the front of the model, behind him is Chandler York. (Photograph: Ford Design Center)

Complete front end and rear end models of each car line are developed in styling clay to the final engineering information. These models include finished sheet metal and plastic surface part edges. Bumpers, grills, and headlamp covers can be removed to observe these part edges during presentations. These models can be precisely positioned on special locators and fixtures in the bridge or CMM, or they can be mounted on a portable stand for presentations or for storage. Here we see supervisor Warren Gaymer instructing the millwright where to transport the model, 1972. (Photograph: Ford Design Center)

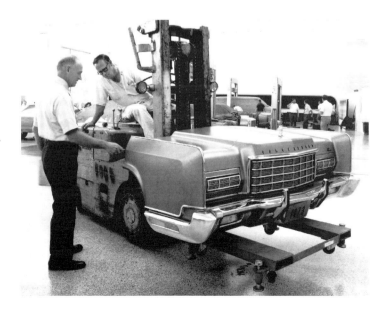

This photograph was taken to celebrate the opening of the new Chrysler Engineering Laboratories in June 1940. Although this is a staged photograph, problems can readily be seen. There are partial full size models, poor model setups, primitive modeling equipment, and the work area is crowded with models, vehicles, and modelers. Clockwise from the upper left hand corner: a designer is working on a blackboard drawing, a model is covered, next a modeler has partially concealed a production 1940 Plymouth with a layer of styling clay so it appears to be a partly finished model, two modelers are working on a front end model that sits against a different body model, three vehicles are lined up, and finally two other modelers are working on another front end model. (Photograph: Chrysler Corporation)

The Norton Tooling Bridge

Prior to World War II, Fred Norton started the Norton Equipment Corporation and began producing equipment for use by engineering and tooling people in model and pattern shops, and inspection departments. The equipment was first cast in aluminum but Norton was experimenting in magnesium casting and soon produced a line of both aluminum and magnesium equipment.

To satisfy the needs of body engineers, Fred Norton developed the Norton Tooling Bridge. This equipment was developed for the accurate three-dimensional measurement of large irregularly shaped objects. The tooling bridge setup was designed as an aid in obtaining an exact match on large dies or stampings that involved related parts. This system of measurement was used in the automotive, aviation, and guided missile industries.

The Norton Tooling Bridge system consisted of two large inspection type pattern maker's angle plates equipped with sliding platform angles to provide universal vertical travel adjustment. The angle plates had hardened steel runners attached to their base to provide a good wearing surface. A bracket with wheels was attached to the base of the upright so that by tilting the unit back 15 degrees, it could be moved easily about. The angle plates could be used independently of each other or together as a bridge.

To form a bridge, a parallel bar would be located by ball head pins onto the platform angles of the two angle plates. A butterfly, or sliding angle, was mounted to the horizontal bar and traveled between the uprights of the two angle plates. This set up provided both vertical and horizontal dimensional control between the angles. These units were all available in cast magnesium.

This equipment could be set up on a surface plate with the uprights positioned along a straight edge. However, Norton also developed base plates that were cast steel alloy precision surface rails. Multiple rail sections could be joined together to form a rectangular working surface around a work piece or a model. The base plates were equipped with leveling screws so they could be set up anywhere on almost any floor.

Norton equipment, including the Norton Tooling Bridge system, was soon adapted by styling studios. The equipment was quite flexible to use and accurate points or template settings could be obtained. However, an accurate setup required clean base plates, clean upright bases, and accurate setting of the adjustable platform angle and all other manually adjustable parts of the system.

Norton equipment was originally based on a five inch grid system but later it became available on an 100 millimeter system.

The use of Norton's smaller magnesium single rib angle plates and magnesium inspection type pattern maker's angle plates are of particular importance to the development of styling clay models. These have become part of the basic styling studio equipment.

The Norton Tooling Bridge system was installed in the General Motors and Chrysler design studios and was the primary dimensional control equipment used in those studios. It had also been installed in the design studios of American Motors, Packard, and Studebaker. The system has been and continues to be used in numerous smaller styling and design modeling studios.

Since the mid 1970s, Gene Perry has managed Norton Equipment Corporation and has directed all operations including the construction of special equipment.

An early Norton Bridge set up installed at General Motors Styling in late 1947. The angles were supplied with two parallel bars, one for across the model from side to side and the other to extend the length of the model on either side. Note that this first installation had wood rails. The Styling Section at that time was in the General Motors Building. (Photograph: GM Design)

Here we see how various pieces of Norton equipment can be used to check a master model. The long mouse scriber is working off of a sliding butterfly that is positioned on the cross bar. (Photograph: GM Design, 1950)

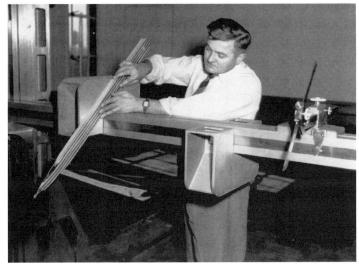

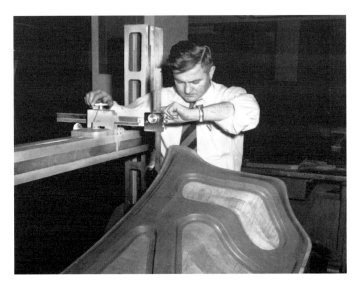

A special three-dimensional pointing system is attached to the Norton cross bar. (Photograph: GM Design, 1950)

The Norton Tooling Bridge is composed of two large pattern makers angle plates, equipped with sliding platform angles. To form a bridge, a parallel bar is installed onto the sliding platform angles and is located with pins. This equipment is available in both English and metric systems. (Photograph: T. A. Hoadley)

One of the most useful pieces of equipment for the individual modeler is a small pattern makers angle plate equipped with a sliding platform angle. The one in the center of this picture is built by Norton Equipment Corp. and comes in various sizes in both English and metric systems. (Photograph: T. A. Hoadley)

A riser plate or a cube is sometimes very useful. This is a five inch riser by Norton Equipment Corp. (Photograph: T. A. Hoadley)

The Progressive Modeling Bridge

In 1953, a greatly enlarged design staff moved into the just completed Ford Design Center in Dearborn, Michigan. This new Design Center featured 12 large exterior design studios separated from each other by motorized sliding partitions. At one end of every studio, there was a window wall facing northeast that looked out onto a patio. The studios were illuminated by indirect light reflected from a high concave ceiling and every studio was equipped with an all new bridge for full scale models. The new bridge was mounted flush with the floor on a steel surface plate. One studio had a bridge with a 100 inches wide, by 144 inches vertical work plane for the design development of trucks. All other bridges had an 80 inches wide, by 84 inches vertical work plane.

This is a surface plate floor mounted modeling bridge built by Progressive Tool and Industries Co. Twelve of these bridges were built and installed by Progressive in 1953 in the then new Ford Design Center. In the photograph is Herman Habitz who designed and engineered the bridge, Charles Stobar who directed the development of the bridge, and Design Center modelers Romeo D'Angelo and Paul Baud. (Photograph: Public Relations, Ford Motor Co.)

Each bridge traveled on wheels attached to its base similar to the previous Ford bridge. The wheels on the new bridge ran on inverted "v" tracks that were mounted below the floor on each side of the machined surface plate. The previous bridge ran on inverted "v" tracks but they were attached to portable rails and the rails were mounted above the floor. This was inconvenient and at times very difficult to work around. The tracks for the new bridge extended in covered pits away from the surface plate and ran to the ends of the studio. This allowed the styling bridge to be moved completely away from the surface plate work area to obtain an unobstructed view of the model.

The new type bridge had a counterbalanced crossbar and side scale holders that allowed infinite movement for dimensional control of the model. The previous Ford bridge had mechanically fixed cross bars positioned at five inch intervals and manually placed scales and spacers.

The new bridge had many advantages over the previous bridge: it aided and simplified modeling and measuring, it could be operated by one person, it speeded up design development work, and it was more accurate.

The study and the development for this new bridge was directed by Charles Stobar, Manager, Fabrication Department, Ford Design Center. The bridges were designed and engineered by Herman Habitz, Supervisor, Inspection Section, Experimental Fabrication Department. The bridges were constructed and installed by Progressive Tool and Industries Company in Southfield, Michigan, under the direction of James Peterson.

During the 1960s, Progressive designed and constructed a series of new portable modeling bridges to replace the original bridges built in the 1930s. These new portable bridges were lighter and simpler than the 12 surface plate mounted bridges, however, they followed the same general construction principles.

The bridge itself was assembled from three large aluminum castings and the rails were constructed from aluminum castings.

Progressive also built several portable modeling bridges that were lighter, simpler, and ran on rails above the floor. These bridges were built in the 1960's and replaced the old Ford bridges from the 1930's. The portable bridges were rebuilt, refinished, and metricated by Lamerson, Inc., in the 1980's. (Photograph: Al Lamerson)

The Schiess Modeling Bridge

In 1967, an all new Design Center was completed in Merkenich (Cologne), West Germany. Passenger cars for Ford of Germany and Ford of Europe were being developed at this location. A greatly advanced bridge was developed and constructed by Schiess A.G., Dusseldorf, West Germany, and installed in the new Design Center. The design for this bridge was directed by the Design Office Supervisors of Fabrication and Modeling, Rainier Kersting, Dietrich Tenner, Heinz Baer, and myself.

There was considerable difference between the Schiess bridge and the Progressive type bridge design. The Schiess bridge was powered by an electric motor, and had digital readouts in the X (longitudinal) axis. All scales could be read by the use of a vernier. The scales were hollow square stock and were very stable, and they ran on rollers.

The bridge traveled on recirculating roller bearings that ran on hardened and ground steel ways. The ways were separate from the surface plate and, once aligned, became the master from which the rest of the system was aligned. This bridge was very precise and allowed for a degree of accuracy in design model development that was not possible before. This bridge was used for design development and real time final prove out work that resulted in master model surface quality.

Schiess also designed and constructed a table-mounted modeling bridge in 1964. This bridge was used for development of scale wind tunnel models and various full scale models of items such as instrument panels, seats, and consoles. This small bridge was manually operated but proved to be quite precise.

Checking the 1/5 scale model against the full scale design model utilizing the full scale Schiess bridge, which was a modification of the Progressive bridge, and the original table modeling bridge.
From left to right are modelers: G. Schoebel, D. Tenner, E. Schwan, Author, and G. Schmidt.
(Photograph: Ford Werke A.G., West Germany, 1960)

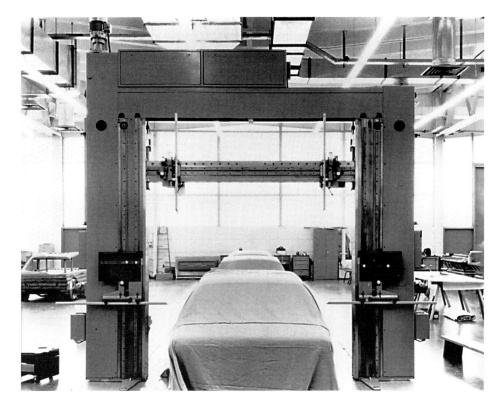

This full size modeling bridge with motor drive and numerical positioning was engineered, built, and installed by Schiess A.G. in 1967. This is a precision measuring bridge that provides the capability of die model dimensional accuracy. (Photograph: Ford Werke A.G., West Germany)

The Schiess bridge movement fore and aft and the cross bar up and down is motor driven. The bridge has numerical readout in its fore and aft position. On the bridge column, from the bottom up, can be seen the numerical readout box, the manual controls, and the electrical control box. Scales are machined square, are hollowed bored, and ride on bearings. Scale tips rotate. Vernier type readouts are provided for each scale. (Photograph: Ford Werke A.G., West Germany)

This is a small table mounted modeling bridge engineered and built by Schiess A.G. in 1964. It was built for the development of wind tunnel study models, instrument panel models, consoles and other small styling clay models. (Photograph: Ford Werke A.G., West Germany)

Digital Electronic Automation - DEA

In 1963, Dr. Ing. Franco Sartorio and co-founder, Ing. Giorgio Minucciani of Turin, Italy, invented an advanced inspection system and founded Digital Electronic Automation. DEA became the pioneer in the development of automatic electronic inspection equipment. Dr. Sartorio had previously been employed in the inspection section of Fiat Auto SpA in Turin, Italy, and he realized the urgent need for improvement in inspection work. The need was for an all new system that would greatly improve dimensional accuracy and sharply reduce inspection time. The answer came in the DEA Coordinate Measuring Machine (CMM).

Under Dr. Sartorio's direction, DEA soon designed and produced CMMs to cover inspection requirements for small table work up to large air frame part inspection.

The first DEA machine was shown at the 1964 Hannover Tool Show in Germany. We were aware of this event at Ford of Germany and I became fascinated with the possibility of using the DEA system in the development of automobile models. I closely watched progress at DEA and Dr. Sartorio aided us in plans for the installation of a DEA machine. Other design organizations were also interested in the system and all waited until DEA was able to produce a CMM with the size to handle a full size model and the ability to scan and mill clay surfaces.

In January of 1967, DEA completed the first large Alpha machine which had been built for the aircraft industry. While this machine was going through final inspection, we prepared a styling clay instrument panel model at the Design Office in Ford of Germany and I transported it to Turin, Italy. The model was set up in the Alpha machine and a DEA engineer, using a point to point mode system, scanned the surface of the clay model. The points were recorded on paper tape and also printed out. The Alpha machine coordinates relative to the model were then offset so that the points would be inside of the clay surface. The points that had been scanned were milled point by point back into the clay model. I returned to Cologne with the model and the surface of the clay was remodeled to the new points. This was the first recorded exercise where a CMM was used to scan styling clay surface, mill the recorded data into a clay model, and where the milled clay model was then finished.

The Alpha was an overhead gantry CMM machine with a vertical column mounted on the carriage. The column traveled back and forth between the two sides of the gantry support towers. Inside of the column was an arm that traveled up and down. On the end of the arm various heads could be attached to accommodate probes for scanning or checking surface, and for milling wood, plastic, or styling clay.

The carriage traveled in the X axis, the arm traveled in the Y axis, and the column traveled in the Z axis.

This machine was designed for the inspection of large parts and it was very precise. However, for it to be used to scan and mill styling clay surface, further development of probes and heads, hardware and software was required.

In the fall of 1968, Ford Design Center, Dearborn, Michigan ordered an Alpha to be equipped with double columns and arms. A machine with this arrangement could be used to work on both sides of a model at the same time; one side could be scanned and the other side milled, or both sides could be milled simultaneously. This machine was delivered in 1971 and put into operation in 1972. It could be controlled manually (with push buttons), or by tape, or computer controlled for automatic surface scanning and milling.

To make this system work, a computer was required that needed more power and greater memory than was currently available at that time. To meet these requirements, DEA designed its own 16 bit process computer, the DEAC 1001, and the supporting software. An operating system was also developed for this computer.

It would have been foolish to have used this sophisticated, precision machine on models that had been constructed to the poor state of the art that existed in 1968 when the machine was ordered. Modeling armatures were unstable and accurate positioning of models was not possible. Points on a model could vary as much as one half inch, from time to time, relative to a fixed reference station. Fortunately by the time the Alpha machine became operational, Ford Design Center's Modeling Systems Unit had designed and furnished all new accurate and stable modeling fixtures, armatures, and positioning systems. By 1976 two DEA machines were operational and all modeling equipment, exterior and interior was completely reliable. During this time I had also directed the development of scanning and milling systems, techniques, and tools.

For the year 1976, the total benefits related directly and indirectly to the use of the DEA machines and the new modeling equipment resulted in a savings to Ford Motor Company equal to 115 people. This included new work such as milling clay models for wind tunnel studies that previously had not been required, and service to engineering and manufacturing departments that was not possible before.

In 1978, Ford Design Center, Dearborn, ordered a new gantry type DEA Lambda machine to be equipped with two carriages and one column and arm on each carriage. The carriages were mounted on extended gantry rails to allow two work stations.

By 1980, DEA had supplied approximately one third of the world market for Coordinate Measuring Machines. There were over 70 models available in sizes ranging from 0.1 to 400 cubic meters. In addition to Ford Design Center, DEA supplied CMMs to several other design offices world wide.

DEA is now a part of the Brown & Sharpe Corporation that also includes Leitz, Tesa, and Roch. Brown & Sharpe markets a complete line of coordinate measuring machines, precision measuring instruments, and custom metrology products.

The Wind Line family of DEA machines start with the small Mistral and increase in size to the Scirocco, Ghibli, and Typhoon. These machines are designed around the new Slant Bridge Technology which has increased stiffness, reduced bridge weight and improved accuracy. These CMMs are moving bridge type machines that are constructed from machined cast aluminum and extruded aluminum forms. These machines are supported and move on frictionless air bearings. The "Wind" series machines are mounted on granite bases.

The Beta, Delta, and Lambda are larger overhead gantry-style coordinate measuring machines. They provide a wide range of measuring volumes and are designed to supply solutions for special applications and to solve customer problems.

There is also the Bravo which is a single column, vertical gantry type CMM. Larger Bravo machines, in a dual installation configuration, are used for "body-in-white" inspection. Smaller Vento machines become measuring robots on automated conveyors or flow lines to provide in-line, cell, or stand alone inspection for small and medium size parts.

The DEA "Surfer"system is a refinement of the "Unisurf" process developed by Dr. Pierre E. Bezier at Regie Renault in the 1960's. Surfer uses the measuring machine as an intelligent point-to-point scanning device for automatic data acquisition of a few optimally positioned points. These points are directly processed through Bezier algorithms and produce a mathematical model of sculptured surface that is subdivided into a number of patches.

All information concerning a product are stored in a central data base, which can be interactively updated. The theoretical definition obtained is uploaded to the compatible CAD system for further processing and it is then transferred to the CAM module for the generation of the NC machining programs. Surfer allows integration and exchange of data between all activities related to the development of the product.

DEA System FIVE or flexible fixturing system uses the coordinate measuring machine to manipulate modular fixture components and arranging them along X,Y and Z axes. This eliminates the need for costly custom fixtures and greatly reduces set up time.

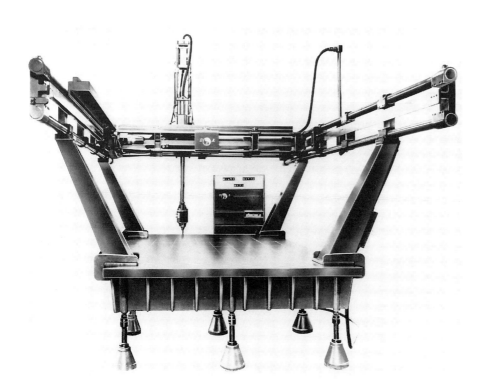

The first Digital Electronic Automation (DEA) machine was displayed at the Hannover Tool Show in 1964, in West Germany. This machine was designed and developed by Dr. Ing. Franco Sartorio in Turin, Italy. (Photograph: DEA Historical File)

The author at the DEA factory in Turin, Italy, February 1967. "To the best of my knowledge, this is the first functional styling clay model scan and mill test. The first large DEA gantry CMM, the Alpha, is scanning the clay model in an automatic point to point mode. Points are recorded on tape and are printed out. Only half of an instrument panel model is required because the design is symmetrical about the centerline. When the model surface was completely digitized, coordinates of the DEA machine were offset in relation to the model so all points could be milled back into the clay surface. The model was returned to the Ford Styling Studio in Cologne, West Germany, where it was cleaned up and finished to the points set into the clay by the DEA Alpha Machine." (Photograph: Author)

Dr. Ing. Franco Sartorio explains the operation of the DEA Alpha machine at the DEA factory in Turin, Italy. Dr. Sartorio and Giorgio Minucciani invented and developed the DEA machine and founded the Digital Electronic Automation Co. The instrument panel half model armature is mounted on a steel plate. Tubes position the armature at two locations inside this partial box. The top, front, and sides of the box form an enclosure for transporting the model. (Photograph: Author)

This DEA Alpha machine was installed in the Ford Design Center and became fully operational for both scanning and milling in 1974. The styling model being scanned is positioned on locators attached to the surface plate of the Alpha machine. (Photograph: Ford Design Center)

A DEA Lambda double gantry CMM at the factory in Turin, Italy. This machine was later installed in the Ford Design Center. (Photograph: DEA)

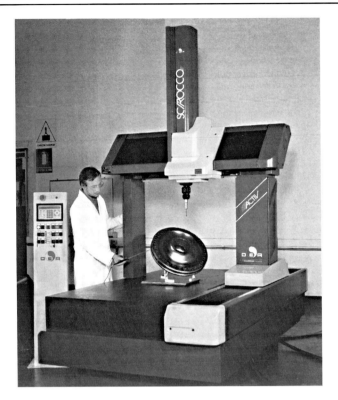

The DEA Scirocco is one of the smaller "Wind Series" of Traveling bridge CMMs. It has been designed around the Slant Bridge Technology which increases stiffness, reduces weight, and improves accuracy.

This DEA Typhoon CMM belongs to their largest "Wind Series" traveling bridge machines.

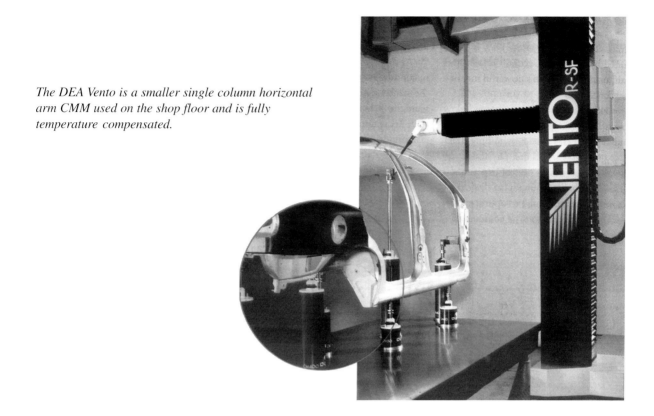

The DEA Vento is a smaller single column horizontal arm CMM used on the shop floor and is fully temperature compensated.

One of the larger gantry machines is the DEA Delta. It is used to inspect large aircraft parts.

The Portage Layout Machine

Another piece of equipment developed for tooling layout and inspection work was the Portage Layout Machine. This machine was also used by design studios in the development of styling clay models.

The machine consisted of a cast iron base with rollers, a vertical aluminum column attached to the base, a counterbalanced aluminum casting with rollers that ran up and down on the vertical column, and a horizontal arm that ran on rollers in the aluminum casting. The Portage Layout Machine came in various sizes and was supplied with various levels of equipment and accessories.

The Portage machine could be run on specially grooved surface plates, or along a rail attached to a surface plate, or on base plates like those manufactured by Lamerson Incorporated or Norton Equipment Corporation.

These units proved to be quite effective in obtaining dimensional data from clay model surface. Small motors and special pointed drill bits were sometimes mounted to the head and used to set points into clay surface.

Many special electronic packages, hardware and software, have been developed and adapted to the Portage machine. Perhaps the first such modification and installation was made by Ford Manufacturing Engineering Office on a large Portage machine. This design and installation was started in 1965 and the completed system became operational in 1967. This was built up for use by the Numerical Control Systems Department, Ford Design Center. The modifications included a special head that allowed points to be recorded from any angle relative to the arm. This machine ran on a portable rail (floor Plate) so that it could be moved up to a model and positioned with leveling screws. The machine was used only for scanning (digitizing) model surface.

Several Portage machines were installed at General Motors Design in the early 1970s. These originally were manually operated units but were later upgraded with computer control and electronic scanning.

One of the most sophisticated Portage machines was built up and installed at Chrysler Design in the mid 1970s. All axes on the Chrysler machine were driven by stepper motors and it was computer controlled. This unit was used for surface scanning and points were recorded automatically with an electronic non-contact probe.

One problem with the Portage Layout Machine has been that the vertical column and arm are rather soft and therefore deflect easily with very little force. To stiffen the column, steel rods have been installed and run from the cast iron base to a bracket at the top of the column. Although this problem still persists, the Portage Layout Machine has been used extensively for both digitizing and milling points.

The Ford Interim Scanner was designed and built-up by the Ford Manufacturing Engineering Office. It is based on a large Portage Layout Machine, mounted onto a portable rail. It utilized a contact probe attached to a universal head. This machine went into operation in 1967 and was used well into the 1980's. During that time the head was rebuilt and many other parts were replaced. (Photograph: Ford Design Center)

A highly modified and enhanced Portage Layout Machine used for surface scanning for many years by Chrysler Design. This machine is equipped with a non contact probe. (Photograph: Society of Automotive Engineers)

The Lamerson Bridge

In 1980 U. D. (Al) Lamerson, founder of Lamerson, Inc., and Ron Lamerson, Al's son, designed and built a table mounted modeling bridge similar in concept to the small Schiess bridge. The small Lamerson bridge was developed for precision work on scale wind tunnel models. This bridge has seen continuous use and is often moved from the Ford Design Center to wind tunnel test sites and other locations. The bridge was originally constructed in 3/8 scale but was refurbished in 1986 and the scale was changed from 3/8 to 4/10. Lamerson has since designed a table-mounted bridge that has electronic scanning and milling capabilities.

In 1984-85 Lamerson designed, engineered, and constructed a bridge for Winnebago Industries, Incorporated, Forest City, Iowa. This was a large bridge capable of handling class "A" motor homes and large trucks. This bridge was also available in a smaller size for passenger cars, small trucks and vans. The length of the work station could vary because floor plates came in one meter lengths. This Lamerson bridge was designed with light weight construction but was very stiff and precise. The operation of the bridge in manual mode at Winnebago is so smooth that all axes of the bridge can be moved with one finger. This bridge design had scanning and milling capability and was available in either English or metric dimensions and operations.

Lamerson completed a series of completely portable and accurate styling bridges in 1996 that are installed in domestic Ford design studios. These point/scanning bridges and their add scale measuring systems have been designed for manual mode operation. This bridge design incorporates many refinements, among those is a system dedicated to the safe and efficient transport of the bridge to other work areas. Lamerson bridges can be special ordered to include scanning and milling capability.

Lamerson has also developed a rather extensive line of equipment for complete product design systems.

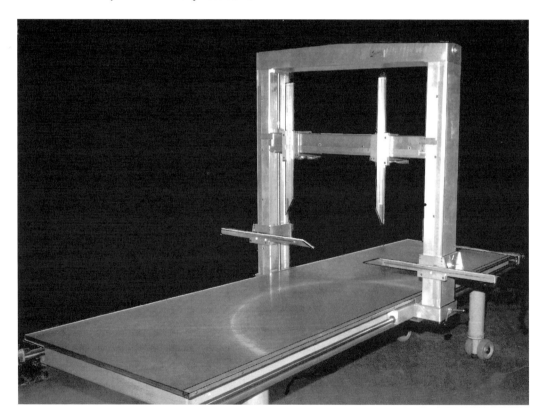

Lamerson designed and built a table mounted modeling bridge similar in concept to the small Schiess bridge. This bridge has seen continuous use for precision work on scale wind tunnel models. It is often moved from the Ford Design Center to wind tunnel sites and other locations. The bridge has electronic scanning and milling capabilities. (Photograph:Lamerson, U.S.A.)

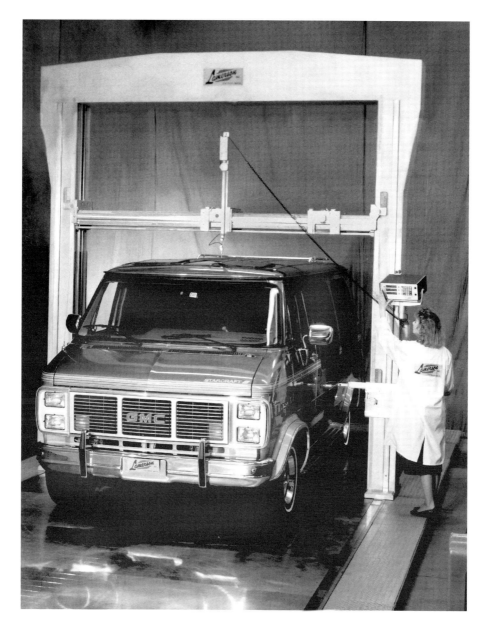

This large Lamerson styling bridge was built for Winnebago Industries, Inc., Forrest City, Iowa. It is able to handle class "A", "B", and "C" motor homes as well as large trucks. It has full scanning and milling capability and operates from CNC controls. It is equipped with antifriction recirculating roller bearings, that travel on hardened ways, and use precision ball screws for positioning of each axis. (Photograph: Lamerson, U.S.A.)

A series of Lamerson styling bridges were constructed and installed in automobile design studios in 1996. These are point/scanning bridges designed for manual mode operation and utilize the Lamerson Add Scale measuring system. (Photograph: T. A. Hoadley)

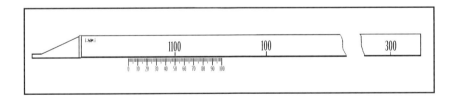

Lamerson Add Scale/Measuring System Diagram.

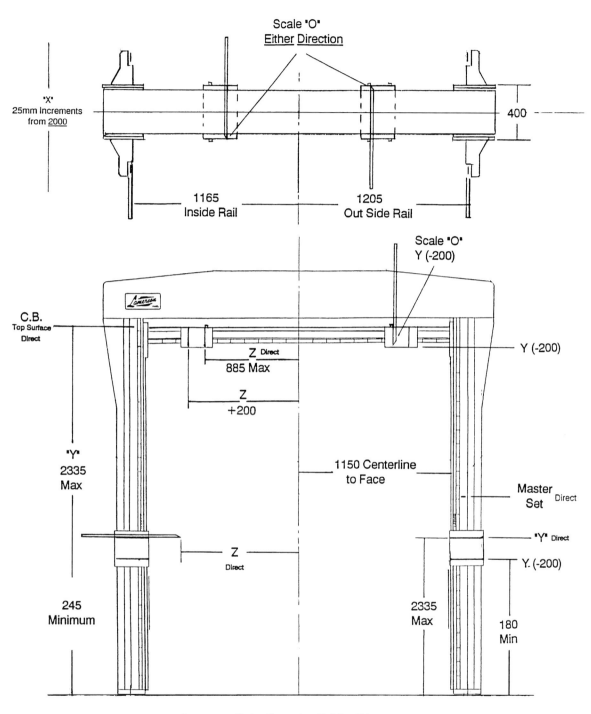

Lamerson Point Scanning Bridge Diagram.

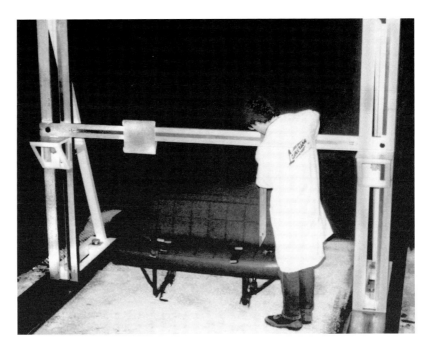

Cross bars for Lamerson's aluminum angle plates are available with adjustable, lockable cursers that travel on roller bearings and rotate from vertical to horizontal. (Photograph: Lamerson U.S.A.)

Lamerson aluminum angle plates are constructed with counter-balanced adjustable platforms. (Photograph: Lamerson U.S.A.)

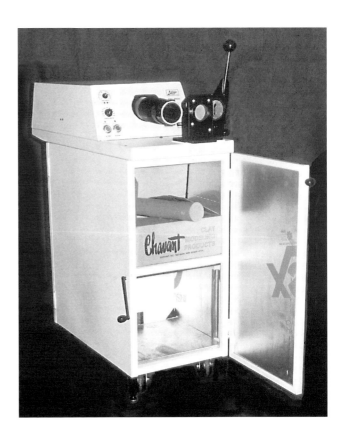

A Lamerson clay extrusion machine showing the swing away head, controls, and the portable cabinet with preheated clay billets and clay storage. (Photograph: Lamerson U.S.A.)

Lamerson clay milling tools of various sizes. Lamerson's tools have been optimized for clay removal and for clean cuts. (Photograph: Lamerson U.S.A.,)

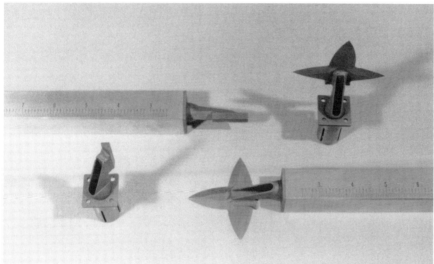

Hollow square scales by Lamerson. Scales are equipped with rotating and removable pointers and scribers, 1980. (Photograph: T. A. Hoadley)

This Lamerson Surface Table is equipped with a milled straight edge, tubular legs, and shock absorbing casters. A Lamerson Universal Fixture is keyed to the table surface. The fixture is equipped with four recirculating ball bearing adjustable mounts used for mounting bumpers, grills, etc. This table can be used for mounting various fixtures and armatures, using other straight edge locations. (Photo: Lamerson U.S.A.)

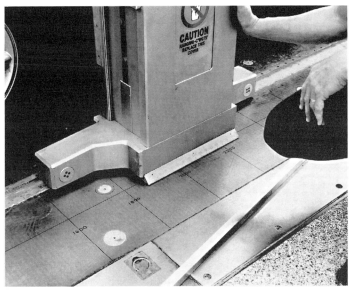

The various functions of the Lamerson Point Scanning Bridge is demonstrated here from these pictures in a design studio. (Photographs Ford Design)

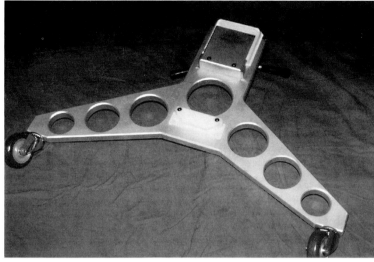

The Lamerson Point Scanning Bridge, may be safely and easily transported to other locations. Covers are removed from the sides of the bridge and the transporter assemblies are set into place and locked with a turn of the handles. Turning the handles further, lifts the bridge from the track. The bridge may be temporarily moved from a workstation to another track location or stored . (Photographs Lamerson U.S.A.)

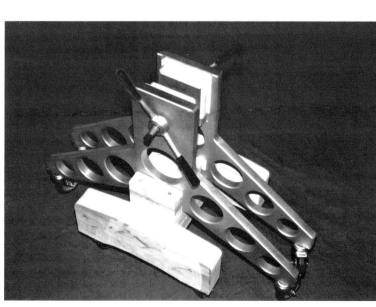

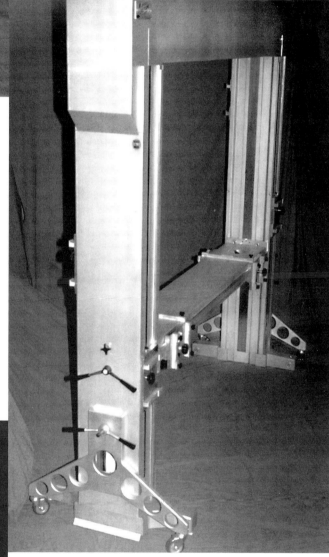

Tarus Machines

During the 1980s, Tarus Products, Incorporated, Sterling Heights, Michigan greatly expanded their share of the coordinate measuring machine market. Today they are one of the largest producers of CMMs, including dedicated 5-axis clay milling machines, used for inspection, digitizing work, and laser scanning. They also produce several types of CNC mills and a gun drilling machine.

Tarus manufacture two basic types of CMMs and these are supplied in several different systems. The standard Tarus inspection machine is equipped with the single column cantilever arm machine mounted to a granite surface plate. The surface plate has a length of 120 inches, height of 24 inches, and width of 72 inches. The machine mounted to this granite surface plate has a travel of X = 96 inches, Y = 60 inches, and Z = 60 inches. This machine, with a different base is available mounted to a steel weldment platform. However, with this arrangement the travel of the X axis is reduced to 48 inches.

Tarus produce a fixed base rail system that also utilizes the single column cantilever arm machine discussed above. This system provides a low profile steel base that can be mounted to, and flush with, a surface plate or other studio or model work station. The system is a fully automatic computer driven CMM. Two of these units can be installed on either side of a studio work station to provide bridge type functions. Each machine has a travel of X = 180 inches, Y = 60 inches, and Z = 60 inches.

The large Tarus clay mill machine comes in a dual column configuration. It is mounted to a cast iron floor plate and is made up of two heavy duty columns with separate carriers and horizontal arms or rams fabricated from aluminum weldments. The machine is equipped with hardened ways, antifriction recirculating roller bearings, and precision ball screws. The machine is level to the existing floor and requires a floor space of 300 inches by 360 inches. The Tarus clay mill machine provides a working cube travel of X = 324 inches, Y = 110 inches, and Z = 110 inches.

Tarus also construct a portable 5-axis clay model milling machine that uses air pads to move about a studio. This machine clamps to existing studio model rails or surface plates. It is self leveling and all controls travel with the machine. The only external connections to the machine are the power supply cable and compressed air line. The travel of this machine is X = 96 inches, Y = 76 inches, and Z = 48 inches. The design of this machine is derived from the large dual column clay mill machine but in a reduced size.

Each of these systems is equipped with Tarus Products CNC controls which include a 20 inch color graphics monitor, diskette and hard drives, and a tape backup unit. Each CMM can communicate with other machines so equipped.

All of the above machines have inspection capability for digitizing with a touch probe or a hard probe (pointer), laser scanning for generating a data base on large surface areas, and milling capability for styling clay and various foams. These machines also provide a graphics menu for the operator to prepare and arrange data for various operations.

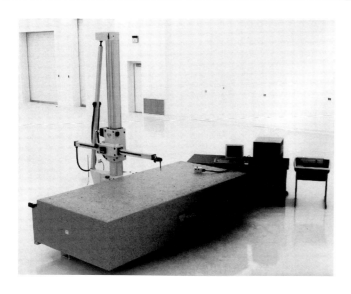

The standard Tarus inspection machine is equipped with a single column cantilever arm machine that is mounted to a granite surface plate. It has a travel of X = 96 inches, Y = 60 inches, and Z = 60 inches. (Photograph: Tarus Products, Inc., Sterling Heights, Michigan)

The Tarus inspection machine with a different base is mounted to a traveling rail. This installation has a travel of X = 48 inches, Y = 60 inches, and Z = 60 inches. (Photograph: Tarus Products, Inc., Sterling Heights, Michigan)

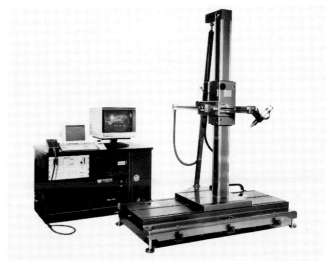

The Tarus fixed base rail system has a low profile steel base that can be mounted above the floor or flush to floor or surface plate. These units can be mounted to either side of a work station and are able to function separately or together as a bridge. It is fully automatic computer driven. (Photograph: Tarus Products, Inc., Sterling Heights, Michigan)

The large Tarus dual column machine functions as a bridge or as separate machines. They are mounted to a cast iron floor plate. Each machine has heavy duty columns and horizontal rams fabricated from aluminum weldments. It has a measuring capacity of X = 324 inches, Y = 110 inches, and Z = 110 inches. (Photograph: Tarus Products, Inc., Sterling Heights, Michigan)

Tarus also manufactures a portable 5-axis clay model milling machine. This is a reduced size machine mounted to a platform that uses air pads to move about. It requires the external connection of a power supply cable and compressed air line. The machine has a travel of X = 96 inches, Y = 76 inches, and Z = 48 inches. (Photograph: Tarus Products, Inc., Sterling Heights, Michigan)

Other Systems

There have been two basic types of measuring equipment used in the development of design models. One has been the modeling or styling bridge developed specifically for that purpose. The other has been tooling, layout, or inspection machines adapted for design model use.

We have traced the first modeling bridge to Gordon Buehrig and followed bridge design through a number of developments. Modeling bridges are now available from Lamerson, USA with CMM capability.

Modeling bridges have several general advantages over other types of measuring equipment: they form a very stable structure to work from; they are very useful in setting templates; and in some cases in dragging templates and sweeps; and they can be moved quickly out of the viewing range of the model. Modeling bridge design has been optimized especially for design model development.

On the other hand, tooling, layout, and inspection equipment has played a significant roll in model development. It is obvious that Coordinate Measuring Machines will play an even greater roll in design development in the future. This will, of course, include bridge type structures as well as single column/single arm and gantry type machines.

There have been many other companies, in addition to those mentioned earlier, that have supplied this market with not only manually operated equipment, but retrofit electronic equipment, and full CMM systems.

In the mid 1970s, VFW-Fokker of Germany, designed, constructed, and installed a CMM scanning, milling system in France that was used by both Peugeot and Renault. In 1979 VFW-Fokker built similar machines for Ford Design in both England and Germany. These machines were for design model development as well as other scanning and milling functions.

A Fokker CMM built in 1979 and installed in Ford Design in both England and Germany. (Photograph: VFW-Fokker)

The Portage machine has been available in Japan from Tokyo Boecki who were licensed to build and market this machine.

Mora in Germany has built and marketed a machine that is a vertical column, single arm machine. The Mora machine is available with a full line of accessories and digital display. This machine is used principally for inspection, layout, and scribing work.

Vickers and LK Tool of England and Brown & Sharp of the United States have designed CMM systems for model scanning, but these companies are best known for machines used in body-in-white inspection systems.

Dual Five-Axis MECOF Milling Machines (Photograph: Global Design Connection, June 1997)

For a number of years SCS-Systematic Computer Services, Incorporated, Geneva, Ohio, have supplied and retrofitted Portage layout machines. They produced and marketed their own CMM system. They have supplied studios world wide with machines equipped for automated electronic scanning (point taking) and milling (point setting). For milling, a small electric motor has been attached to the end of the arm and points are drilled into styling clay with a special drill bit.

MECOF, an Italian company, have been constructing and installing mills dedicated for use on styling clay models. Their latest installations are at Ford design studios in Dunton, England and Merkenich, Germany.

There are many companies supplying computer graphics and other computer operated viewing systems. These systems are interfaced to work with CMM computer and data systems. The automobile companies are putting a lot of time and money into these new developments.

More recent developments have added improvements to these capabilities. Steinbichler Optical Technologies have developed the first automatic robotic digitizing system. A white light digitizing sensor combined with a robotic solution offers greater flexibility for complex geometry. Engineers can measure and digitize unlimited 3-D form without the use of a CMM.

Another company, Paraform, Incorporated, provides greatly improved software and 3-D laser scanning services. Through improved levels of structure and usability to 3-D data, Paraform permits the creation of computer - generated models of complex forms. Paraform's software features a set of tools to create dense polygonal meshes from raw scanned data, and enables conversion of a dense irregular polygonal mesh of arbitrary topology into a parametric smoothed surface. Paraform's 3-D laser scanning services has the capability of scanning an object at exceptionally high resolution and digitizing it more rapidly and efficiently than traditional approaches. The utility of resulting scan data is superior to that obtained through alternative methods.

Control Data Systems Inc. and other companies including Evans & Sutherland, Intergraph Corporation, Computer Designs Inc., and Hewlett Packard in addition to Alias|wavefront are now supplying computer aided modeling systems for rapid development of 3-D free formed mathematical surface modeling.

Control Data Systems Inc. have developed ICEM SURF. The system obtains surface modeling speeds through a combination of automatic operations and real time interactive manipulation. Digitized data can be handled in raw form. Surface can be developed when starting data is incomplete, inaccurate, or there is a mix of digitized data, curves and surfaces. As with other systems, surface is developed in a patch structure and is independent of scan structure.

These mathematical surface modeling systems have been derived from the "Unisurf" process developed by Dr. Pierre E. Bezier at Regie Renault during the 1960s.

Alias|wavefront have released Auto Studio V9.0, a unique design and styling software directed specifically at transportation design. By adding Studio Paint 3D to the system, software tools are available for sketching, 3-D modeling, rendering, design animation, and engineering and manufacturing integration. You may input scanned or CAD/CAM data, or you may create surfaces using basic modeling tools. You can check highlights and reflections, joint lines and surface continuity, and translate manufacturable surfaces into CAD/CAM ready files.

There are also systems that construct hard models directly from CAD data. Stereo lithography (SL), has proven most valuable in producing complicated mechanical prototype parts in a very short time. After the outer and inner surface of a part has been developed in three-dimensional CAD data, a Stereo lithography apparatus (SLA) is used to construct prototype parts for design verification. 3D Systems, Valencia, California, is one of the companies that has developed this process.

In 3D Systems' process, an ultraviolet laser-generated beam traces a single layer of the part from CAD data onto the surface of a vat of liquid polymer. The ultraviolet causes the material to harden, the part is lowered a small amount, recoated with resin, and another layer is formed.

Other systems accomplish similar results. The DTM Corp., Austin, Texas, has developed selective laser sintering (SLS). DTM's Sinterstation beams laser radiation onto specialized powders to transform CAD data into three-dimensional objects. Helisys, Torrance, California, produce patterns from multiple layers of laser cut sheets of an adhesive paper. This system is called laminated object manufacturing (LOM). Cubital Ltd., Raanana,

Israel, can produce prototype parts through solid ground curing. Parts are built up from layers of photo-reactive resin. Stratasys, Eden Prairie, Minnesota, are able to produce parts by extruding and depositing a semi-liquid thermoplastic resin. All of these systems produce complicated prototype parts or patterns from CAD data. These prototype parts all require engineering design verification but do not need aesthetic surface development.

Another company, Item Products, Inc., sell standard catalog sections that can be assembled into typical structures for model development work and display purposes. While they may prove satisfactory for displaying models, they will not provide the stability nor the accuracy required for precision modeling. Also, a positioning system for these units does not exist.

This outline represents a broad spectrum of some companies and some equipment used in industrial design and design model developments. New electronic design systems are being developed all the time and it is difficult to say what will be in use even a few years from now.

Where to purchase various pieces of equipment, tools, and mathematical surface modeling systems can be found in the Resource Directory.

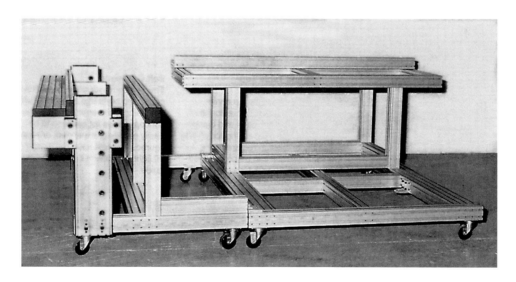

Standard Item catalog sections are used to construct typical interior buck fixtures. However, while fixtures constructed from these sections may be satisfactory for display models, they will not provide the stability nor accuracy required for precision modeling. (Photograph: Item Products, Inc., Houston, Texas)

PART TWO

DESIGN MODELING

CHAPTER 3 - An Overview

Design Modeling in Industrial Design

The term and the profession, industrial design, is a phenomenon of the 20th century. Nearly all of the mass produced items that we use every day have gone through various stages of design development.

In ancient times, many handmade articles including tools, vessels, utensils, and weapons were created not just for function but with artistic beauty in mind. This can be seen in libraries and museums under the classification of "decorative arts". Many of the articles were decorated with a pattern or ornamental design. Some patterns and motifs became signs or symbols for a certain clan, nation, or culture of people. The addition of ornament did not affect the usefulness of an article, it was just decoration or adornment, however it did fill a human need. These articles were made by artisans by hand while industrial design determines the form and/or decoration of objects which are made by machine.

During the Industrial Revolution, numerous mechanical devices came into existence. Many of these were created by inventors and engineers who lacked training or talent in artistic design. New products, new materials, and new methods of manufacture brought about higher production and lower cost and thus created mass markets and sales for machine made articles.

The need for better designed products with applied artistic design or styling, became quite evident during the tremendous industrial expansion of the 1920s. The smart manufacturer sought the advantage of improved product appearance. Designers who had been struggling to get into industry, found themselves in great demand and industrial design emerged. Greater competition, created partially by the Depression, and pushed forward by the ugent needs of World War II, cultivated an atmosphere that thrived on industrial design. The culmination of these events put industrial design in the forefront of a new industrial revolution. For more information on the history of design see: Harold Van Doren, *Industrial Design*, McGraw Hill Book Company, Inc.; John Heskett, *Industrial Design*, Thames and Hudson; and Michael Lamm and Dave Holls, *A Century of Automotive Style: 100 Years of American Car Design*, Lamm-Morada Publishing Company.

Products being designed fall principally into four different groups: 1. Consumer products; 2. Commercial products; 3. Capital or durable goods which include machine tools; and 4. Transportation vehicles.

Design modeling emerged because many of these products, during design development, required accurate three-dimensional models to properly visualize the design and to sell the design to the client. The need for design models continues to grow today because of expanding markets, new materials and methods, and because many smaller companies and studios now develop their own models.

Model makers for the industrial design profession originally came from allied skilled crafts, such as die, pattern, and ceramic model making, and plaster ornament making. In addition, certain industries, such as wood furniture manufacturing and the carriage (or wood auto body) industry, all contributed artisans to industrial design model making.

Many designers prefer to develop their own designs in three dimensions or at least to rough in the form, if they do not have the time to finish the model. Some persons trained in the industrial design disciplines prefer to work in three dimensions.

The role of design modeling in industrial design is clear; while a client may give directional approval to a design theme from a 2-D illustration or a 3-D visual interpretation, the client normally will not approve the design until it is developed into a three-dimensional finished model. The task of design modeling in industrial design is very important because the completed model (along with digital data or drawings) is usually the final product of a design development project.

Training

Model making, utilizing various materials, is taught in industrial design courses in educational facilities that teach design. Transportation design courses usually have classes that teach automobile modeling using styling clay. Many courses are available in local colleges to aid persons interested in design and design modeling, who may not be able to attend special colleges teaching industrial design.

Regular art school courses may be available locally where a person can learn drawing and sketching and especially sculpturing. Courses in design, color theory, art history, ceramics, silver smithing and engraving are very helpful. Remember, the design modeler is given the task to optimize the aesthetic aspect of design, from two-dimensional representations, into three-dimensional models.

Mitsubishi Eclipse-Li Chih Fu. Art Center College of Design, Pasadena, California. (Photograph: Steven A. Heller)

Yamaha - Vinnie Bumatay. Art Center College of Design, Pasadena, California. (Photograph: Steven A. Heller)

In addition to artistic talent and training, a design modeler needs technical training and shop experience. A course in mechanical drawing is essential and body surface drafting or ship lofting can be most valuable. Shop classes or apprenticeship courses are necessary to learn to operate various shop tools and bench tools. This knowledge is required to be able to support any form of model construction. If such courses are not available, the student may be able to learn through apprenticeships in a company doing this type of work or through self study.

For additional information on shop tools, materials, and methods see the *Model Shop Manual* by Joseph J. Farrer. The Model Shop Manual can be obtained from Joseph J. Farrer, (retired) Model Shop Supervisor, Art Center College of Design, 1700 Lida Street, Post Office Box 7197, Pasadena, California 91109-7197.

Cadillac Eldorado - Jay Bernard - Center for Creative Studies, Detroit, Michigan. (Photograph: Carl Olsen)

Chevrolet Pickup Truck - Chris Volpe - Center for Creative Studies, Detroit, Michigan. (Photograph: Carl Olsen)

Design Modeling Materials

Design models may be constructed from any one of many different materials. As an example, if the form is simple and the finished article is not large, it can be fabricated from the material the form represents such as a detailed turned or spun metal part. It makes sense to construct the appearance model from the materials and tools the design suggests. If a small hard surface model is desired and the form is simple and no changes are in order, the model may be constructed from wood, plaster, metal or plastic. However, if the model is more complicated and represents several different materials in the finished product, or if the forms are complex or large, or many changes are anticipated, then the model should be constructed from styling clay laid up over a stable armature or frame.

There are many advantages in using styling clay for industrial design projects. These advantages include:

1. Unlimited freedom of expression in surface development.
2. Precision and accuracy in model development to meet all engineering requirements.
3. Unique qualification for computer controlled scanning and milling systems.
4. Unique qualification for three-dimensional engineering and master modeling systems
5. Ease of transporting clay models anywhere when they are constructed on lightweight stable armatures.
6. Reusability of styling clay that is not contaminated.

Only a few companies manufacture styling clay. Two of these companies are Chavant, Inc. in New Jersey and American Art Clay in Indiana. Chavant, Inc. manufactures by far the majority of styling clays for use world wide. In Japan, the Too Corporation manufactures and markets Chavant clay under a license agreement. Chavant clay is also manufactured and marketed in England by Wilkins Campbell & Co. in partnership with Chavant, Inc.

There are several different types of styling clays with variations in composition. The essential difference between them is their hardness at room temperature, and the temperature at which they become soft so that the clay can be laid up and easily worked. The composition of styling clay is approximately 10% powdered clay, 30% oils and waxes and 60% filler. The actual clay formulations are highly-refined, closely-controlled mixtures derived from proprietary formulas.

Early modeling clays were rather soft. The hard styling clay formulation was developed in the early 1930s. The clay formulations do change from time-to-time as improvements in clay composition are made. Reasons for change include the availability of new materials, the changing raw material market, and environmental requirements. Therefore, there is ongoing development and testing of new clay formulations.

You may have wondered about the claymation characters of California Raisins, and other similar animations. These are not made from styling clay. Instead they are formed from a soft high- oilbased clay sold under the trade names of Plasticine or Plasteline.

History of Styling Clay

In a paper presented at a meeting of the Society of Automotive Engineers in 1920, George J. Mercer explained automobile design as it was being practiced by body builders at that time. In this paper, Mercer described the use of modeling wax, or modeling clay on full size models.

During the period of time that Mercer was referring to, modeling clay was made by the Chavant company in New Jersey, which was then owned and operated by Mr. and Mrs. Joseph Marra. Modeling clay was softer than styling clay and required less heating to make it pliable and easily applied to the modeling buck or frame surface. It could be built up, changed, finished, and painted the same way as styling clay is today. Modeling clay had a natural grey green color.

There was a hard sculpturing clay available from Europe that was dark red in color. However, the Chavant modeling clay was the standard material being used by body builders and other industrial designers. Harley Earl, the head of GM's Art and Colour Section, may have been knowledgeable of this dark red European Clay. Joe Thompson was an exceptional modeler working for Earl. They wanted an improved modeling clay, so Earl asked Joe Thompson to investigate having a harder modeling clay formulation developed.

History of Styling Clay (Cont.)

Joe Thompson worked with Joseph Marra in the late 1920s to develop the hard styling clay for General Motors. This clay was tinted dark red and except for variations in the formula, it is still being used today.

Ford used a slightly harder type of this formulation but in the natural grey green color up until the late 1940s. Ford clay is still slightly harder than the styling clay used by General Motors but it has a lighter red color.

Chrysler clay, made by American Art Clay Co., Inc., Indianapolis, Indiana, is a hard dark red modeling clay. This is a hard clay at room temperatures but requires less heat to make it soft and workable. Chrysler has used both drawer type clay ovens and the Bulldog mixing type clay ovens. Chrysler uses Chavant styling clay in its advanced California studio.

Chavant, Inc. was established in 1892 by Claude Chavant and his wife, with the help of Mr. Benjamin and Mr. Goldenhorn. When Claude Chavant died, Goldenhorn took the company over until the mid teens when Mr. and Mrs. Joseph Marra bought the business. Joseph Marra died shortly after the hard styling clay was developed and Mrs. Marra continued on with the business until 1962. It was then purchased by Paul F. O'Neil, who is the present owner.

This historic background of Chavant, Inc. was obtained from Mrs. Marra through Paul O'Neil in December, 1993.

Design Development Stages

Styling clay provides unlimited freedom in the development of surface. Because of this, much care and expertise are essential to maintain proper dimensional control of the model. In other words, when styling clay is used, it is very easy to exceed or infringe on vital package dimensions.

A clear understanding of the design theme is recommended prior to starting a clay model. Design themes can be studied in two-dimensional line drawings, sketches, illustrated drawings, or computer aided design studies. The preferred themes can then be developed into three-dimensional clay models. When required, styling clay can be used to develop a "picture" in three dimensions to aid in determining the theme. A design study is usually made prior to commencing a clay model.

To create a proper construction of surface, knowledge and experience in basic surface development criteria are essential. The design modeler must possess a combination of artistic talent, skill, knowledge, and experience. These attributes are absolutely necessary to develop aesthetically pleasing lines, forms, highlights, proportions, and silhouettes, all of which must be taken into consideration in three-dimensional design.

To develop a satisfactory clay model, full size master sections of the chosen design theme need to be drafted (or drafted to the scale of the model to be developed). This is necessary so that a modeling armature can be constructed upon which the styling clay will be applied. The modeling armature should be light weight, strong, and stable. It should also provide sufficient latitude for change.

To support engineering requirements, including the later installation of various parts and accessories, a continuous update of the master sections should be maintained to assure functional build requirements.

As the design theme develops in the roughed-in design model, changes or modifications can easily be tried. If the model is symmetrical about a center line, one side of the model can stay with the original theme development and the other side may be freely modified.

When the clay form is completed, it is given a final surface cleaning or steeling and slicked (smoothed with a plastic slick). The surface may be painted or covered with painted Dinoc (a decalcomania film). The "bright work" (parts of the model representing polished metal that are modeled in clay) can be covered with aluminum foil. Other materials may also be included as parts of a finished clay model. These might include polished or painted metal parts, plastic parts such as lenses or ornaments, and glass. Finished fiberglass parts or production parts may also be included in the completed model.

The techniques of styling clay model construction, development, and finish are described in later chapters.

Casting Clay Models

After the clay model has been completed and approved it may be necessary to cast the model. This is done to maintain a permanent record of the approved design and for engineering or tooling purposes. To accomplish this, the model must be prepared for constructing a negative. This includes removal of any loose parts and stripping the Dinoc if the latter had been applied. All undercuts must be filled and draft provided when using hard casting materials to assure removal of the negative from the model and a positive part from the negative. Draft is the taper given to a model so that a negative can be easily withdrawn. Also, this is the last opportunity to make any corrections or requested changes on the model. The surface is cleaned once again and if a multi-piece negative is required, those surfaces are dammed off so each piece can be cast separately.

The surface of the model must be prepared for the type of material to be used. The negative could be made from plaster, epoxy, polyester, or silicone, or in some cases, a combination of two of these materials. Some of these materials require elaborate clay surface preparation, especially when the negative is intended to be used as a tool for casting prototype or production parts.

The quality of a positive cast, made from a negative taken from a clay model, depends on the preparation of the clay model and the care that went into making the negative. The use for which the positive cast is intended, would be a controlling factor in the construction of the negative. This quality factor could range from a "quick splash" cast for tooling and manufacturing studies to a high quality accurate, die model cast.

Detailed procedures for casting the clay model will be found in chapters dealing with this subject.

Design Model Integrity and Accuracy

Models constructed from styling clay can provide the same degree of accuracy required of any master model constructed of impreg or other hard materials. Impreg, is multi-layer mahogany impregnated with a plastic material.

There are three factors that control the precision and dimensional accuracy of clay models:

1. Stable model frames and armatures.
2. An exact method to position the model.
3. Accurate model measuring and
   marking or milling.

Foremost in assuring model integrity is the construction of a stable model frame and armature. Next, is an effective method to position and reposition the model as design development progresses. If these two factors can be assured, then the accuracy of a design model will depend primarily on the care and precision taken by the design modeler within the limitations of the equipment available.

Of course not all clay model developments need to achieve milled master model accuracy. Therefore, models constructed from styling clay are constructed to a level of precision and accuracy required for their particular use.

These two photographs show a conventional cube assembly of highly accurate impreg master models, finished to inside of metal. Individual panel models are milled from engineering lines or numeric data and hand finished. Impreg or other plastic master models, are constructed to fit together around a cube structure on a surface plate. Cubed models are shown for surface and jointure approval. Kellering models are processed from master models.
(Photograph: Author)

This composite male master model, was processed from the feasibility styling clay model. It was cubed with impreg hood and door models made by Visioneering, Inc. The highlights and surface continuity were true and flawless. This method for producing master die models has been proven feasible. Total development time took 140 labor hours, 5 days time, and minimal material costs. The model weighed only 78 pounds.
(Photograph: W. A. Stanley)

Model Measuring and Marking

For smaller clay models not requiring a high degree of accuracy, a simple base can be made from 3/4 inch plywood. Preferably this should be coated or have a Formica covering to provide a hard and clean work surface. This base, plus standard scales, an angle, aluminum extrusions for straight edges, a surface gauge, and a level will provide an adequate setup for many models. An effective method for positioning and securing the armature in this setup, is highly recommended to assure integrity in the control of the model. To accomplish this, pins can be set into the plywood base work surface and holes can be drilled into the armature so it can be positioned by the pins. An angle or bridge can be constructed out of dry white pine or mahogany.

More accurate models are made with specialized equipment. This includes steel surface tables or surface plates with machined rails; light weight aluminum and magnesium angles, horizontal bars and scribers; and height gauges, surface gauges, scales, and sweeps.

Precision modeling bridges and single-or double-column measuring machines are available that assure accurate dimensional control of models. These machines have been developed specifically for the dimensional control of styling clay models. Although they were developed for the automobile industry, they are now available in various sizes and are being implemented into other industrial design operations. These machines provide computer controlled point-to-point measuring and marking. Some also provide surface scanning, line milling and surface milling capability.

More information concerning clay model measuring and marking will be found in a later chapter.

CHAPTER 4 - Equipment and Arrangements

Design Studio Equipment

The equipment and supplies that are required for a design studio to construct styling clay models depends on several controlling factors. These include the size and type of models to be built, the method used for dimensional control of the models, the data retrieval system or how surface information will be obtained, and how the models that are built will be utilized. It is advisable to take all of this into consideration in the planning stage. There are, of course, certain basic pieces of equipment that are needed in any studio that uses styling clay for design model development work. We will review these first along with basic supplies.

To start a design development project, the services of an industrial designer and an engineer are normally required. These services may be supplied "in house" as a part of the design operation or they may be purchased. Equipment for these services will also be itemized but under separate headings.

This list does not include personal tools that the individual is expected to have. Although some of the equipment that is listed may be owned by the individual, this situation varies. Personal ownership of the more expensive or larger pieces of equipment is not usual.

In addition, fabrication services are essential. This includes wood working, metal working, plaster and plastic, paint, and trim. These services can be purchased if they are not available within the design operation. Nevertheless, there are basic pieces of shop equipment that are necessary for design modeler use. These will be shown along with the other equipment.

Computers, software, peripheral equipment and supplies, along with office equipment and supplies, and standard building facilities and supplies are not shown in these lists.

The number of pieces of each type of individual equipment required will depend upon the number of people assigned to each function of the design operation.

Capitalized Basic Equipment

This is equipment that capital has been allocated for in an approved budget or project and that has an extended useful life.

Modeling Equipment

Clay Oven- designed to heat styling clay up to 150°F

True Sweeps or Radius Sweeps 60 inch parallel set #1-25

Blackboards to display illustrations and drawings

Work Tables - 4' x 8' wood construction

Surface Table or Surface Plate - size determined by use.

Angle Plates - magnesium or aluminum 5"x10"x20" or 125mm x 250mm x 600mm (or similar)

Cubes or Box Parallels - magnesium or aluminum 5"x10"x15" or 100mm x 200mm x 300mm (or similar)

Modeling Equipment (cont.)

Drill Press - 10 inch

Workbench - wood

Surface Gauge - 10 inch

Table Saw - 10 inch

Band Saw - 15 inch

Bench Vise - heavy duty

Sander - combination belt/disk

Grinder - 6 inch grinding wheel

Swivel Chairs - cushioned, adjustable

Taboret - with drawers

Vernier Height Gauge - 18 inch or 450mm as needed

Hydraulic Floor Jack and Other Equipment for Transporting Models As needed

Note: Some studio equipment can be constructed in-house from expensed materials. If the proper piece of equipment is not available when needed, it may be necessary to use something else or to improvise.

Design Equipment

Drawing Table - 60" x 37-1/2" (or similar)

Roll Files - 2-1/2" x 43" tube size

Swivel Chair - cushioned, adjustable

File Cabinet - legal 4 - drawer

Flat Files - 5 drawers

Light Table - 36" x 48"

Paper Cutter - 36" rotatrim

Taboret - with drawers

Combination Lamp - adjustable

Reference Table - 60" x 30" (or similar)

Drafting Machine and Scales - 37-1/2" x60", 18" scales

Engineering Equipment

Flat Files - 5-drawer

Reference Table - 60"x 30" (or similar)

Drafting Table

Floating Straightedge - 72" (to fit drafting table)

Swivel Chair - cushioned, adjustable

Fluorescent Lamp - with adjustable arm

Taboret - with drawers

Light Table 36" x 48"

Radius Sweeps - 60" standard #1 through 50

Straight Edges - 48", 60" or 72" depending on need

Drafting Machine (37-1/2" x 60") with 18" scales

Layout Table - size depends on products developed

Expensed Basic Supplies

*Expensed supplies are purchased from an allotted
fund and may be considered expendable.*

Modeling Supplies

Pens - ballpoint

Pencil Sharpener - regular point

Pencils - soft and medium lead

Lined Paper Pads -8-1/2" x 11"

Poster Board- light-medium weight

Masking Tape - various widths

Markers Permanent-Black, Red, Blue, Green

Paint Spray Cans - various colors and finishes

Black Photographic Tape-various widths

Plexiglas - 1/8", 1/4"

Dinoc - as needed

Lexan - 1/8", 1/4"

Roll Files -2 -1/2" x 43"

Styling Clay - billet type

"C" Clamps - various sizes

Heat Gun - three range

Strippable Vinyl - spray cans

Ship Curves - small set (See Resources)

Hand Drill - 3/8" chargeable

Mechanic's Tools

Drill Bits - wood and high speed metal

Hard Board - masonite 1/8", 1/4"

Polyurethane Foam - 4 Pounds preferably

Square Aluminum Tube - 1"x6', 1-1/2"x8', 2"x8'

Feeler or Thickness Gauge Stock 0.004", 0.007"

Mouse Scriber wood, Aluminum, or Magnesium 6", 15", 36"

Battens and Splines -Wood and Metal (See Resources)

Extruded Aluminum Bar - 1/8"x1"x6', 3/16"x1-1/2"x8', 1/4"x2-1/2"x8'

Scales or Rules - Stainless Steel or Aluminum 12", 36",60", and 30cm, 60cm, 100cm

Utility Knives and Graphic Arts Knives - handles and blades (X-ACTO, Alvin, Surgrip)

Art Supplies

Utility Knives - and graphic arts knives

    (X-Acto, Alvin Surgrip, X-Calibre RT)

Comfort Shears

Adhesive - spray can

Fixative - spray can

Transparent Tape - clear

Drafting Tape - various widths

Masking Tape - various widths

Black Photographic Tape - various widths

Frisket Film - sheets or rolls

Mi-Teintes Pastel Papers - 19"x 25" various colors

Tracing Vellum - 14"x 17"

Sketch Pad 14" x 17" and 19" x 24"

    (marker pro-layout by Canson or similar quality)

Saral Transfer Paper - sheets or rolls - various color

Erasers - pink pearle, kneaded, artgum

Layout Paper Pad - 14"x17"

Pencil Sharpener - regular point

Colored Pencils-Fine Point - verithin set

Specialty Markers - white, black, greys

All Purpose Marker - various colors

Fine Line Marker - various colors

Colored Pencils - soft thick prismacolor set

Drafting Supplies

Tracing Paper roll - inch or metric grid

Tracing paper sheets - 18" x 24"

Drafting Pencils - various degrees of hardness

Pencil Sharpener - draftsman's point

Drafting Tape - various widths

Masking Tape - various widths

Erasers - various

Shears - Drafting room shears

Note: Triangles, ellipses, scales, etc. are usually personal tools, but could be supplied.

Specialized Equipment

One of the most useful pieces of special equipment for modeling is a clay extrusion machine. When modelers are using a large amount of clay moldings and flat stock, the clay extrusion machine is a great time saver. A special de-aired styling clay billet is used with these machines. This billet is the proper size for the machine's cylinder and it is de-aired to remove entrapped air that is in a normal clay billet. If a clay extrusion is made that has air entrapped, the air will cause blisters to appear on the surface of the extruded molding. The blistered surface destroys the molding.

Clay extrusion machines are available and can be purchased. They are portable and plug into any 120V electrical outlet. See Resource Directory.

Additional measuring equipment becomes necessary when larger models are developed and when more exact dimensional control of models is required.

Larger models may call for some type of bridge and a large surface plate or bridge rails for the bridge to run on. The type of bridge and work surface depends on the accuracy requirement and how clay surface information will be obtained.

Smaller models that require accurate dimensional control, should be built up on armatures that attach to a surface table fixture.

The above equipment is available but generally it must be purchased on special order. Obtaining this equipment takes time, thus the time factor should be considered in the planning stage.

Designers sometimes need special lighting equipment (Macbeth Light) to check color samples and fabrics. Some type of special equipment for show areas and conference rooms may also be required.

If a CMM (coordinate measuring machine) is used to mill and/or scan the model, then several pieces of CAD (computer-aided design) equipment will be required for modeling, design, and engineering. This again requires time to obtain estimates, determine equipment requirements, and place orders through company channels. See Resources for various pieces of specialized measuring equipment.

Studio Arrangements

The arrangement of studios that develop styling clay models will vary depending upon the size of the overall design facility, the size of the models, how the models will be utilized, and the preference of management.

A small design facility may have all operations in one room. The various functions can be separated with either permanent or portable partitions. Blackboards on casters are very useful for mounting drawings, sketches, and illustrations; and for use as portable partitions.

In any arrangement, it is quite important that shop tools be located behind partitions and remote from where design, drafting, and clay model development work is performed. Wood dust or metal particles can easily contaminate styling clay and cause considerable trouble when working clay surface.

Larger design facilities will have some functions in separate rooms. Fabrication services should be located in separate areas remote from the design studios. Engineering facilities may be divided between a small support group in the design studio but having the main engineering complement in a separate area.

When it is possible, only those people directly involved with the styling clay development work should be assigned to the studio where the work is performed. This will aid in maintaining security of the models and reducing confusion within the studio.

Designers and engineers are normally in the studio where the model development work is being done, although it is not unusual to have these functions completely separate. The decision to locate these functions in a separate location might depend on space utilization or the preference of management.

Large models obviously require more space than small models. They require a larger work force, more supplies, and larger equipment. Studio arrangements for large models will be different from those studios that construct small and medium size models set up on tables or smaller surface plates.

When out-of-doors presentations of design models are necessary, it is desirable to have the studio adjacent to the courtyard where the presentations will be made. In addition, a corridor must be maintained to transport models to indoor show areas and to fabrication services areas as required.

This is a contemporary studio scene in General Motors Design. (Photograph: GM Design)

The designer in the right foreground is using color and lighting to evaluate the shape and surface of a design proposal on a high-definition monitor. Clockwise, left foreground, a design engineer is working on a package layout of the design proposal. The design engineer far left may be checking engineering package requirements, jointure of panels, hinge lines and door swings, etc.
Next, a design modeler is developing a design proposal on a 2/5th scale styling clay model; a designer is completing a blackboard rendering; and the studio manager is adding a bit of decor to the side of a finished model.
In the center background, another design modeler is utilizing a coordinate measuring machine to develop surface on another 2/5th scale styling clay model, and to the far right a studio designer or stylist is developing idea sketches and renderings for management review.

CHAPTER 5 - Traditions, Tools, and Techniques
Keys To Achievement

This chapter gives detailed information concerning tools and their use, and presents some basic guidelines to follow.

In discussing tools with Charles Stobar, he said, "my hands are my tools." An artist's or artisan's skill and expertise is the result of the interaction of the brain and the hands. A tool may perform the task the brain commands but it is controlled by the hand. A tool in the hand of a skilled person can do wonderful things but in the hand of an unskilled person it can accomplish very little. Charles Stobar was a talented sculptor and model maker. He worked for both General Motors Design and Ford Design. While at Ford, he was Manager of the Fabricating Services Department. He also owned and managed a design and model studio and shop.

The fundamental steps in any art form, are more or less universally applied. Nevertheless, technique can differ to a great extent by a person's training, experience, skill, talent, creativity, and the tools that are used. As an example, an experienced skilled person can accomplish a given task with various tools and different techniques. A person with limited training and experience may be able to accomplish the same task but in a very restricted method.

To develop exceptional skill and to be able to accomplish a given task in the shortest possible time, it is necessary to learn each fundamental step that the task requires. After each step has been learned, a person can develop his or her expertise to reduce the time required to accomplish the task. By understanding each step, it is possible to use short cuts and perhaps even skip some steps and still accomplish the same final result. If a person does not learn the steps properly or completely, the end result may never be quite right and the work may tend to be somewhat careless. To learn to do a job quickly and skillfully, it is first necessary to learn to do the job correctly and well.

The Earl of Chesterfield said, "Whatever is worth doing at all is worth doing well." Cicero said, "Whatever you do, do with all your might." The Apostle Paul wrote in Colossians 3:23, "Whatever you do, work at it with all your heart, as working for the Lord, not for men," NIV. Certainly, to be successful in your work, it is important to always do the best you can whatever the circumstances. Don't be overwhelmed by negative criticism or attitudes, nor discouraged by conditions. Don't be satisfied with mediocrity. Be positive and joyful in your work and you will enjoy your work and succeed in your endeavors.

Design Model Development Steps

To better understand design model development, let us divide the process into separate steps and examine the tools and materials that are required.

1. Make idea sketches.

2. Prepare finished drawings or illustrations.

3. Interpret the preferred design on a layout over a dimensional package drawing.

4. Construct a modeling armature or buck based on this layout.

5. Set up the armature to known base lines and stations.

6. Make templates from the three view layout drawing.

7. Prepare and skin coat the armature with clay.

8. Add warmed clay and set templates and points.

9. Develop the model according to the templates and points.

10. Modify as necessary to obtain the desired design theme while holding required hard points and master sections.

11. Make the model symmetrical.

12. Finish the model; add Dinoc, aluminum foil, etc. for presentation.

Starting a Design Model

Let's assume that a design has been chosen and at least a rough three-or four-view drawing has been drafted. From this, an armature has been constructed, located, and mounted on a properly prepared work surface. The armature has been shellacked and the first layers of clay have been rubbed well into its surface. Templates have been made from tracings or copies of the drawing and are ready to be set into warm clay on the model's surface.

The steps that follow are generally the same whether the model represents something small such as an ornament or handle, or something larger like an appliance or console, or a large model representing some type of vehicle or piece of equipment.

Setting Templates and Points

Templates are set into warm clay that has been rubbed onto the armature in the area of the template section only. This should be above the roughed in clay surface. Never rough-in clay above the template sections before templates are set, because the hard rough clay would have to be tooled down in order to set the templates. The exception to this would be if the model is being built up to mill or to set points into the clay surface. In these situations, templates should be used to determine approximately how much clay should be built up on the armature. Points can be set into either hard or soft clay (that is cool clay or warm clay), however, points set into hard clay are much more precise.

Use some method to position each template and then move the template back and forth through the warm clay until a smooth and exact narrow template surface remains. Scribe a line on this surface on the location of the section represented by the template. This is the section from the drawing transferred to the model. Some templates are set into a model as master sections to control the surface development. Other templates are used as guides to follow in roughing in a model.

Warm clay can now be carefully built up between the template sections. When this is accomplished, the clay is ready for tooling and roughing in the design.

Styling Clay Scrapers

A clay scraper is used first to clean up the clay surface. This tool is sometimes called a rake because it has teeth that have been milled or filed into its sharp cutting edge. Clay scrapers come in various sizes and weights, and range from about five inches long down to one inch. A larger or smaller tool is used depending on the size and contour of the model. The tool's teeth vary depending on the size of the scraper. A large scraper has larger teeth than a small scraper.

Work the appropriate scraper in a crisscross pattern to develop an even surface. Warm clay is added as needed. The model is first roughed-in to the template sections. If it is found, as the surface is cleaned up, that these template sections do not provide the desired form, then add or remove clay free hand when there are no restricting lines or points to follow. If there are master sections or hard points that must be held, work around these to develop the surface.

The toothed scraper will leave a textured surface. You may wish to go to a smaller scraper as the surface evolves so that a finer texture develops. The form of the model is easily read in this textured surface.

When the form reaches the point where further clean up is required, then it is necessary to switch to other tools.

A description of various styling clay scrapers and where they may be purchased will be found under Resource Directory.

Wood Battens

Battens (sometimes called splines) are strips of wood used to scrape the roughed in clay surface. They are usually made from maple, although sometimes they are laminated with maple on the outside edges, but alternating with strips of mahogany through the width of the batten. Battens are made in many sizes, ranging in length from about four feet down to one foot. The longer battens are wider and thicker and the shorter ones are narrower and thinner and more flexible.

The battens are several times longer than the width of the scrapers that have been used. When battens are scraped over a clay surface, they cut away high areas and show up low areas that must be filled with warm clay. Fill and scrape until the surface is even. Naturally, a batten can only be used on a surface with a minor contour. A surface with considerable form or a complex configuration will require other tools when being cleaned up such as styling clay steels.

Metal splines, made from hard aluminum or steel, are used like battens but being metal they hold a sharp edge longer.

A description of the various sizes of wood battens and metal splines will be found under Resource Directory.

Styling Clay Steels

Steels are made in many sizes and a variety of shapes. They are cut from blue spring steel and have thicknesses ranging from 0.005 to 0.060 inches. Larger, thicker steels are used on large surfaces with minor contours. Small, thinner steels are used on smaller models and surfaces having greater contour. Special thin steels are used when steeling fillets and radii. Elliptical shaped steels are used on more complex surfaces.

Most steels need to be held firmly in both hands when steeling the surface. The steel should be bent to form the contour of the surface.

A batten will clean off the larger high areas and fill the larger low areas of a model, but it will not leave a smooth surface. When using a steel, all of the minor high points are easily cleaned off but all of the low points must be filled. Steels are also used in a crisscross pattern and a lot of filling with warm clay is required. When finished, a properly steeled surface is perfectly smooth, but it has a dull finish, therefore it must be slicked.

Styling clay steels of various sizes, shapes, and thicknesses, and where they may be purchased will be found under Resource Directory.

Plastic Slicks

Plastic slicks are used to bring out a high luster on the styling clay surface. Slicks are made from plastic sheet in various sizes and thicknesses. The edges and corners of a slick are rounded and highly polished so that there are no visible scratches.

Larger, thicker slicks are used on larger surfaces with minor contour. Smaller thinner slicks are used on surfaces with more form. Special slicks and plastic tools may be used on models with complex form and fine detail. Slicks are used in a crisscross pattern. Like steels, slicks generally need to be held firmly with both hands and bent to form the contour of the surface.

When the styling clay surface has been slicked, it is polished with a soft cloth that has been dipped in cool water. The wax in the clay brings out a high luster on the slicked surface of the model.

A description of some plastic slicks and plastic tools will be found under Resource Directory.

True Sweeps (Radius Sweeps)

True sweeps are made from plastic, wood, or anodized aluminum. They are available in various lengths and they are numbered. A true sweep is a portion of a circle or radius. Each number of a sweep relates to a rise of one eighth of an inch in a true radius, relative to a straight line 60 inches long. A number one sweep has one eighth of an inch rise in 60 inches. A number two sweep has two eighths of an inch rise. A number three sweep has three eighths of an inch rise, and so on.

A true sweep need not be 60 inches long; however, the same number sweep has the same radius whatever the length. True sweeps are sometimes made to a small scale size, in which case the controlling factors would be adjusted to the scale dimensions.

True sweeps can be used as templates. When a major portion of a line follows a sweep, two points on the line can be located on the model for the sweep to connect.

Sweeps can also be used as templates to bridge across two sections that are developed on a model. In either case, warm clay is applied and the sweep is used as a template.

True sweeps are sometimes used to drag a clay surface. When a portion of the surface follows a constant sweep, the surface can be dragged in hot clay with the sweep. To do this, it is necessary to develop two or more sections at right angle to the sweep. These are used as guides and are covered with steel tape (feeler gauge stock) for the sweep to run on.

Sweep charts in both English and metric will be found under Charts and Resources. Sweeps can be made from the dimensions found in the charts. Also, lines for any sweep can be plotted on a model or drawing from chart dimensions.

Descriptions of sweeps and where they may be purchased will also be found under Resource Directory.

Ship Curves

Ship curves come in 56 different shapes. They are made from acrylic sheet plastic and were developed for drafting measured ship drawings. Large scale ship curves are made from mahogany. Both sizes have been used in coach design and in body design work. They are also very valuable when developing lines on design models and lines for templates.

These and other curves, their description, and where they may be purchased will be found under Resource Directory.

Drag Templates

When a template is used to drag a surface, styling clay scrapers and wood battens are not used. Templates for dragging may be made from metal or plastic sheet, hard board, or plywood. A template should be finished with a perfectly smooth edge so no scratches will be left after the surface has been dragged. The dragged surface is steeled to take away any unevenness and minor low areas are filled and steeled. The surface is then slicked.

A template that is dragged against the edge of a sweep or another template, should be attached to an angle or a special template holder. If an angle is used to hold a template for dragging, a nose adaptor or follower should be utilized to maintain the template 90° to the tangent of the sweep. A template may also be dragged against a surface that has been protected with steel tape or metal extrusions.

Sources for angles and other modeling equipment will be found under Resource Directory.

Dinoc

When a styling clay surface has been cleaned up, steeled, and slicked, Dinoc can then be applied. This material is available by the roll or by the foot and is 36 inches wide. Although rolls can be purchased in various colors, it normally comes in beige.

The Dinoc film (decalcomania) is a transfer material. The film has a paper backing to which it is attached with a water soluble adhesive. The Dinoc may be painted any color and finish, but it is necessary to add a plasticizer to the paint. The Dinoc Company was founded in Cleveland in 1938 and was bought by 3-M in the early 1960s. Dinoc used on clay surface is listed by 3-M as "Model Maker's Film".

After a sheet of Dinoc has been painted and dried, it can be applied to a finished clay model. The sheet is precut to the approximate size of the area of the model on which it will be applied. Some additional material must be left on the precut sheet to allow for stretching and trimming.

The precut sheet of Dinoc is dipped in a pan of warm water. The clay surface should then be sprinkled with water from a large wet sponge. When the paper backing is thoroughly wet, the film will easily pull away and will hang as a flexible sheet of paint. Several persons may be required for this task, depending on the size of the surface to be covered. The painted film is then laid on the clay surface and more water is sprinkled on. Using sponges, squeegees, and slicks, the Dinoc film is pressed to the clay surface and the water is forced out. The water on the clay surface acts as a vehicle for applying the film. The film is stretched and squeegeed down in areas where more material is needed.

A heat gun or hair dryer can be very useful in stretching and forming the Dinoc, especially in recessed areas and on surfaces having a lot of form. A heat gun can also be used to soften and re-attach Dinoc if it pulls away from the clay surface.

The edges of the film are all slicked down and trimmed with a sharp knife or X-ACTO blade. Where two surfaces meet that require two sheets of Dinoc make the trim on normal breaks, design lines, or joints of the item that has been modeled. Use a straight edge, sweep, or curve to cut the film on the exact line on the model. The two sheets may be cut at one time and the excess removed to make a neat trim.

In the back of the book under Resource Directory, you can find where to purchase Dinoc.

Strippable Vinyl

If you have a completed clay model that you want to finish in color but do not wish to disturb the surface with either Dinoc or paint, you can coat the clay surface with Coat "N" Strip. This is a moisture barrier, strippable, protective vinyl coating. This material is particularly useful when finishing textured clay areas and smaller models where the clay surface cannot or should not be disturbed.

After the Coat "N" Strip has been sprayed on and has dried, other paints and finishes can be sprayed over it. Make sure the Coat "N" Strip has been sprayed on heavy enough to form a film that can be peeled off. A thin coating of this material will not peel easily.

Coat "N" Strip or vinyl paints under other names can be found in stores selling modeling supplies and is listed in the back of the book under Model and Industrial Supplies.

Aluminum Foil

Aluminum foil can be applied to finished clay surface to represent bright metal. It can also be applied to painted and polished plaster or fiberglass reinforced plastic (FRP) casts processed from styling clay models. The aluminum foil is available in several thicknesses and widths, and comes in various colors and finishes including polished, satin, and brushed.

For best results, the clay surface should be carefully steeled and slicked. When applied, the aluminum foil will reveal the exact surface that it overlays. The foil is fairly soft and can be stretched and drawn to fit the surface.

Before applying the foil, observe the model to determine how large a piece of foil will be required and where to plan to make cuts and joints. Highly polished slicks and plastic tools must be used to apply aluminum foil.

Precut the foil and with both hands, stretch it down over the model. Use a slick or plastic tool to draw and stretch the metal and work it down over the surface. Take it as far as possible until it begins to wrinkle or tear. Slick it down at that point and then make the necessary cuts and trims. Use a very sharp knife or X-ACTO blade. Aluminum foil is applied just as Dinoc is applied, but it is not nearly as flexible. If two or more pieces of foil are necessary, overlap the pieces next to each other and make one trim for both pieces. Use a straight edge, sweep, or curve so that a perfect trim line will result. When possible, trim on normal breaks, design lines or joints. When it is not possible, make trim lines where they will not be seen, such as under an edge or bead. Aluminum foil will adhere naturally to styling clay.

It is sometimes necessary to apply small pieces of foil where it has been impossible to stretch it to cover all of the surface. In these cases, cover the more visible areas first, then cut the foil and work it down around the rest of the surface. Piece in and trim as necessary. Practice and experience is required to obtain confidence. Be careful not to apply so much force that the clay surface is deformed.

When applying aluminum foil over plaster or FRP casts, the surface must be perfectly finished, polished, and cleaned. Spray adhesive can be applied to the back of the sheet of foil before it is stretched over the model. The process is similar to applying foil over clay models except more force can be applied without deforming the surface. Because of this, the foil may tear more easily so that great care in its application is essential. After it has been applied, aluminum foil can be painted with various colors of transparent paint to represent lenses of glass or plastic.

Regular aluminum foil may be used but generally this is too hard. The preferred aluminum foil for this use should have an 0 or soft temper, one side bright finish, and have a gauge or thickness of 0.0008", 0.001", or 0.0015". Temper indicates the hardness of the material. Normally 0.001" thickness foil is used although a thinner or thicker foil can be used in special circumstances. Especially prepared foil in various widths and finishes can be obtained at the address shown under Resource Directory.

Plaster and Ceramic Steel Tools

Several tools normally used in plaster model work are also valuable in developing styling clay models. Various sizes of chisels and fine steel tools are very useful. Plaster mold tools and knives also work quite well in styling clay. Where to purchase these tools can be found under Resource Directory.

Wire Tools and Wood Tools

Wire tools are used on small design models and models requiring fine detail work. Wire tools are also used for cutting grooves, trimming edges, and softening or rounding corners of models.

Wood tools are used to build up styling clay in small or tight areas and to run fillets. They are also used to develop patterns and texture on small models and models with fine detail. The use of wood tools in styling clay is similar to their use by sculptors using water clay.

Some wire tools and wood tools can be purchased from artist supply stores. Some are available along with other modeling tools from companies manufacturing tools for styling clay work. These tools can also be made by the individual. Special wood tools can be made on the job at the time they are needed.

Where to purchase these tools will be found under Resource Directory.

A model of a decorative glass lamp is built up over a plaster form attached to a plywood base. Master work lines from the design have been laid out on the base. After master lines have been developed in clay and protected by feeler gauge stock, a clay scraper or rake is used to clean up the surface. Lamp design is by Paul V. Potter, Ann Arbor, Michigan. (Photograph: T. A. Hoadley)

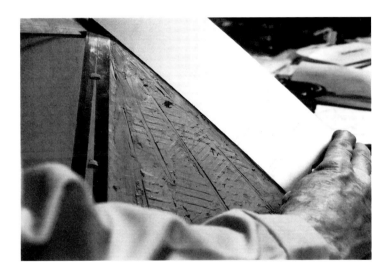

After using a scraper, a sweep is used against established sections to create lines on or near the desired surface. (Photograph: T. A. Hoadley)

A flexible batten is used to remove excess clay. (Photograph: T. A. Hoadley)

Continued use of the batten smooths the surface and reveals areas that require more clay. (Photograph: T. A. Hoadley)

A steel is then used to finish the surface after filling the low areas with warm clay. (Photograph: T. A. Hoadley)

Wood tools are used for details. (Photograph: T. A. Hoadley)

The finished model prepared for construction of a plaster negative. The various clay modeling tools that have been used surround the model. Plaster casts processed from this model will be used to form parts for a decorative glass lamp. (Photograph: T. A. Hoadley)

The finished hanging glass lamp. (Photograph: Author)

A drag template is ideal for developing the surface of a wheel cover model. Make sure the edge of the wheel is smooth and even. Build an armature out of wood or foam and attach it to the wheel. Install a wood dowel in the middle of the armature with the top of the dowel being the proper height of the center of the wheel cover model. Bond the dowel to the armature. Make the template to the major line of the wheel cover surface. In this case, the template includes a removable piece that represents the deepest part of the scallop pattern. A copy of the drawing has been attached to a sheet of Lexan with spray adhesive and the template has been cut out and cleaned up on the line representing the cross section of the surface. Drill a small hole in the top of the dowel at the actual center of the wheel. Install a small nail on the centerline of the template so that it will protrude and set into the hole in the dowel. (Photograph: T. A. Hoadley)

With the piece removed, the template represents the normal surface of the wheel cover. The template rides on the dowel in the center and on the edge of the rim at the side. The template is positioned by the nail that is attached on the center line of the template. To start the model, the armature is shellacked and when that is dry, hot clay is applied and built up. The wheel cover surface is roughed in with the template, but the clay must cool and harden before final surface can be finished with the template. (Photograph: T. A. Hoadley)

From lines laid out on the drawing, a mouse or scriber is used to scribe the edges of the scallop pattern onto the clay surface. (Photograph: T. A. Hoadley)

This wood tool is used to fill and shape each scallop area before going on to other tools. It has a 45° knife like edge at one end and a spatula shape at the other end. "It is one of the tools I cannot do without."
(Photograph: T. A. Hoadley)

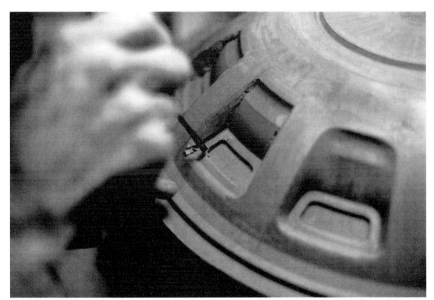

After the wood tool has filled and shaped the small openings at the bottom of the scallops, a half round steel carving tool (or plaster carving chisel) is used to trim the corners.
(Photograph: T. A. Hoadley)

A wire tool is used to rough in the sides of the scallop.
(Photograph: T. A. Hoadley)

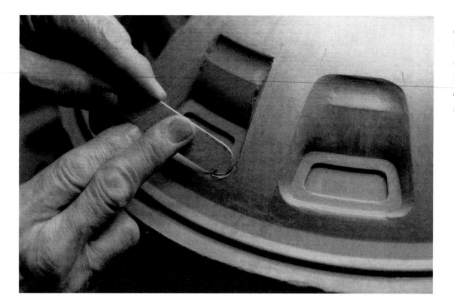

A re-shaped tongue depressor makes an excellent tool for shaping small inside corners. The outline of this shape is not a radius, it is developed like an ellipse. (Photograph: T. A. Hoadley)

A small steel is used to clean up the sides of the scallop. This steel has a straight edge on one side, a curved edge on the opposite side, and elliptically shaped corners of different sizes. (Photograph: T. A. Hoadley)

The styling clay model of the wheel cover is finished and is ready for making a plaster negative. (Photograph: T. A. Hoadley)

This rather elaborate template drag set up was designed and developed by Stephen Stringer for E&G Classics, Inc., Columbia, Maryland. Mr. Stringer, a well known design modeler and consultant, is explaining the operation of the machine. (Photograph: T. A. Hoadley)

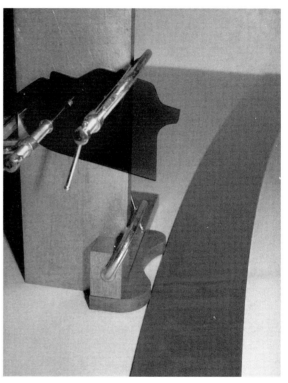

When dragging against a sweep, a wooden follower is clamped to an angle plate to obtain properly dragged surface. The follower holds the vertical surface of the angle plate at a right angle to the tangent of the sweep. By aligning the leading edge of the template line with the nose of the follower, the dragged surface will accurately follow the sweep. (Photograph: T. A. Hoadley)

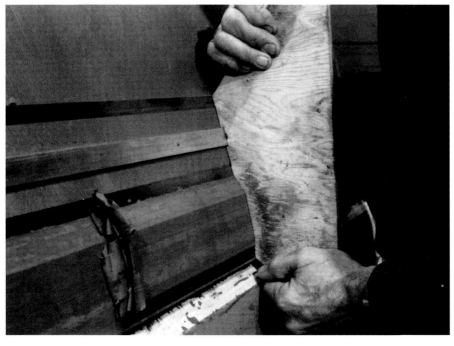

A simple drag set up can be utilized where fixturing or a surface plate can not be used. In this situation, a beveled step is being dragged in with a plywood template. The surface above the bevel and at the very bottom was first cleaned up and steel tapes have been fixed to these surfaces. The aluminum extrusion is pinned to the surface with small nails. The surface is in a #1 horizontal sweep. The plywood template rides on the three steel tapes and it is positioned vertically by the aluminum extrusion. The template is undercut where it would otherwise make contact with finished or cleaned up clay surface. It is necessary to steel the dragged clay surface to obtain a good finished. (Photograph: T. A. Hoadley)

Gil Treweek and Glenn Daubenmeyer apply Dinoc to the surface of a model. Dinoc is a plastic film that can be painted any color and can be formed to fit any surface. This model is a combination of clay and fiberglass, 1975. (Photograph: Ford Design Center)

Debbie Kelman uses a groove-cutter to define a trunk lid opening and Gayl Cosselman smooths a window surface with a steel, 1975. (Photograph: Ford Design Center)

The upper photo of a sleeper cab and the lower photo of a van roof inner liner,
illustrates how large styling clay models, use the same type of tools as smaller models.

CHAPTER 6 - Beginning A Design Model

The Need For A Modeling Armature

Styling clay differs considerably from plasteline or from what is known as school clay. At normal room temperature styling clay is hard and must be tooled with special scrapers to achieve the desired shape and surface. Styling clay becomes soft and pliable when heated so that it is easily formed and bonded to itself or other materials. Styling clay may be built up into very small solid models but usually it is laid up over an armature or over another surface.

Because styling clay provides unlimited freedom in the development of surface and form, it is necessary to maintain proper dimensional control of the model. To do this it is essential to construct a stable but lightweight modeling armature. The armature should be sufficiently strong and rigid to support the clay plus any other items to be assembled to the model. The armature must also withstand the stress and strain of the work on the model. Depending upon the size of the model, the armature also may have to support the weight of the modeler.

Since the model may be moved from time to time for reviews, presentations, casting, etc., there should be built into the armature the means for lifting and carrying the model. A model can be transported virtually anywhere if the armature (and frame if there is one) is rigid and stable, and the clay has been properly laid up over a firm sub-surface. If the model is to be transported over a great distance, care must be taken to control environmental conditions such as temperature and other weather conditions, and other factors such as vibration and model support.

While it is important to provide latitude for change, it is most desirable to limit the thickness of clay from perhaps less than one inch to no more than two inches.

You may ask, how is it possible to know the configuration of a new design before the model has been constructed? The answer lies in the gathering of information prior to starting a design development project. This includes design objectives, design sketches and illustrations, engineering drawings, and package drawings. The development of an accurate frame and armature drawing depends on this advance information.

Design Illustrations and Sketches

After the gathering of sufficient information, actual work on a design is begun. Many rough sketches will be made until a theme develops. Then tighter sketches around the theme or themes will evolve and finally a few more finished and more detailed illustrations will follow.

When the client and the designer agree on a particular theme to be pursued, a three or four view line development must follow (side, front and rear elevations, and top plan view). This can start as a chart tape drawing over a package drawing and be followed by a line drawing or a computer graphics development. How this process is accomplished depends on how the drawing will be used, the training of the people involved with the project, and the type of equipment available. If you are in a shop where electronic equipment is not available, you will make a line drawing. If on the other hand you have a computer graphics system, an electronic plotter for drafting, and perhaps a scan/mill machine, you could utilize this equipment providing time can be scheduled for its use on this project. What is necessary is a three or four view development representing the approved theme illustration.

Engineering Drawings

It is most important to gather all engineering information pertinent to a design development. This information, whether it is in the form of drawings, sections, advance information, or actual parts, should be reviewed and appropriately added to a package drawing.

Drawings or sections that are needed but are not available must be constructed from information that is available. Drawings to be developed from information might include hinge lines and openings for doors or covers, latches, attachments, and structural members.

Sections for all edges and openings must be either taken from production units or developed new. This information is essential and must be taken into consideration when developing a design model.

Packaging

A package drawing starts as an advance layout of the unit to be modeled. The first draft package drawing is developed from advance information including all engineering information that can be obtained. The purpose of the package drawing is to establish the parameters around which the design must follow. This includes the placement and clearances around all components, various positions of moving parts, hinge lines and openings for doors and covers, and seating positions if that is required. The package drawing is updated as more and better information becomes available.

A package drawing may start simultaneously with advance sketches. The design theme, as it emerges, should be realistic and represent compatibility with the package drawing. However, the design theme should not be controlled by the package when changes that are within cost objectives will permit more acceptable or superior design features to be developed.

Assimilating The Information

Having followed the above steps, a drawing or computer aided design development of the approved theme will be available. Of considerable importance, the drawing will incorporate all package requirements. This theme drawing provides the information necessary for building the design model.

The drawing should be drafted to the scale of the model to be developed. If it is not, another drawing, either an enlargement or reduction, must be drafted or processed. If for some reason this is inconvenient, then the master sections must be developed to the proper scale. The drawing must also include a dimensional grid system of reference lines that should relate to engineering reference lines. Master sections would include a center line, if there is one, and a series of both vertical and horizontal sections from which the form will be developed.

This outline represents an ideal scenario, however, this may not always happen. Sometimes a design theme will be chosen but all package information may not be available. Other times package information is complete but there is difficulty in choosing a design theme. If development time is limited, you may be requested to proceed with a model. When a situation like this occurs, you will design and construct the armature according to the best information available. As the development of the model progresses, it may be necessary to modify the armature to accommodate the package or to satisfy the design theme. This can be done by modifying the foam (polyurethane or polystyrene) on the armature. In any case, do not jeopardize the integrity of the model by having for instance, too much clay in an area where it is not properly supported, or reduce the sub-surface to the point where it is no longer firm or stable.

Designing An Armature

The type of armature to be designed depends on the size of the model to be built, its use, and the accuracy required. A simple, limited-size armature can be constructed from plywood or foam or a combination of the two. As the size of the model increases and there is a need for mobility and/or improved accuracy, the armature must be constructed over a frame that will provide the desired structural stability.

To determine the size and configuration of the armature, overlay the theme drawing with a sheet of tracing paper. Align or trace the grid, then back off from the sections of the design theme the thickness of the clay to be applied and draw new sections on the tracing paper parallel to the existing sections. The new sections will represent the surface of the armature. If the armature is to be foam over plywood or over a metal frame, draw a general thickness of the foam and develop a geometric form that can be constructed as a sub-surface to the foam. Allow ample thickness of foam for preshaping to provide the proper thickness of clay.

On a model where a frame is necessary, plywood can be bolted to the frame and sheets of foam can be bonded and screwed (using large wooden washers) to the plywood sub-surface. Or blocks of foam (4" to 5" thick) can be bolted directly to a metal frame and bonded together. Polyurethane foam can also be sprayed on a sub-surface of plywood, fiberboard, or paper. It can be built up to a thickness of several inches. Equipment used for spraying insulation is ideal for this. On a model that will be transported, weight should be kept as low as possible while maintaining the armature's strength and rigidity. The use of an aluminum frame, several inches of foam, and a controlled thickness of clay will allow even a large model to be transported almost anywhere.

Designing An Armature (Cont.)

A metal frame for a modeling armature can be fabricated from aluminum or steel tubing. The tubing should be either square or rectangular rather than round for better attachment of plywood, foam, and other parts. The frame should be of welded construction and be cross braced for rigidity. The tubing can vary from 1-1/2" or smaller square steel up to 2" x 5" rectangular aluminum extrusions. The frame should be designed to accept the strain of the weight of the clay and the stress of the work on the model while providing a stable modeling structure. Locators should also be provided to position the frame and consequently the model. For transporting the model, special areas for lifting or a jack pad should be built into the frame.

On a model where a frame is not necessary, blocks of foam can be bonded together or sheets of foam can be screwed and bonded to plywood. Plywood can be used to construct a closed box that has corner braces and bulkheads for rigidity. The box need not be six sided nor in the form of a cube. Instead, it should represent the general form of the proposed design inside the clay and inside the foam.

Being a box that is closed on all sides will provide a structure with a great deal of torsional stiffness.

If variations or changes to a proposed design are to be limited due to stringent package and design requirements, the clay can be laid up directly over shellacked plywood. This, of course, depends on an armature form that would limit the thickness of clay to something less than one inch to no more than two inches. This is practical whether the plywood formed the structure or whether it was bolted to a frame. However, this is not recommended if you anticipate that part way through a design development program you may have to remove the clay and the plywood to modify the frame.

These are general instructions for armature design. There are other materials that you can use. In practice, I have had great success using armatures that were constructed as described above. A successful design modeling armature is one that is rigid and stable, can be moved about without cracking or affecting the clay, does not require changes to the frame, and is quickly and accurately positioned and repositioned.

Aligning The Armature

To align the armature, a work surface or work table is required. The work surface needs to be larger than the model to provide space for some type of model control. The surface may be a cast iron surface plate, or a steel or granite table, or it may be machined rails laid out and leveled around the model. A simple work surface can be a sheet of plywood reinforced and leveled. The type of work surface depends on the size and weight of the model, the accuracy required, and the equipment available.

The work surface around the model needs to have a grid that corresponds to the reference lines of the three or four view drawing of the design theme. It is desirable also to have straight edges on the work surface around the model to aid in controlling the model. The work surface or the straight edges attached to the work surface can have metric or inch increments marked out on them or scales can be attached to them.

The most desirable of course would be a styling bridge or a coordinate measuring machine that can mill points, lines, and surface. These machines have their own surface plates and mensuration system.

The armature should be equipped with some type of positioning system. When the armature is constructed, locator pins can be assembled loosely. The female half of the locators, or the other half of the positioning system, must be accurately assembled and fixed to the work

surface. Next, the completed armature would be mounted on the locators on the work surface. Since the locator pins on the armature are assembled loosely, the armature should be adjusted to the grid on the work surface prior to tightening or fixing the locator pins into their proper position.

In most cases, accuracy tolerance of the armature structure is not critical. Variations in construction are balanced out. The armature structure is positioned to its proper height and its optimum position side to side and fore and aft. When this has been accomplished and checked, the locator halves on the armature are tightened and fixed. They may be pinned and bolted, or welded, or screwed to the armature, but they must be securely fixed. At this point, the armature becomes an accurately aligned structure for building the model. A model built on the armature can be removed and then returned or moved to another location and set up on other locators that have been accurately positioned. Each time the model is dropped down on locators, it is accurately set up and requires no further aligning.

Even a small model, not requiring high precision, needs to be attached to its work surface so it does not move about. It can be removed for presentations and casting and repositioned for additional work.

Master Sections

At this stage, the armature structure has been accurately positioned but the armature surface must be checked and prepared. If blocks of foam are used and pre-shaped before they are bonded to the frame, the foam can be the correct thickness. However, even with this and any other process used to build up the armature, the armature must be checked.

What is needed now are templates of the master sections and other sections from the drawing of the design theme. Copies of these master sections can be made or they can be traced on tracing paper along with the appropriate reference lines. A copy made on a machine could shrink so it is sometimes advisable to trace the sections if a high degree of accuracy is important. Spray the back of copies or tracings with adhesive and attach them to the material from which the templates will be made.

Material used for templates will depend to some extent on the accuracy necessary and size of model being constructed. Materials include posterboard, fiberboard, plywood, many types of sheet plastic, sheet aluminum and sheet steel. Accuracy is much less important if it is the first go around on a theme model than it would be on the final prove out model. Master sections are laid out where there are areas on the surface of the model that cannot be infringed upon. These are sometimes called "hard points." It is important to have accurate sections in these areas.

The templates represent the sections of the clay surface but by setting them in their proper location, the foam surface can also be checked. The space between the template and the foam should equal the thickness of the styling clay. If there is too much foam, it should be cut away; if not enough foam, more should be added.

Cardboard or posterboard templates can be cut with a sharp pair of shears. Final clean up with sandpaper should be in the same direction as the line and not across it. The cardboard edge can be hardened by applying shellac. Other materials can be cut with a coping saw or band saw. In cutting the template, never cut to the line. Leave the last part for sanding or filing.

You can assume that the center of a line on paper or velum is the section. An accurate template properly finished should have half of the line on the template still visible.

A vertical belt sander and drum sander can be very helpful in cleaning up a rough cut template. The sanding or filing must be done at right angle to the face of the template. If the template is made from a thick piece of plywood, the back side of the template can be beveled. Again, it is important in final clean up that you sand or file in the same direction as the line and not across the cut.

To align the template, reference lines should be left exposed on the template surface. The template may be cut on other reference lines that permit it to stand on the work surface or to be attached to an angle or cube. Templates can also be located from a modeling bridge.

Computer Aided Design

If a computer graphics system is used in developing the various views from the theme drawing, the data obtained from this development can be used to draft the sections. This can be accomplished on an electronic plotter and drafted to the proper scale. Electronic plotter copies are ideal for making templates. Processed data can also be used in a coordinate scan/mill machine to align the armature and check the foam surface.

Other computer processes such as solid modeling, 3-D computer modeling, virtual reality (VR) and holography are sometimes used to research and develop theme designs. Data from these developments can be used in the design and preparation of armatures. The end developments from these processes, however, do not preclude the need for clay models.

This photograph shows an excellent set-up for developing a motor home instrument panel. This set-up was constructed at location using materials on hand. The work surface is Formica finished particle board accurately positioned and attached to a tubular steel frame. The armature is built up out of layers of foam. Note the drag template attached to one of the two wood angles and the finished dragged clay surface. (Photograph: Author)

The work surface for the forward part of the instrument panel represents the surface below the lower windshield opening. Templates have been set on each ten inch section and those surfaces have been covered with steel tape feeler gauge stock. The areas between the sections will be filled with warm clay and cleaned up with wood battens and steels. (Photograph: Author)

To give the model realism, marker sketches are used to illustrate instruments, controls, vents, etc. This advanced instrument panel was designed by Dennis Otto, Director of Product Design, Gulf Stream Coach, Inc. (Photograph: Author)

Final Armature Preparation

Using the template sections, the armature surface must now be checked and adjusted to provide the proper thickness of clay. If the model will have tall vertical walls or sides, it is recommended that thin cleat strips be attached to plywood armatures. On foam surface armatures, a router can be used to mill inverted bevels or cleat-like grooves into the foam. These strips or grooves will provide a footing for the clay to hold onto.

Only one more task remains before the styling clay can be applied. Although styling clay will adhere to many surfaces, it is always advisable to shellac the armature before clay is applied. The shellac can be reduced or thinned with 50% alcohol to speed drying. Two coats of reduced shellac are recommended and should set over night to assure that the shellac is completely dry. Styling clay will not adhere to damp shellac.

Determining Styling Clay Requirements

Clay has a weight to volume correlation of 90 pounds per cubic foot. This ratio holds true only in an absolute sense. In other words, if there are not air pockets within the clay and the compression factors of the clay billet is uniform, then 90 pounds will fill a cubic foot. When clay is manufactured, there is always some air entrapment and generally when clay is built up on an armature, pockets of air will be introduced.

To calculate the amount of clay needed in a solid object, a user must estimate how many cubic feet or what volume of clay is required. The standard formula is Volume = Length x Width x Height. Multiply the length, width and height measurements in inches and divide the answer by 1,728 inches (the number of cubic inches in a cubic foot). Multiply your answer by 90 to obtain the number of pounds required.

Irregular forms should be estimated in individual sections and then added up. This calculation was provided by Jack North, in "Chavant Clay Matters", July 1, 1993.

Laying Up The Styling Clay

The armature should now be ready to build up with styling clay. The armature has been designed to the shape of the design theme illustration and the dimensional limitations of the package; the armature structure has been accurately positioned on the work surface; the foam was laid up and checked to be within dimensional requirements; and the armature is prepared for laying up hot clay.

The clay must be heated to a soft workable consistency. The temperature of the clay will depend on the particular styling clay that is being used. The first layer of clay should be no thicker than one eighth of an inch and should be rubbed in hard with the thumb and forefinger to obtain a good bond. You push the soft clay with the thumb and pull it back with the forefinger between the first and second knuckle. You may also use the butt of your hand and switch this procedure to your other hand. The idea is to get the clay well rubbed into the armature surface. If the clay is uncomfortably hot, gloves may be worn during this procedure.

The next layer of clay can be thicker and this time you want to fill the cleats on the plywood or the grooves in the foam, if there are any. Each layer of clay should be well rubbed into the previous layer.

If you will be using templates to set in the sections, check the clay build up with the template. The rough clay build up should always be below the section edge of the templates. It is too time consuming to tool down rough clay to set templates. Templates are always set in warm soft clay.

If the model is to be milled, the clay buildup should be above the sections. The clay milling cutter should be milling hard clay. However, the clay buildup on the armature should be controlled so that too much clay is not added. When milling clay surface, excess clay (beyond the depth the cutter can mill) must be tooled down and areas below the cutter paths must be filled with warm clay.

All armature and clay buildup work to this stage can be accomplished by staff personnel other than design modelers. This is possible if support personnel are available. However, a design modeler should check the preparation of the armature and the clay to assure that it meets modeling requirements.

Obtaining A Good Clay Bond

The importance of obtaining a good clay bond in the first layers of a styling clay buildup cannot be over emphasized. This same importance of obtaining a good bond also exists when laying up a new layer of heated clay over an old clay surface. If a good bond is not obtained, the new layer of clay may become loose and cause all sorts of problems.

There are several things that should be done when building a new layer of clay over an old clay surface. First of all, scuff the old surface with a wire brush or the toothed edge of a clay scraper. This will improve the surface adhesion. The old surface can also be heated with a heat gun. Softening the old surface in this manner will greatly aid in obtaining a good bond.

A similar situation exists when clay is applied over a metal or fiberglass surface. If it is not necessary to protect the surface, it can be shellaced before warmed clay is applied.

If the metal or fiberglass surface must be protected, apply masking tape over the entire surface to be covered with clay. Use only a masking tape with good adhesive characteristics. This will protect the surface from damage. On top of this layer of masking tape, apply carpet tape or other thick double-sided tape. This layer of carpet tape will create an excellent surface for obtaining a good clay bond.

Do not apply the carpet tape right to the edge if the clay surface must feather out. Instead, stop the carpet tape back a little way, and apply shellac over the masking tape up to the edge where the clay surface begins to feather out.

Special Situations

There are design models that do not require especially constructed armatures. Models falling into this category would be appliques, ornaments, moldings, and various after market products. It would also include additions to or changes to some type of existing composite tooling. These developments would all be modeled on a cast, or a tool, or the surface of the manufactured product for which they are designed.

A simple armature such as a piece of wood or angle, or aluminum sheet formed as needed can be attached to the surface of the manufactured product for which the item is being developed. Or, this could be a cast or a partial cast of the product, or it can be fixed and built up on a work surface.

Masters for plastic injection parts can be made from design developed wood models. Masters for engraved or embossed ornamental parts may be made in metal.

Styling clay is also used to build up models that take the place of wood patterns required for castings. These may or may not require an armature but they do require special processing to develop both the outside and the inside of the part or the pattern. Also, the model may have to be built to shrink dimensions.

Wind tunnel models for the aerodynamic study of automobile designs are built up in styling clay in usually one fifth or two fifth scale but sometimes full size. These are very special models built to exacting dimensional standards and tolerances. Armatures for these models are built up in light weight aluminum or fiberglass and form a structure similar to the structure of the vehicles they represent. Inside these models is an open space for the installation of various test equipment including those to measure pressure points.

The underbody and chassis for scale windtunnel study models are built up separately from the rest of the model. This permits the engineers to develop and install major mechanicals according to the latest advance, prototype, or production information available. It also permits one underbody and chassis model to be used with several body types and styles during the same series of tests.

The windtunnel study models are exact copies of the styling models in their design development phase. These aero models are used to measure the various aerodynamic forces that affect the vehicle as it travels through the air. These models are tuned, adjusted, and modified during windtunnel studies to reduce or correct aerodynamic deficiencies. Changes made in a windtunnel will be examined later on a styling model in the studio and will require approval before being incorporated into a production program.

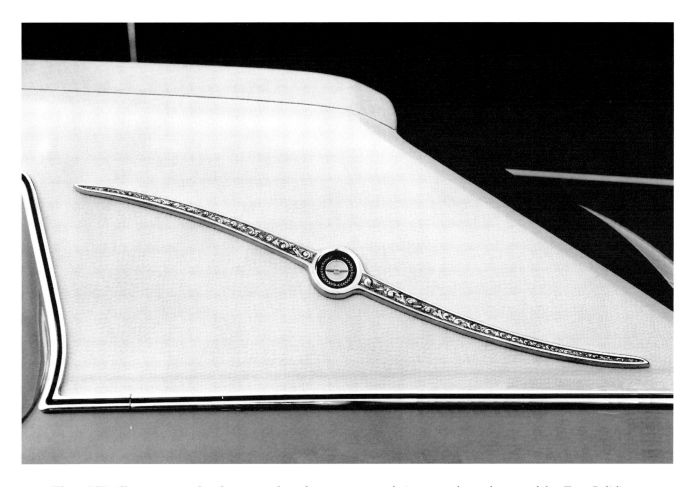

These "C" pillar ornamental embossments have been custom made in copper by sculptor modeler, Tony Palidino. These embossments were chrome plated and set into a plated fiberglass part. (Photograph: Ford Design Center)

Steel plastic injection tools for these Big Rig Spinner parts have been copy milled, or Kellered, from wood master models. The shrink factor of the chrome plated ABS plastic injection material has been incorporated into the master models.
In this picture the part is still on the die immediately after the plastic injection machine has been opened. (Photograph: T. A. Hoadley)

Positive side of plastic injection tool. (Photograph: T. A. Hoadley)

Author discussing sample parts with Quality Engineer, Sylvester Smith. (Photograph: T. A. Hoadley)

Preparing a Big Rig Spinner for show. (Photograph: Pat Cragin)

One blade of a five bladed propeller is developed in solid clay on a surface plate. Templates for the outline and cross section are set in the warm clay surface. The areas between template settings are filled and the model is roughed in. (Photograph: Jake Free)

The surface of the blade model is cleaned up and is ready for construction of a negative. The Three-Dimensional Engineering and Master Modeling system is used to produce the underside of the blade and the mold. The completed blade model is used as a pattern to produce the mold for casting the propeller. (Photograph: Jake Free)

A finished five bladed propeller processed by Master Modeling. The propeller design and development is by Jake Free. (Photograph: Jake Free)

Jake Free designs, engineers, develops, and markets propellers and other products. The propeller model that is shown above, and other propeller developments, are used on world class man powered water craft. These pictures show Free with his water craft above the water surface, just the propeller and the hydrofoils that lift the water craft are below the surface. The steering hydrofoil in front and the main hydrofoil below the seat were also developed by Free using the 3-D Master Modeling System.
The entire craft was designed and constructed by Free including the floats and mechanical drive.
(Photographs: Free Enterprises, Elkhart, Indiana)

These work platforms were mounted onto brackets that had been fabricated, machined, and bolted to the tractor's accessory attachment pads. This created an accurate work surface to develop the model. (Photograph: Design Center)

Aero dynamics and windtunnel studies have been vitally important in the design development of many European automobiles for most of this century. Until the middle of the 1970s, windtunnel studies were only occasionally used in the United States and therefore of only minor importance. This photograph shows a scale model prepared for windtunnel studies in the early 1930s by Buzz Grisinger at Chrysler Art & Colour. (Photograph: Ford Design Center)

In the late 1950s and early 1960s, the author developed a system for the aerodynamic study and tuning of styling clay models in the German windtunnels. Shown here is a one-fifth scale aero test model in the small windtunnel in Stuttgart, August 1962. The model is the 1964 Taunus 17M built by Ford Werke, A.G. (Photograph: Technische Hochschule, Stuttgart, Germany)

Dietrich Tenner modifying a model in the small wind tunnel in Stuttgart, Germany. (Photograph: Ford Werke A.G., West Germany, 1960)

The system developed in Germany for testing styling clay models in the windtunnel is further developed, refined, and expanded by the author at the Ford Design Center, Dearborn, Michigan.
A three-eighths scale aero test model is being milled in the DEA Alpha two headed CMM by Bob Barrow. All sections and lines milled into the styling clay model are being roughed in by design modeler, Bob Laich, 1976.
The model is keyed to its fixture, the fixture is keyed to the table, the table is positioned by locators onto the surface plate of the CMM. (Photograph: Ford Design Center)

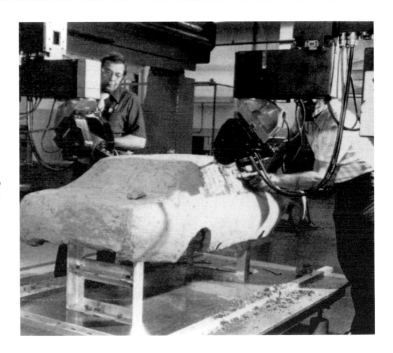

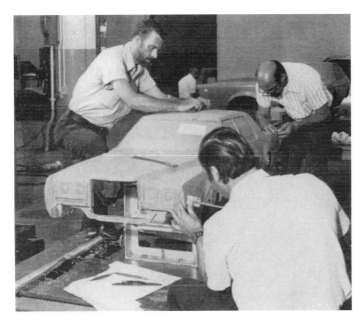

The three-eighths scale aero test model is being cleaned up by design modelers Russell Heitman and Bob Laich, after all sections and lines have been milled into the styling clay. When the model is finished it will be shipped to the windtunnel for testing, 1976.
Notice that the model is built on an open aluminum fabricated armature. The chassis with under body, engine, drive line, axles, suspension, wheels, etc. will be assembled and keyed to the body. Since the body is open, pressure point tubes and other test equipment can be easily installed. The chassis is separate from the body so that it can be prepared in the same time frame. Also several body types and styles can use the same chassis, 1976. (Photograph: Ford Design Center)

An aero test model in the windtunnel. Smoke streamlines trace the air flow. (Photograph: Ford Design Center)

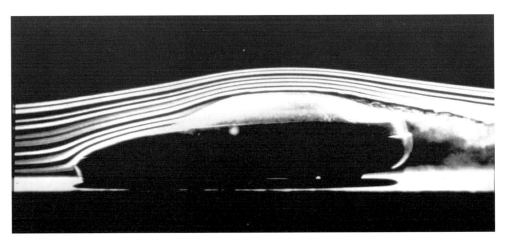

Checking airflow on a styling clay aero test model in the windtunnel. (Photograph: Ford Design Center)

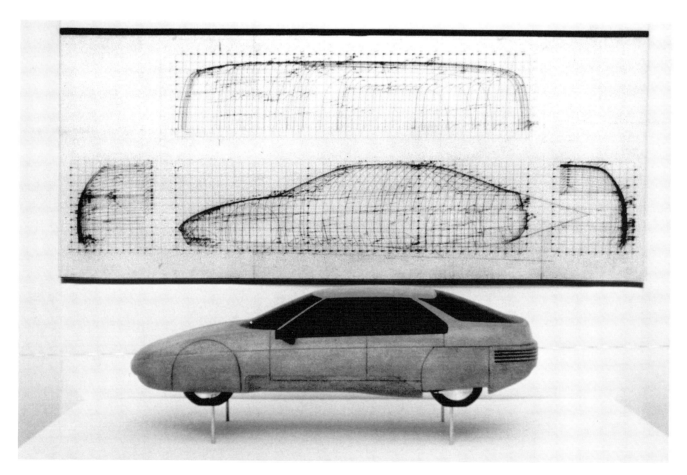

This picture shows a four view computer generated and drafted surface layout drawing that was scanned from the finished full size model. In the foreground is a styling clay model of the Ford Probe IV that was milled from computer data and finished for final windtunnel study. (Photograph: Ford Design Center)

A two-fifths scale aero test model is built on an armature that is keyed to the updated surface table support fixture. The table can be keyed to the scan/mill surface plate with locator pins and stands. In the background at the far right, can be seen the small Lamerson bridge used by both the studio and the windtunnel, 1983. (Photograph: Ford Design Center)

Design model development for front and rear, left and right hand splash guards are built up in styling clay on sheet aluminum armatures attached to the vehicle. Design and development is by Tom Stone. (Photograph: Assurance Advisors and Investigators, Dearborn, Michigan)

The splash guard models are finished in clay, painted, and presented for approval. Negatives are made from each model right on the vehicle. Completed parts are cast in flexible urethane through the use of Three-Dimensional Engineering and Master Modeling. (Photograph: Assurance Advisors and Investigators, Dearborn, Michigan)

CHAPTER 7 - Design Model Development
Setting Templates

Templates can be set after styling clay has been laid up on an armature constructed to the rough configuration of the design. The templates should be set in place one at a time. If there is too much clay on the armature it must be tooled off so the template is free of the rough clay.

Align each template by using the reference lines on the template surface. On table models, align vertical templates to the grid on the work surface. Templates can be notched so they rest against the straight edge. Templates for large models can be stabilized by attaching them to an angle block or bridge with "C" clamps. If templates are clamped to an angle, the angle should rest against the straight edge.

Horizontal templates may be set up on blocks adjusted to the proper height or set against lines scribed into vertical template settings on the model. All template settings must agree with the master-theme drawing. It is advisable to set all vertical templates in one view before setting horizontal or cross templates from another view.

When the surface has been prepared and the template has been aligned, move the template away from the station and apply warm soft clay on the model in line with the template section. Apply clay in a line no wider than from 1 inch to 3 inches wide (25 mm to 75mm) depending on the size of the model and the number of templates. Immediately, while the clay is still warm, drag the template through the soft clay. Make sure the template is orthogonal. Drag it back and forth, adding soft clay as needed along the section until there is a clean drag an inch or so wide all the way. Then set up an angle plate with its face on the section station and scribe a line on the dragged surface. This is the template section.

There are several things to do if the clay on the model cools and sets up before the template can be brought into its proper position:

1. If the template is made from a hard material, tap the back edge of the template with a mallet to bring it to its proper position and then tap the sides of the template back and forth with the mallet.

2. Tool off the warm clay that had been added and re-drag but this time add less clay.

3. Tool off the warm clay that had been added and re-drag only a portion of the template at a time. Repeat this process consecutively until the whole section has been dragged.

When the line has been scribed on the dragged section, tool off some of the excess clay on either side of the scribed line. Be very careful not to disturb the line.

Fill in the rough areas between the template sections after all templates have been set on one side or one area of a model including any cross templates. Be careful to rub the clay in well to avoid any air pockets in the clay buildup near the surface of the model.

To protect the scribed lines, modelers sometimes will tape off one side of the line. This is particularly effective if black photographic tape is used. By using black tape the lines stand out and are easily read. The sections can likewise be compared to each other.

Plastic fish (gut) line is also used to protect lines scribed into clay surface. In addition, fish line is used to protect the edges of design lines and creases. The fish line can be laid right into a scribed line and easily pressed in along the edge of a crease. The surface can be steeled and the fish line, imbedded in the clay, does not move.

A styling bridge can be used to set templates by clamping each template to the bridge. The bridge set-up is moved back and forth until the section surface has been dragged.

Points can be used instead of templates by plotting in consecutive points along each section. By utilizing a styling bridge, points can be set in manually with a pointing scale.

Points can also be set in with a surface gage or a height gage. Scribe a line on the surface of the model by using an angle block and mouse or scriber. To do this, set the angle on the desired station on the side, front, or rear of the model and scribe a line in the area where a point will be taken or set in. Adjust the surface gage at the proper height and at an angle adequate to reach the point area. In this manner, you can either set a point into the model or retrieve a point from the model.

Points can also be milled in using special equipment with a motorized head. An electronic layout machine can be controlled either automatically or manually to accomplish this. Points from a stored data base are milled into sections consecutively after the machine has been set up on each section station. Points set into a surface require cleaning up to obtain a section similar to a template. Surface can also be developed by using many points on sections milled close together.

Coordinate measuring machines, working from stored data, can mill sections and lines into clay models using tapered line cutters. These machines can also mill surface utilizing a ball cutter. The data base for this work would come from the computer graphics development of the design theme. Data could also come from a model previously electronically scanned or from other stored data sources.

Sections milled into clay can be preserved by brushing talcum or spraying white or silver paint into the grooves. Section lines milled into a clay model are similar to lines that have been set in with templates.

Surface milling requires a considerable amount of processed data and time for milling. Surface milled with a ball cutter leaves cusps on the clay surface that must be tooled and steeled off. Cusp size depends on the size of the ball cutter and the spacing of the cutter paths. Equipment for milling surface is expensive and requires support personnel and available operating time. A flat cutter can be used on a convex surface with a minor amount of crown, but the resultant surface must also be steeled.

Roughing In The Model

It is time now to rough in the model. All templates have been set and sections have been scribed. The areas between the sections also have been filled.

By using a toothed scraper, you can clean away the high points of clay. As you work, fill in the low areas with warm soft clay. The toothed scraper should be held at approximately 60 degrees to the clay surface. Hold the scraper firmly and shave the clay. Work the scraper by pulling it at an acute angle to the sections. Then work the scraper in an acute angle to its last cut in a crisscross manner. By judiciously scraping and filling, the surface is soon brought to a relatively smooth texture.

At this stage, the form of the model is very easily read. However, since the clay has not been steeled or slicked, there are no highlights. Highlights can be plotted with a highlight gauge and outlined with black tape. It is therefore possible to get a quick picture of the design very early on. The edge of a combination square protractor head may be used as a highlight gauge. This can be done by setting nicks along a line of the contour of a clay model's surface at a preset angle of the protractor. Use the level of the protractor to set the nicks. You can develop a 30°, 45°, or a 60° highlight line.

Why Design Models Are Needed

The design theme usually originates on an illustration or series of well finished sketches. These illustrations are interpreted into a master theme drawing. However, by using a computer aided industrial design (CAID) program, a 3-D perspective model may be created from a 2-D Studio Paint sketch. This information can, in turn, be reproduced into a full size three-dimensional styling clay model by conventional means or the model surface can be milled through the use of a coordinate measuring machine (CMM).

Persons who are not familiar with automobile design, may assume that a sophisticated 3-D computer modeling development should be the end of the design process, that a model is milled and finished just to check that everything looks good. But at this point, the design may be lacking in character or execution. Because of this, the designer may decide to alter a line or two and change the form here or there. The engineer, after preliminary checking of the model, may decide that a certain surface has to change for manufacturing reasons, clearance for a mechanical part, or for government regulations. Cost studies may conclude that the material of some part must be changed for cost reasons and a different material will require altering the surface of that part. So this is the beginning of a three-dimensional styling clay model for final surface development, presentation, and comparison. There are always several finished models prepared for comparison at the time of design approval. These are all the result of model development and evaluation.

There are other factors that need to be considered here. Designers normally work in two dimensions while modelers work in three dimensions. Although some designers work comfortably in either 2-D or 3-D, many designers lose a good design idea when they put their 2-D sketch into correct perspective or into package. A designer may make a terrific sketch with a good idea but may be unable to translate it into a good 3-D design. It is the modelers task to capture that sketch idea or feeling in a model. Many good design ideas have been saved by a capable design modeler.

A well designed automobile, and this applies to other products as well, is the result of good teamwork and leadership. A good design requires more than a good original theme, it requires a well thought out model, positive engineering support, and a manufacturing organization that is responsive to the development. Good teamwork and leadership starts from the top. People in management must be supportive. They can instill a feeling of accomplishment and excitement into the design project and stress cooperation among the various entities involved in the development.

Hundreds of sketches are made by designers. Some of these will be further developed into finished 3-D computer modeling studies. These visual model interpretations will be reviewed and modified by design management and company officials, and some will be used in market research clinics. This same process takes place with conventional sketches and illustrations. But only a few of these will be further developed or milled into styling clay models.

When a model is milled, data may come from several sources. The theme can come from the 3-D computer modeling development, but package data will already be fixed in the program such as window plane surface and door openings. Other surface may come from parts of existing production vehicles carried over into a new program. Still additional surface data may come from a previously studied 3-D computer model or styling clay model development. These areas may already be milled into a new model before the data from a new theme development is added.

Let us look a little closer at computer aided industrial design and coordinate measuring machines. These really are excellent development systems. Perhaps the greatest value of CAID is in transferring the designer's sketch into dimensionally correct visual data. Although these systems do have limitations in going from an illustration directly into a finished three-dimensional model, they can aid the design engineer's task and the design modeler's development work and do so accurately in a much reduced time frame.

In automotive design, surface development usually evolves from one side of a model to the other and back again. The CMM can become a tool of the design modeling team, accurately milling in surface on command. As a measuring machine, the CMM records surface data from those areas that are modified or developed directly on the model. This data is then recorded and used to mill updated surface on the other side of the model. As development work progresses from one side to the other and the model becomes finished, surface data is already stored in the computer and is available at any time for engineering and manufacturing studies.

3-D computer modeling is not a panacea, while it does reduce model development work it does not replace styling clay models. I believe final surface tuning requires the eye and hand of a skilled modeler on the clay surface. Styling clay models will continue to provide three-dimensional surface definition.

Hard Points

When changes are in order, it is sometimes necessary to protect the "hard points" by setting wood dowels or blocks of wood into the clay surface. These blocks and dowels are accurately positioned at the critical areas on the master sections. They become points of reference that cannot be infringed upon. When the model is completed, but before finishing, these wood dowels or blocks can be removed.

Free-Hand Modeling

The changes that were listed above are often not large changes. They are being made to capture the character of the theme design and to satisfy certain engineering and manufacturing concerns. The model at this point usually has not been seen by the client. All effort is toward meeting engineering and manufacturing requirements and finishing the three-dimensional model of the two-dimensional design theme illustration, or the 3-D computer model development.

Changes are made free-hand to the clay surface. Lines are adjusted, forms are modified, and the model undergoes general tuning. This work can all be done without templates or drawings. Results will depend upon the expertise of the modeler and the input of the designer.

Creating Surface Free Hand

Many designers prefer to develop their design in three dimensions right on the model. If they have a sketch or an illustration or only an idea, it can be tried out in the clay development. It may be very difficult or nearly impossible to put lines down for some designs without first putting them into three dimensions.

When developing surface free hand, it is necessary to work around hard points or check them periodically, especially for a production model.

Advantages of Styling Clay

The advantage of small clay models is that you can work more freely creating surface free hand without being held so closely to hard points. Also surface can be developed much more quickly in a small model than in a full size model.

Changes are common and expected during design development. It would be great if a model could be constructed and finished for appearance just to obtain final approval for engineering and tooling. If that were the case, other types of model building material would suffice and a hard model might be very desirable. But unfortunately, that is not the case. Styling clay, therefore, provides the best medium for design development of models.

Foam (polyurethane or polystyrene) models are fine for a quick picture, but as soon as a series of changes are made, foam becomes a real liability. Cutting into the surface is not difficult unless you must hold hard points and master sections. If changes require the surface to be built up, then more blocks of foam must be added or the surface will have to be built up with styling clay or one of the hard modeling materials.

Bondo consists of a polyester resin and styrene monomer. It is used on wood or on fiberglass casts for model development; however, constructing Bondo models require several times longer to make and finish than do clay models. Bondo is a very hard material and must be sanded. It requires a lot of time and care to develop a good surface. Also, unlike styling clay, changes in Bondo are very difficult to do and require a lot of time.

Plaster modeling has been used successfully for centuries and requires considerable skill, but it is messy, requires time for build-up and it has many of the drawbacks of other hard materials.

As noted in Chapter 3, the primary advantage of styling clay over other materials is unlimited freedom of expression in surface development. Styling clay is either equal to or better than other model construction materials as outlined in the six advantages. However, there is an additional advantage. When styling clay has been builtup over a finished painted surface or production vehicle or part, the clay is easily removed after redesign of the item or part has been completed. Hard material cannot be removed without damage to the surface.

Many times when a model is developed in a hard material, such as wood and Bondo, the development goes into production to the chagrin of the designer (if not the client also) due to limitation of time, money, and the professional ability of the artisan constructing the model. This should not happen. Models constructed from styling clay can be quickly altered and tuned to meet the designer's and the client's full satisfaction.

It is not an exaggeration to say that the ability to make fast, accurate changes either for styling or functional reasons is possible only with styling clay. The validity and significance of this statement has been demonstrated many times during reviews with engineering or presentations to the client. Those people who are not familiar with styling clay development are amazed to see a requested change roughed-in within a few minutes right in front of their eyes.

In many models made of Bondo or other hard materials, lack of model precision and finesse is quite evident. Without the costly outlay of capital for equipment and systems used in die model and pattern shops, the sanding and buffing that are required with many hard models only makes the surface development worse while the surface becomes highly polished. The result is an inferior surface development, as contrasted by the versatility and satisfaction that styling clay affords the designer and modeler.

A Tarus machine being used for checking points in the development of a styling clay model. The sections have been milled and the surface roughed in. (Photograph: Tarus Products Inc.)

A ball cutter is seen here milling clay surface. It is attached to a five-axis mill on a MECOF machine manufactured in Italy. (Photograph: Ford Design Center)

Non-contact X-Y-Z data measurement began with a single point laser diode triangulation method. A laser spot projected onto a surface was viewed at an angle with the diode as a receiving detector. This was recorded as a single X-Y-Z data point. It was necessary to reposition the sensor for each laser point measured. Technology improved and the single point diode was extended to a single line laser scanning device. For this the sensor was repositioned for each line. Coordinate Measuring Machines (CMMs) are used by the automobile industry to accurately position and reposition models, and to scan and mill surface. Model surface is developed, milled, scanned, recorded, and sections are cut and studied according to predetermined package X-Y-Z coordinates. CMMs have been ideally suited for laser point and line scanning. The next technological development was made by Electro-Optical Information Systems (EOIS). Using white light, a fringe pattern projection device with hundreds of lines was projected simultaneously and the fringe pattern image was collected by a solid-state video camera. This combination of camera and projector is called a moire sensor. With this device enough data can be collected in a single measurement to generate a high-density X-Y-Z data array of 200,000 data points over a 400 x 500mm grid. The patch size is determined by the moire sensor optics. Typical data accuracy for a 3" x 3" patch is 0.001". Fringe processing techniques were studied and applied in laser interferometers during the 1960s and 70s. Major break throughs in moire techniques were made possible in the early 1980s because of more powerful computers and more sophisticated algorithms. In 1980, typical EOIS array processors weighed between 5 and 10 pounds, cost $75,000, and required a special positioning system for the sensor and part. A special-purpose moire system cost between $200,000 and $500,000. Only the aerospace industry could afford these systems. In the early 1990s, EOIS redesigned it's moire sensor head and produced the Mini-Moire™. By 1994, EOIS sensor heads weighed only 10 ounces and cost $7,500. The Mini-Moire is attached to a Renishaw PH-9, PH-10, or MIH articulating head mounted to standard industry CMMs. The challenge for moire sensor technology for surface scanning is not data collection, but the formatting and interfacing of the data to conventional surface development software type packages. Another company, Imageware, has developed such a system. The mass of points collected by the data array sensor is formatted into a sophisticated 3-D computer modeling program. The surface can be smoothed or massaged as in systems using data generated by conventional scanning methods.

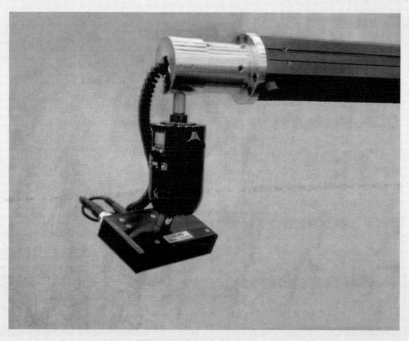

Mini-Moire™ set up to scan a windshield.

John S. Andrews

1961 Taunus 17M, front three quarter view, November 1960, Turin Automobile Show.

A well developed design and a successful program are by-products of good teamwork. An example of this is the 1961 German Ford Taunus 17M. The full size design model was approved in September 1958 and the new vehicle was in production and in dealers showrooms two years later. The new model was publicly introduced at the November 1960 Turin Automobile Show. This was the result of good teamwork and leadership emanating from the top down.

John S. Andrews became General Manager of Ford-Werke A.G. in January 1958. He put together a team of men who headed product planning, timing, design, engineering, and manufacturing. Andrews was able to organize these executives and their staffs (who came from diverse backgrounds, training, and nationalities) into a team dedicated to produce an outstanding automobile in a restricted time frame. In addition to the new 17M there were two extensive facelift programs to be completed and in production in one year and another all new program for the Taunus 12M that followed.

The all new 1961 Taunus 17M won several awards and many other accolades for design and for engineering and manufacturing innovations. Not only was the design trend-setting but the comfort, interior space, fuel economy, acceleration, and speed were greatly improved. The drag coefficient was reduced 25% from the previous model, the weight was reduced 210 pounds, the all new 4-speed transmission met Andrew's stipulation that it shift like "a knife through warm butter"; this new design had achieved his goal.

Wesley P. Dahlberg, head of the design office in Ford-Cologne, was responsible for the design of the new 17M. The model had many first time features not seen before on a low priced European automobile. These features included:

1961 Taunus 17M, rear three quarter view, November 1960, Turin Automobile Show.

Wesley P. Dahlberg

> o *Compound curved side glass*
> o *Compound wrap-over windshield*
> o *Large oval headlamps giving improved illumination*
> o *Curved rocker panels*
> o *Hatch type hood*
> o *Sheet metal aprons below the bumpers front and rear that completed the body's surfaces*
> o *Hidden "B" pillars on both 2 and 4 door sedans*

There were many other features including an overall elliptical appearance giving this car a very unique look. Production of the new 17M increased by several fold and Ford-Cologne's share of the market also increased. This was a very successful new model launch.

John Andrews did this through friendly persuasion and teamwork. To put this task into its proper perspective, this was still post war Western Germany. The devastation and debris from World War II were still a common sight. Busses, trains, street cars, interurban rail cars, and bicycles were the normal means of transportation. One of the greatest difficulties was a shortage of workers. (The Design Office initially included 15 employees). The company brought in workers for all types of jobs from Spain, Italy, Yugoslavia, Turkey, plus some employees who came from the Eastern Zone. Many of these people were scarred physically and/or psychologically by the war. Living accommodations had to be constructed for these workers and their families and they had to be trained. There were shortages of all tools and equipment so new factories had to be constructed.

For John Andrews and his team to have accomplished this task with success was truly an outstanding achievement.

New, more advanced MECOF five-axis milling machines have been installed in Ford's Small and Medium Vehicle Center design studios in Dunton, England and Merkenich, Germany. These dual five-axis milling machines were developed jointly by Ford and MECOF and manufactured in Italy.

These machines take much of the labor out of design modeling by duplicating computer 2-D data into 3-D design models. The designers provide a sketch and imput key coordinate points that follow the flow of primary lines. Those points are then entered into a computer program, and are converted mathematically to produce a complete surface grid of the design.

But a surface developed by advanced technology, lacks the refinement and finess that is available when the hand is on the model. Experience, emotion and creativity work together with a complexity that cannot be duplicated by technology.

Dual Five-Axis MECOF Milling Machines (Photograph: Global Design Connection, June 1997)

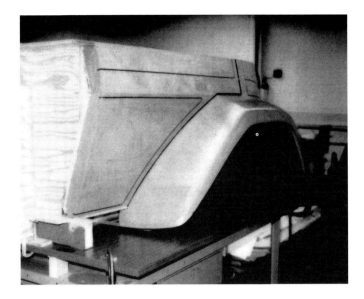

A design development for a J. I. Case backhoe fender starts with a strong rigid plywood armature. This armature is designed by the author using engineering information and design sketches drawn by Case staff designer, Dennis Otto.

The armature is mounted to a plywood platform, leveled and clamped to a table. The model is roughed-in with templates from design drawings. This rather simple set up meets the level of precision and accuracy necessary for engineering development.

The fender is then "picture" modeled around a few master sections and sketches. The model is shown to management. A revision is requested and roughed-in during the presentation. The development is cleaned up and released to engineering. The cab portion of the backhoe is developed for reference and includes the previously established outline for the fender intersection.

A Case International backhoe tractor is shown with the new fender.

(Photograph: Author)

CHAPTER 8 - Finishing The Model

Cleaning Up The Model

After all modifications have been made to the model, it will be necessary to finish the clay surfaces. On many smaller models and on portions of some larger models, there will be fine detail that must be cleaned up with small tools and steels. In addition, most models have areas that can be dragged.

Templates can be made for dragging-in constant section detail and surface. Templates for this purpose should be carefully made and highly polished. It may be necessary to drag these templates against a straight edge and steel tape. Steel tape for dragging can be made from feeler gauge stock. Templates can also be clamped to an angle block and dragged against the work surface and a sweep or curve. Special setups, as necessary, may be made for dragging templates to create compound curved surfaces.

Moldings and some types of graphic design details will require clay extrusions. Special dies are made for clay extrusion machines. These dies must be drilled, filed, and tried out to obtain the proper section and finish. Clay extrusion moldings are cut and fit and then bonded to finished clay surface with a clay solvent such as turpentine or other thinners.

Larger models may have surfaces that are rather flat or have only moderate crown. Flexible wood battens, or metal splines and sweeps, are used to scrape over the clay surface to further remove the high areas. The batten is many times longer than the toothed scrapers and will easily show up the high and low areas of the surface. Hold the batten firmly with two hands and bend it to the curve of the surface. Scrape the edge over the surface and shave off the high areas. Crisscross the surface with the batten and fill the low areas with warm soft clay.

To make clay extrusions, de-aired clay billets are slid into the cylinder of the machine. The die, with the exact shape of the desired molding, is inserted. The breech is closed and locked. Power is applied and the speed of the piston and travel of the clay extrusion is infinitely controlled.

Checking Highlights and Reflections

Highlights can be seen on any upper surface that reflects light. This of course includes fender and body sections, and the edges of the roof, deck, and hood. In addition, highlights will be seen on the reflective surface of grills, moldings, ornaments, bumpers, fins, and blips. Highlights should be checked on instrument panel surface, instrument cluster frames and pod surface and edges. Failure to plot highlights will create some surprising reflections.

Highlights can be plotted on a rough surface with black tape but for the show they must be checked visually. The clay surface will be slicked with a plastic slick that has rounded polished edges. The slicked clay surface should be polished with a soft cloth or sponge that has been soaked in cool water. Since styling clay contains wax as one of its ingredients, the slicked and polished clay will take on a high luster. Highlights will be easily seen on this polished clay surface.

The highlights may need to be adjusted. Please remember, as the curve of a surface is modified to raise or lower a highlight in side elevation, the highlight will also move in or out in the other views. So highlights must be viewed from all angles. It is also very important to plot the highlights when making a surface drawing or computer graphics development of surface.

Reflections can be seen in any highly polished surface such as a window. A polished surface will reflect and make visible any surface irregularities. A poor surface development will broadcast surface distortions. It is just as important to check surface reflections as it is to check highlights. Any design model, but particularly those that will have a polished surface, should have a polished surface finish prior to completion of the model. This can be accomplished with polished clay, Dinoc, or painted strippable vinyl. Surface reflections need to be checked and the surface development corrected if distortions appear.

Highlights can be plotted before a surface has been finished. First it is necessary to lay out and clean up one line and a master section at right-angle to the line. In this case, the line represents the window reveal moulding. A master section has been modeled free hand, cleaned up, and is marked with a 45° protractor setting. One or more highlights can be marked on a section utilizing a protractor with an adjustable level. You can check a 30°, a 45°, or any other degree highlight that you wish. (Photograph: Author)

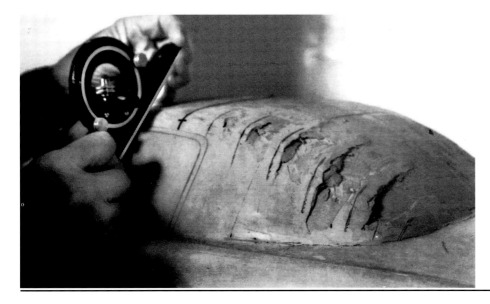

Rough build additional sections randomly with warm clay by working each way from the master section. Using a batten or a spline smooth off the highlight area of these additional sections to run well with the cleaned up line. Carefully mark each of these sections with the protractor. (Photograph: Author)

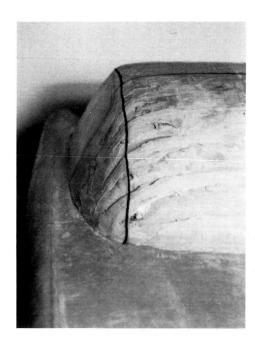

Run a black tape through the center of each highlight mark. Compare the run of this black tape in all three views with adjacent lines and surfaces. (Photograph: T. A. Hoadley)

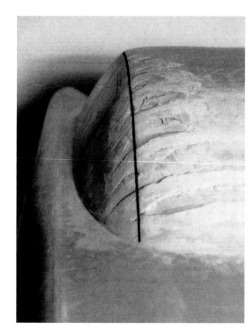

Adjust the sections accordingly to achieve the desired highlight. This can be done before building up and finishing the surface. (Photograph: T. A. Hoadley)

Fitting Loose Parts

All loose parts that are to be attached to the finished model must be fitted to the model's surface. Loose parts include lettering, ornamentation, latches, handles, lights, reflectors, glass, controls, grilles, vents, etc. Some of these parts may come from an item that is in production while others may be prototype parts. Some parts such as lettering and ornamentation may be crafted especially for this show.

Some of the loose parts will require modification to the part or to the model. For instance, instead of installing a complete radio chassis into a model just the face plate and controls would be installed. Also, parts such as handles may need a boss on the clay or a recess for the handle. After fitting, remove all loose parts so the clay surface can be finished.

Surface Finishing

The entire clay surface must now have a final steeling. After steeling, the type of finish preparation will depend on the type of finish that is planned for the model. If the model will be shown in clay, the surface should be slicked and polished. If a painted decal film is to be applied, the surface should be slicked, but it is not necessary to polish it. If the surface or a part of the surface will have a texture, such as leather grain, then the surface must be treated with a texturing tool.

If the model is to be painted with a color over strippable vinyl, the surface can be slicked and also textured if required. However, if the model is to be painted with a polishing lacquer over primer, the clay surface should not be slicked. Instead it should be sealed with shellac or another sealer such as R&M Undercoat 811 Clear Adhesion Promotor.

The color chosen for painting the model is a very important factor in the success of a model's presentation. Painted test sheets of Dinoc film should be tried out on the model to check the color and at the same time to check highlights and surface. Likewise, a model that is being primed and painted can have undercoats of color, sprayed on between layers of primer to check the color. Surface form has a great effect on color particularly when metallic or opalescent paint is used. The upper crown of a surface can exaggerate the tint of a color and the lower turnunder can exaggerate the shade of a color. The value of color is effected by reflections and shadows, so it is easy to see how the anticipated result from a carefully chosen paint chip may not always be met and therefore require additional study.

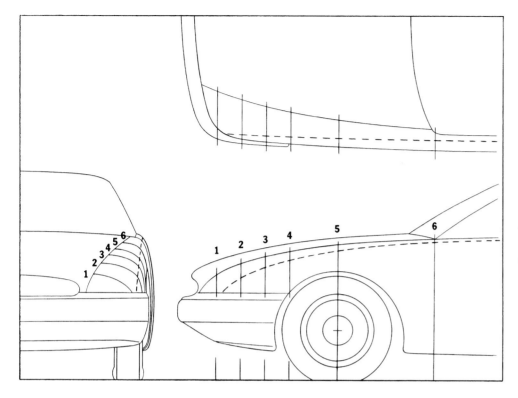

This theoretical surface development shows several fender sections, numbers 1 through 5, coming forward from a master body section number 6. The dotted line represents a 45° highlight line. Notice that the highlight line drops away from the fender line in the side elevation view and splays out in the top plan view. (Drawing: Author)

In this development, the fender surface has been modified to raise the highlight line in the side elevation view. In doing this, the highlight has moved in-board as seen in the top plan view and the front elevation view. (Drawing: Author)

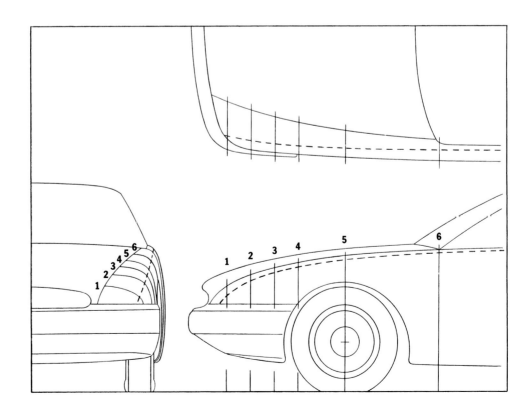

Final Preparation

After the clay surface has been painted, the model will undergo final preparation. Some areas of the model may have to be blacked out with flat black paint. Other areas of the model may require bright or satin metal finish. To accomplish this, the proper aluminum foil color and finish would be applied to either the portion of the painted surface to be bright metal or to fresh clay extrusion moldings bonded to the model and finished.

All loose parts that had been previously fitted and removed would then be reapplied to the model. These parts at this time may need special attention such as color or texture.

Joint lines or openings may be represented with narrow black tape or tape painted the same hue as the model but a darker shade. Painted tape may also be used to emphasize or represent intended undercuts and texture.

Show Set Up

When all details are complete, the model will be set up in the presentation area. The presentation may be in a special indoor showroom or outdoor court yard, or it may be in a hurriedly cleared area especially for the presentation. While the show area may range from poor to excellent, the objective is the same: present the model in the best situation that the environmental conditions will permit. A check list of conditions to watch for include:

1. Watch out for and correct any unsightly background.
2. Carefully review and correct any disturbing reflections on the surface of the model.
3. Place the model in the best possible lighting situation. If it is necessary to show the model under banks of fluorescent lights, position the model so the major surface runs with the lights and not at an angle to the lights.
4. The color of the floor or table under the model will be reflected from the model's lower surfaces. It is advisable to have some type of underlayment on which the model will be positioned. If it is a large model, it is sometimes necessary to paint the entire floor surface under and around the model.
5. The position and attitude of the model in relation to the position and attitude of the other objects in the show is very important and should be carefully planned.

When the model and other items in the presentation have been checked and rechecked and all conditions have been reviewed and optimized, then the show is ready to commence.

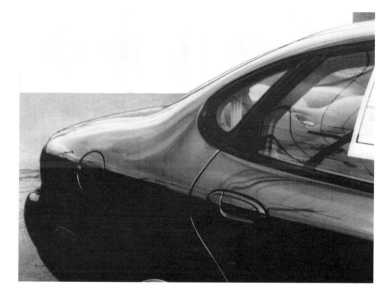

The pictures on the left, showing reflections from the deck lid and quarter panel of a new Taurus sedan, illustrate a surface development problem. These pictures were taken at a Ford dealers lot early in March 1997. The pictures show that the section at the center of the deck lid is convex but sections going to the outside become ogee, that is they have a reverse curve or are concave starting about half way up the deck lid. Reflections from this surface show a depression (a hollow) in the surface development. This depression carries over onto the quarter panel.

This condition could have been easily seen on the styling clay model. However, a surface depression would not have been seen so easily on a computer development unless the operator ran a series of flow lines through the deck lid and the quarter panel.

How did this happen? Perhaps originally the ogee ran all the way across the deck lid. If so, the center section silhouette would have had this reverse curve on the model. Maybe someone didn't like this silhouette and requested that it be changed to a convex form. A change might have been made to the center area of the deck lid without correcting the rest of the surface. This change (if it was a change) might not have been checked on the model, nor on the computer surface development, nor on the cube. The convex center of the deck lid should run across to the sides. The concave area could be reduced and moved up to just below the window and become a fillet between the deck lid and the glass. This is what originally may have been intended but the fillet became too large and extended half way down into the deck lid. It's too bad that no one corrected this on the clay model. Changes to the tools and dies to correct this is very costly but this change was made soon after and the surface corrected.

CHAPTER 9 - Model Changes

Model Changes After The Show

During a presentation where directional approval is scheduled, it is normal that a number of changes or adjustments to the design will be requested. First of all, the designer, who has lived with the development from the beginning, will see certain changes he would like to make, so naturally, he will have some new sketches or illustrations. If the model has two sides, there will probably be some differences between the two that will also require sorting. In addition, this may be the first time the client has seen the model. If so, he will have had a fresh impression of the design, but maybe it is not quite what he had in mind.

At this point, the model in its development may get directional approval, but approval may cover detail-to-detail and area-to-area. A record should be kept of the recommendations and remarks made by the client and the responsible people in charge of the development process. Also, the model and other objects in the presentation should be photographed.

At the earliest possible time, the approvals that have been given and the changes that have been requested should be reviewed and a plan of action should be established. This is done so that there is a clear understanding by all concerned as to the work to be accomplished and the schedule to be met.

Sketch Interpretation

Work on the model at this stage will be free-hand. While a certain amount of time will be spent sweetening lines and form, much of the time will be spent in sketch interpretation. What is important here is to interpret two-dimensional sketches quickly into three dimensions in styling clay. Using a clay knife and a few other tools, some warm clay and perhaps some black tape, a two-dimensional sketch can be quickly roughed-in on the model.

The goal is to achieve on the model the character or the feeling of the sketch. Since the proportions or the perspective of the item in the sketch may be exaggerated, it might be impossible to interpret the sketch exactly. But a design sketch will illustrate an idea and do so with an artistic feeling. It is this feeling from the sketch that you must attempt to capture in the model.

It is important to rough-in a sketch in three dimensions quickly because the idea in the sketch may not work out. It may be necessary to rough-in several ideas before one is found with real design appeal that meets all criteria. This is basic to good design development and is referred to as "Rapid Visualization".

Working to Engineering Tolerances

As changes are made and work progresses, it is necessary to check these modifications with engineering and package requirements. This process can be aided if the hard points represented by wood dowels and blocks are still set in place. In any case, the areas, lines, and points that are of special concern to engineering personnel must be checked to assure functional build requirements.

If the model has two sides, one side will lead the other and will become the master side. If the two sides are to be symmetrically opposite, then the master side will have to be duplicated on the other side. If the two sides are to be somewhat different one from the other, those differences will have to be carefully controlled. As the model approaches finality, recheck all hard point and fixed package information relative to the changes made on the model.

One of the more interesting designs from the 1920's was this Aero-Phaeton rendered by Roland L. Stickney for LeBaron. The illustration is beautifully balanced and is quite inspiring. This design was used by LeBaron for Lincoln. While many of the individual design elements of the illustration can be seen in the photograph of the Lincoln, much of the inspiration of the rendering was lost. Of course Stickney took some dimensional liberties in his creation. Changes from standard package included lowering the chassis, replacing the standard rear bumper and stretching the illustration. On the other hand, the Lincoln development failed to follow the design on several points, all of which were important. It should have had white sidewall tires and wheel covers. The fenders and the running board riser should have been body color. The front fender lacked the beautiful form of the illustration. The second cowl lacked form and finish and appears to be a piece of wrapped metal with a raw edge. Also, the tail fin change made it look like a chicken's tail feathers.

The Lincoln Aero-Phaeton was a very unusual and striking design but it lacked the magic of Roland Stickney's rendering. This is a good example of a poor interpretation of an inspiring design.

Recording Changes

The model started as a three-dimensional development of the design theme illustration. Sections were derived from the theme drawing or computer graphics development and the model became a representation of that development. Now changes have been made for which there is no record.

Depending on the need for surface information, changes can be simply recorded on the theme drawing or a surface layout can be drafted. If equipment is available to scan and digitize the model, then the surface can be recorded and drafted digitally. Sections can be compared to the package drawing and studied by engineering and manufacturing personnel.

If the model is to be made symmetrical about a center line, the master side will have to be transferred to the other side. This can be done by templating the model, or by pointing it off with a styling bridge, or by copying the master side with a scan/mill coordinate measuring machine.

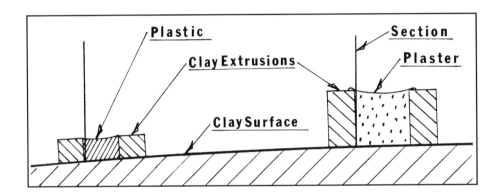

Templating The Model

If templates are to be made, sections to be templated must be scribed on the model. Reference lines or sections 90° to the sections to be templated must also be scribed on the model. Templates can be made from light weight cardboard or poster board. They can also be cast from any one of a number of casting compounds such as plaster, epoxy, or polyurethane.

To cast a plaster template requires damming off the section along the scribed line. Clay extrusion moldings with a cross section 3/8" x 3/4" or 10mm x 20mm can be used for this purpose. One molding should be laid along the low side of the scribed section and the other molding laid approximately 3/4" or 20mm from the first molding on the high side of the section. Casting on the high side of the line will cause the exposed inside edge of the negative template to be the scribed section. The plaster cast can extend to the work surface or to a block or angle on the work surface. This will provide a quick and accurate means to align the template on a drawing.

Before casting a quick set tooling plastic template, the surface inside the dam should be protected by applying the proper sealer and parting agent. The casting compound should then be mixed and the dam filled. The cast can be strengthened by laying in reinforcing material while filling the dam. If the template is on a vertical surface, a jacket must be made by closing the dam with another clay extrusion.

When the casting compound has set up, remove the cast and sand or grind off any high edges so that the section side of the template will lie flat on the theme drawing. Since reference lines exist on the cast template, new sections can be drafted by tracing the inside edge of the template after the reference lines have been aligned.

Quite accurate templates can also be cut from poster board that is heavy enough to hold its shape, but easy to cut. All you need besides the poster board are a good pair of shears, a simple pencil compass, and some sandpaper. You may wish to wrap the pointed leg of the compass with tape so that it will slide across the clay surface without damaging the model. Pre-cut the poster board to a rough contour of the section. Hold the poster board to the scribed section to be templated so that it touches two places. Open the compass and put the pointed leg on the section to be templated and the pencil end on the poster board. Align the compass so that a line passing through the pencil tip and the point will be at right angles to the reference lines of the section. While holding the compass in that mode, draw a line on the poster board by sliding the pointed leg along the section. Trim off the excess poster board and refit to the scribed line. It may be necessary to redraw the line and re-trim the poster board a few times.

When the cut template is very close, do any final clean up with sandpaper. If the section is too large for cutting the template from a single sheet of poster board, make the template by cutting two or more pieces of poster board and putting them together. While holding two pieces of the template on the section, attach them together with double sided tape and then staple them together. This should also be done with sections that are too complicated to cut from a single piece of poster board.

Be sure to mark reference lines on the templates so that there will be at least two right angle coordinates. Reference lines can be scribed from an angle plate and from a height gauge. Large poster board templates can be reinforced by stapling the templates to thin wood strips.

When the changes have been completed and checked for feasibility, it will be time to clean up and refinish the model for another show.

CHAPTER 10 - Completing The Model

Design Approval

As the model approaches the final stage of design development it may have gone through a series of presentations and changes. People responsible for engineering, manufacturing, marketing, and cost would have had a final review of the model and possibly request a few minor adjustments. They would then give their approval. The model would be shown again to the client and receive final approval for engineering and tooling. After receiving final approval, the master side of the model would be completely scanned or templated for a full surface layout or computer graphics development. This has been called the design feasibility phase in automotive design.

This is the theme model given clay approval for the Lincoln Mark VIII. Notice the bubble top, the hollow side section, and the simulated grill. (Photograph: Ford Design Center)

The Lincoln Mark VIII final feasibility model has incorporated all of the changes required by engineering and manufacturing. While the theme of the model given clay approval remains, the details of the production model are now complete. (Photograph: Ford Design Center)

Fine Tuning The Model

This is the opportunity to incorporate the minor corrections that time did not permit before. First, however, if the model had been covered with Dinoc, this film must be removed. If the model had been painted over strippable vinyl, that too must be removed.

All surfaces should be checked for highlights and reflections. The width and angle of all flanges should be checked. All draft angles should be checked for proper draw angle. This is necessary, when hard casting materials are used, to assure that the negative can be removed from the model, and more importantly, that positive casts can be removed from the negative.

Draft angles need not be related to a line 90 degrees to the base of the model. A negative may even be locked in if an attempt is made to pull it straight off of a model. There are situations where a negative can be removed by rotating it off. This can be checked on a drawing by using an overlay or a trammel bar compass.

All crease lines, highlights, and openings should be checked from all viewing angles to make sure that they run well with each other and with the silhouette of the model. This last point is very important. While viewing the model from all vantage points, observe the run of the highlights, openings, crease lines, or other design lines to

assure pleasing and proper proportions with the silhouette. Let your eye travel around the model at different heights and pay particular attention to the silhouette. It may be necessary to adjust surfaces or creases or openings to obtain a pleasing and proper relationship of these design elements. Although these considerations are very important when developing automotive type models, they can also be important when developing other types of models.

If final changes are made to the model, they should be picked up and recorded on the draft. If the draft or computer graphics development indicates that certain adjustments should be incorporated on the model, then the model should be updated to the draft or to the computer graphics data.

Not all design projects need a surface layout; however, all design model developments must have control through master sections.

If the model is basically a dragged section, then the drag template is the master section. Additional templates would be necessary only for the endings of the model plus any details within the dragged section. Depending on the need, the surface on which the model is dragged can be templated for reference.

Preparing The Model For Casting

If the model is to be finished and cast, then it should be carefully prepared. If it is to be used for tooling purposes, then precision and exactness are necessary.

Wood blocks or dowels representing hard points must be removed and the voids carefully filled. Fish line protecting a crease, windsplit, or other design line must also be removed. However, before removing the fishline carefully steel the surface to one side of the line. The fish line can then be removed and the line itself can be adjusted as necessary. Black drafting tape, available in various widths, can be used to protect the line and make it more readable while making adjustments to it. You can move the tape from one side of the line to the other as adjustments are made and the surface is steeled. Remove the black tape when the line is finished.

Reference lines (these are sometimes referred to as keylines or keypoints) representing sections from the three views of the drawing, should be scribed onto the model surface at strategic locations. This should be done to

provide a means to locate templates and set up casts of the model later on. These reference lines should be scribed with as small a tolerance as possible since in the cast they normally represent the most accurate way to locate sections.

Parts that had been added to the model, such as handles or knobs or some type of ornamentation, must be removed and the areas where they were located must be cleaned up and finished. This is necessary so that when the cast is finished, the loose parts will fit the surface.

Likewise, any area of the model that will be cast as a separate assembled part must be properly identified and outlined. This could include covers, lights, control housings, and instrument clusters. Or, it could be a working or moving part that is formed into the surface such as a lever or a vent. There will be more information on this subject in a later chapter.

When all of these conditions have been met, it is time for surface preparation for casting the model.

CHAPTER 11 - Design Development Examples

This chapter shows, pictorially, the development of several different design modeling projects. The first is of a truck cover that has become an industry standard. The second comprises the development of the front and rear caps of an aerodynamically improved motor home. The third contains the multi-piece model development of an award winning tractor.

A prototype Leer truck cover is mounted on a Chevrolet S10 pickup. (Photograph: Leer Inc., Elkhart, Indiana)

The three-quarter front view of the production Rockwood motorhome is very dramatic. This unit became very popular and was in production for seven years. It was developed under the direction of Vern Wamsley and the staff of Product Spectrum. The design was by Dennis Otto. (Photograph: Rockwood, Inc., Millersburg, Indiana)

A series of prototypes are built-up from parts cast from master epoxy negatives taken directly off the styling clay design models. (Photo: Case International, Racine, Wisconsin)

Pickup Cap

This preferred design illustration for a pickup cap was chosen from several developed by Dennis Otto for Leer Inc. (Photograph: Author)

A full size black tape drawing of the preferred design is illustrated on tracing paper and mounted to a plywood board. The board, trimmed to fit inside of the pickup box, is painted the color of the pickup truck. Number three design is approved. This series of photographs show the development of a large surface without the aid of a measuring device. (Photograph T.A. Hoadley)

The truck is weighted down and blocked-up with jack stands so that the top of the box is level. A surface layout proposal drawing is made by the author using an overlay to the black tape illustration. An armature drawing is developed to utilize available tubing and plywood. Since no large changes to the design are expected, only approximately one inch of clay is required over the plywood. (Photograph: T. A. Hoadley)

The tubing for the armature frame is cut and welded and the plywood is attached with self tapping screws. The assembly is located and clamped to the pickup box. The plywood is shellacked and a layer of clay is rubbed well into the surface of the plywood. (Photograph: T. A. Hoadley)

Plywood templates are laid out from the surface layout drawing and accurately cut out and finished. Templates are carefully set into soft clay and the roof surface is modeled in. (Photograph: T. A. Hoadley)

Male templates are set into the clay surface representing the recessed pattern and window area. This surface is modeled in and cleaned up. (Photograph: T. A. Hoadley)

The edge at the bottom of the cap is developed. Three steel tapes are bonded to the clay and an aluminum straight edge is pinned to the surface. A template of the cross section is dragged over hot clay by the author and held in proper alignment by the steel tapes and the straight edge. (Photograph: T. A. Hoadley)

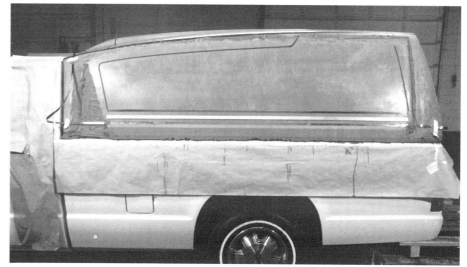

The recessed pattern is laid out on the clay with black tape and the surface surrounding the pattern is developed. (Photograph: T. A. Hoadley)

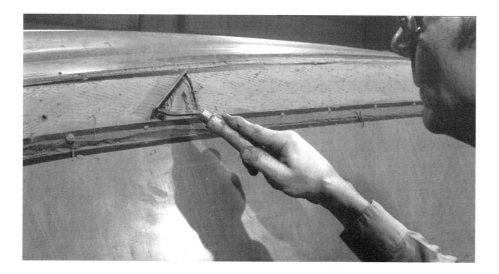

This close up shows how the styling clay is built-up and the surface roughed in with the tooth scraper. Black tape is used to develop the lines. (Photograph: T. A. Hoadley)

Work continues in cleaning up the surface surrounding the recessed pattern. The illustration and tape drawing can be seen in the background. (Photograph: T. A. Hoadley)

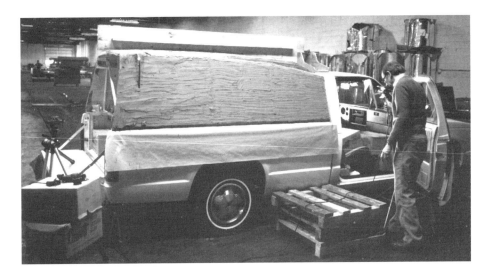

The next series of photographs show step by step how the recessed pattern area is developed.
First a skin coat and then a thin layer of clay is built-up on the side panel of the cap armature. (Photograph: T. A. Hoadley)

Next, grooves are cut into the clay so male templates (short narrow sweeps) can be set into the clay surface above the armature. These templates are individually set into warm clay. One template is at a section near the front and the other at a section near the rear of the recessed pattern area. (Photograph: T. A. Hoadley)

A female template is adjusted to the section and to the pickup box and is leveled. The female template is used to locate and accurately position the male template. Each male template is set separately and clayed into place. (Photograph: T.A. Hoadley)

After the two male templates are set, a long plywood #2 sweep is used to drag three narrow vertical arbitrary sections between them. These three sections are cleaned-up and steel tape is bonded to them. These sections stabilize the sweep as the surface is dragged in. (Photograph: T. A. Hoadley)

The long plywood sweep is used to drag and fill the areas between the steel tapes and the male templates. (Photograph: T. A. Hoadley)

The surface has been roughed-in with the long plywood sweep. (Photograph: T. A. Hoadley)

The steel tapes are removed and the surface is further cleaned-up with a large 3/8 inch thick wood batten. High places are cleaned off and low places are filled with hot clay. (Photograph: T. A. Hoadley)

The recessed pattern area is further cleaned-up with a large 0.060 inch thick steel scraper. (Photograph: T. A. Hoadley)

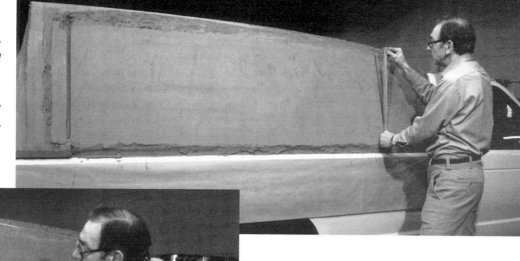

The male templates are removed from the surface and the grooves are filled with hot clay. The entire surface area is further cleaned-up with the large steel. (Photograph: T. A. Hoadley)

The surface is smoothed with a plastic slick. (Photograph: T. A. Hoadley)

The surface is polished with a damp cloth. Notice how the wax in the clay surface shines. (Photograph: T. A. Hoadley)

Before completing the cap model for casting, the pick-up truck with the styling clay model is driven out-of-doors for viewing and minor roof adjustments.

A prototype Leer truck cover is mounted on a Chevrolet S10 pickup. A second truck cover model was developed for full size trucks. This model was developed in a Bondo type material to determine the advantages or disadvantages of these materials. Professional design modeling methods were used on the Bondo model and the surface workout was equal to that of a styling clay model. The advantage in using Bondo is that when finished you have a hard surface model. The disadvantage is that it takes approximately four times longer to develop surface in Bondo and make developmental changes. Although you have a hard model when finished, it is still necessary to make a master model (plug) for production tooling. Modifications were made to reinforced casts of these two designs to create new tools so that pick up covers would fit all domestic and imported pick up trucks. (Photographs: Leer Inc., Elkhart, Indiana)

Motorhome

To start this design model of the Rockwood motorhome, a prototype buck is built up from engineering drawings. It is positioned in the work area, blocked up, and leveled. Steel frames are constructed and bolted to the prototype buck front and rear. These are the structures that will support the clay models. Full size plywood templates are cut and sanded exactly to lines from a surface drawing developed by the author. These templates include all necessary reference lines.

Plywood is attached to the steel frames front and rear and these are sprayed with polyurethane foam to within one inch of the templates. Where too much foam exists the foam is cut back. (Photograph: T. A. Hoadley)

The foam is shellacked and a skin coat of clay is rubbed into the surface. The templates are positioned and blocked into place. (Photograph: T. A. Hoadley)

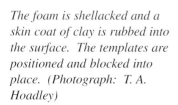

Hot clay is rubbed-in at the edge of the template while it is moved back and forth to form a narrow band. The template is again accurately positioned and a line is scribed in the clay along the edge of the template which represents the section. (Photograph: T. A. Hoadley)

True sweeps are used to develop the surface between template settings. After horizontal sections are developed with sweeps, smaller section templates are used to drag in the rest of the surface between template and sweep settings. Black tape is used to emphasize lines and retain template settings. As the surface contours are built up, the corner surfaces are rounded and softened for improved aerodynamics. (Photograph: T. A. Hoadley)

The grill armature is constructed as a separate model to fit into the front cap. Head lamp cans are located while the grill armature is orthogonally positioned on a table. Head lamp cans are modeled integral with the grill. (Photograph: T. A. Hoadley)

The grill armature is positioned into the front of the cap model. Head lamps are installed into the head lamp cans. Templates of the back surface of the grill bars are set and the surface is dragged in with a sweep. (Photograph: T. A. Hoadley)

Grill bars and head lamp trim are made from clay extrusion moldings and bonded to the clay surface with turpentine. The clay mouldings are carefully aligned and steeled. The grill surround is completed and cleaned-up by the author, John Bird, and Ken Gillette. A master negative of the hood has been constructed and removed. See the chapter on Three-Dimensional Engineering and Master Modeling. (Photograph: T. A. Hoadley)

A close-up of the corner shows the fine finish and detail modeling by Ken Gillette. All surfaces are accurately controlled with templates and sweeps. (Photograph: T. A. Hoadley)

A fork lift truck prepares to lift the grill model and pull it free from the front cap. The grill is carefully pulled away as the design engineer, Bill Conway, watches.
(Photograph: T. A. Hoadley)

The grill is pulled free from the cap and set on a table. The front cap model will be cleaned-up and primed for construction of the negative. The grill model will be processed separately.
(Photograph: T. A. Hoadley)

The grill model has been attached to a rollover fixture and tipped over 90° for final clean-up and processing of the negative.
(Photograph: T. A. Hoadley)

The design model of the rear cap is developed in a way very similar to the front. Since the surface extends across the back in an unbroken plane, full width templates are used and these are mounted on strips of wood attached to the side of the motorhome at the proper heights. (Photograph: T. A. Hoadley)

While standing on a portable platform, the rear cap surface is cleaned-up by Ken Gillette and John Bird. (Photograph: T. A. Hoadley)

Clay mouldings made from a clay extrusion machine are bonded as texture surrounding the tail lamps. A tail lamp plug is set into place by John Bird. (Photograph: T. A. Hoadley)

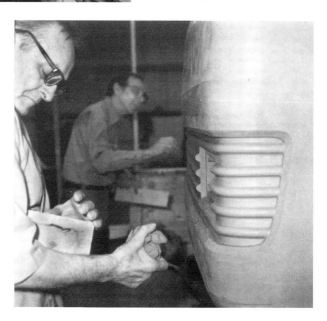

The rear cap model is finished. It will now be prepared, along with the front, for constructing negatives. (Photograph: T. A. Hoadley)

The clay surface is sealed and sprayed with surface primers. A plywood board clamped to a forklift truck is used as a platform to stand on by the person sanding the surface. (Photograph: T. A. Hoadley)

A plywood flange is attached to the front edge of the rear cap model. After several light coats of PVA have been applied and waxed, a polyester surface coat is built-up. (Photograph: T. A. Hoadley)

A close-up of the tail lamp and texture area after it has been sprayed with a polyester surface coat. (Photograph: T. A. Hoadley)

Several layers of polyester resin and fiberglass are built-up. (Photograph: T. A. Hoadley)

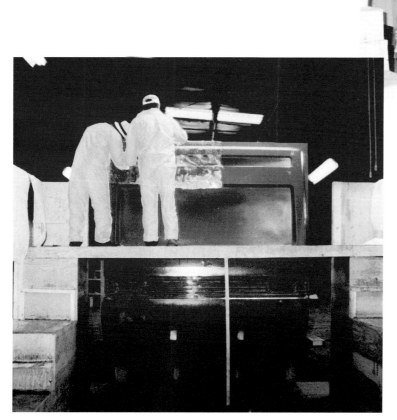

The fiberglass and polyester resin is rolled-out after each layer is applied. (Photograph: T. A. Hoadley)

The polyester/fiberglass build-up is completed. A structure to support the negative is started. (Photograph: T. A. Hoadley)

The framing is carefully assembled, braced, and bonded to the negative. Note the legs on the assembly of the reinforced supporting structure. (Photograph: T. A. Hoadley)

The three-quarter front view of the production Rockwood motorhome is very dramatic. This unit became very popular and was in production for seven years. It was developed under the direction of Vern Wamsley and the staff of Product Spectrum. The design was by Dennis Otto. (Photograph: Rockwood, Inc., Millersburg, Indiana)

Rear view of the production Rockwood motorhome. (Photograph: Rockwood Inc., Millersburg, Indiana)

Tractor

The Case International Magnum Tractor earned first place in its class in a competition sponsored by the Industrial Designer's Society of America (IDSA), 1988. Ralph Lanphere and Greg Montgomery were presented with the award. (Photograph: Case International, Racine, Wisconsin)

A series of prototypes are built from parts cast from master epoxy negatives taken directly off the styling clay design models. (Photograph: Case International, Racine, Wisconsin)

The design responsibility for the exterior is credited to Ralph Lanphere, Mgr. J. I. Case Design Center; Dennis Otto, Staff Designer; and Greg Montgomery, Montgomery Design. (Photograph: Case International, Racine, Wisconsin)

This prototype tractor closely resembles the theme illustation shown in the third picture in the sidebar below. (Photograph: Case International, Racine, Wisconsin)

The three pictures in this side bar illustrate the evolution of a design theme. The first picture is of the original working prototype for the Case International Magnum Tractor. This prototype, developed by Ralph Lanphere and the Case Design staff, established the theme that included: a flat sloping hood; a horizontal band with built in lights that divided the grill and ran back along each side of the hood; a windshield with a curve in plan view that extended down around the sides of the hood; a cap roof with a light panel at the front; and a separate air cleaner/air conditioner box that hung-off the back of the roof. Inside there was an instrument and control panel that appeared to extend back from the hood and engine side panels. But the prototype appeared unfinished and the design was not unified. It was a combination of several unrelated design elements.

The second picture shows an 1/4 scale model developed by Montgomery Design that again carries the above general design theme. The design is more integrated but the surfaces are stiff and the cap roof still appears detached.

To start the Case-International 'Magnum' tractor, full size surface layout proposal drawings are drafted by the author. From these drawings, armatures for the cab roof and windshield are constructed. The armatures are attached to a prototype cab frame assembly. A work platform is built around the perimeter of the roof. A scaffold is built for the modelers working on the roof. Rough clay is built-up on the armatures. The illustration on the easel in the background was rendered by Greg Montgomery, Montgomery Design, Hinsdale, Illinois. (Photograph: T. A. Hoadley)

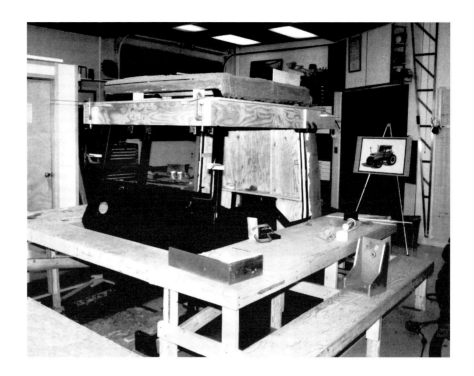

The upper windshield now slopes back but has a horizontal break below the top of the hood and the lower divided windshields angle back to the floor of the cab. These windshield surfaces, straight in side view, appear hollow and create an awkward vee in the sides of the hood. The grill is flat and the grill surround frame is not well developed. This causes a problem, particularly at the top, where it appears hollow. Also, there is still an open space between the hood and the cab.

After many sketches by designers and discussions between design, engineering, and management personnel, several important decisions were made. It was decided that the windshield should have a compound curve; the hood should extend back to the cab; the roof lights should be recessed into the front of the roof; and the hood and grill should have a positive form. Design illustrations were made depicting how these changes would affect the design.

The third picture shows the illustration that displayed the revised theme best. This illustration by staff designer Dennis Otto was used by the author as the inspiration for the design model development.

Notice the forward thrust apparent in the illustration and the rounded forms that are suggested. A cowl is shown that finishes the area between the hood and the cab; the horizontal band has a definite ending; the windshield has a pleasant forward leaning curve; and the roof has a softer leading edge.

Several master negatives from the finished clay models were required following completion of the design development. These were needed to cast a series of parts for the buildup of a number of prototype tractors.

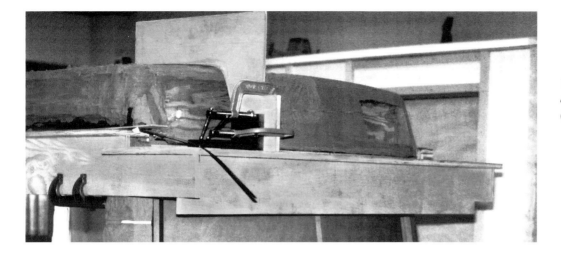

Templates for the roof are accurately positioned in hot clay. (Photograph: T. A. Hoadley)

The roof goes through several surface changes and highlights are checked before final clean-up. (Photograph: T. A. Hoadley)

A texture is dragged into the front surface of the roof. (Photograph: T. A. Hoadley)

The roof front texture and light depressions are finished. (Photograph: T. A. Hoadley)

This shows a detail of the corner of the roof including a portion of "A" pillar and door frame. (Photograph: T. A. Hoadley)

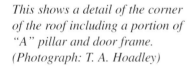

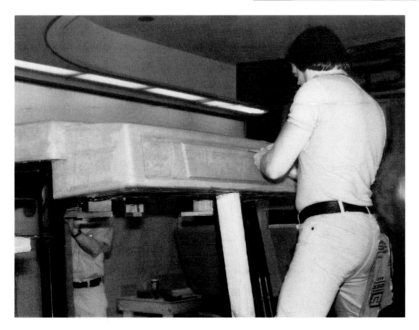

The air cleaner box at the rear of the roof is developed by Tim Kirkpatrick. (Photograph: T. A. Hoadley)

The windshield surface is established by setting several horizontal and vertical templates. The areas between templates are completed by dragging a sweep across steel tapes bonded to the surface where the templates have been set. A vertical straight edge (square aluminum extruded tubing) is accurately positioned and used as reference to insure the windshield opening dimensions. (Photograph: T. A. Hoadley)

A change is made to the left hand windshield opening and this change is duplicated to the right hand opening by Robert Doehler. In the center background can be seen the well insulated walk-in clay oven. (Photograph: T. A. Hoadley)

The windshield and "A" pillars are cleaned-up and prepared for the construction of a master negative. (Photograph: T. A. Hoadley)

The mechanical tractor prototype is positioned and leveled, and armatures are constructed for grill, hood top, and hood side lower panels.
Clay is applied to the shellacked wood grill armature by the author. A skin coat of clay is always built-up first by rubbing the clay well into the surface. (Photograph: T. A. Hoadley)

The clay is further built-up and templates are set into the hot clay. Steel tape is bonded to the templated surface at the center and at each side of the grill. Tim Kirkpatrick drags the surface with a sweep.
(Photograph: T. A. Hoadley)

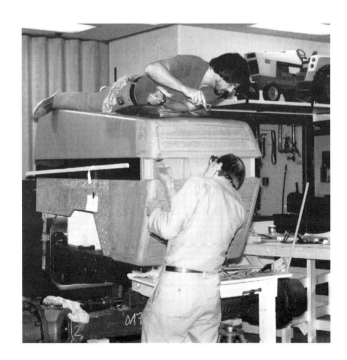

The hood top is dragged-in and cleaned-up by Tim Kirkpatrick. Light pockets are modeled in by the author.
(Photograph: T. A. Hoadley)

The grill model is finished and approved and is prepared for the construction of a master negative.
(Photograph: T. A. Hoadley)

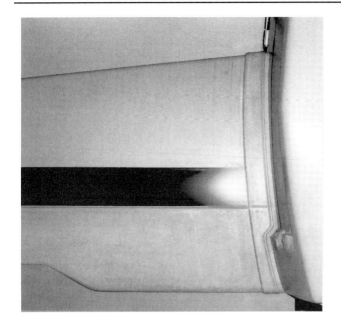

Reinforced epoxy casts of the grill and the windshield with the pillars are installed on the mechanical prototype to aid additional design development work. The hood and lower engine side panels are developed in clay and completed. A modification to the windshield lower opening is roughed-in. The cowl or collar between the hood and windshield is finished. (Photograph: T. A. Hoadley)

The right hand cab side panel is modeled in clay from engineering drawings and is prepared for constructing a negative. The left hand side uses an existing door. (Photograph: T. A. Hoadley)

A cast of the right hand cab side panel is mounted to the frame. Previously developed fenders are installed and modified. (Photograph: T. A. Hoadley)

A surface layout proposal of the instrument panel is drafted by the author from Greg Montgomery's illustrations and an engineering drawing. The styling clay model is roughed-in from templates made from the surface layout proposal. The model is first built-up in a tractor interior cab buck, but is removed and mounted on a separate stand for final development and clean up. (Photograph: Greg Montgomery, Montgomery Design)

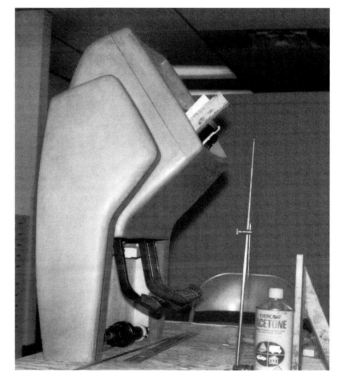

The instrument panel is shown to management and changes are requested. The model is revised and cleaned-up for final presentation and for the construction of master negatives. (Photograph: T. A. Hoadley)

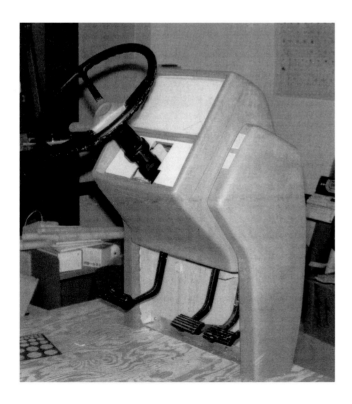

Design responsibility for the tractor interior is credited to Ralph Lanphere, Mgr. J. I. Case Design Center and Greg Montgomery, Montgomery Design. (Photograph: T. A. Hoadley)

*Production Tractor-Exterior
(Photograph: Case International,
Racine Wisconsin)*

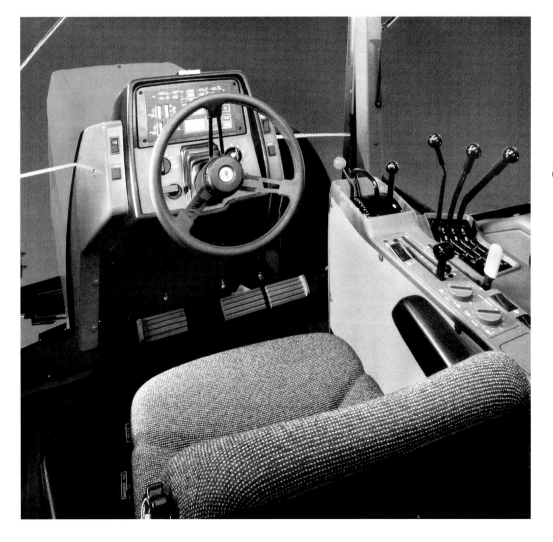

*Production Tractor -Interior
(Photograph: Case International)*

CHAPTER 12 - Casting Preparations

Testing New Materials

First of all, run test samples on any unfamiliar or new material, before using it on a design model that may have had several hundred man hours development time. Drag and finish a few small clay samples and run tests until confidence with the material is achieved.

Special Considerations

When constructing negatives, the type of preparation required for design models depends on the material to be used and the intended use of the negatives. Surface preparation for plaster and plastic negatives will be found in the chapters covering the use of these materials.

Larger or more complicated models may require piece molds. Piece molds are made when there is insufficient draft on a model for a single mold. There are two or more separate parts in a piece mold.

Some models have areas that must be molded by themselves. A formed-in scoop or handle represents such an area. A separately molded area can be a removable piece from a larger overall mold. It is, therefore, a type of piece mold.

Some models will be cast for record purposes. These may have one or more positive casts fabricated and finished for display or marketing use. They may also be used for developing various levels of model range of the item, and for developing ornamentation or a logogram. However, models cast for record purposes do not require precision negatives.

On the other hand, some models are cast for tooling purposes. Actual production tools, such as used for producing fiberglass or vacuum formed parts, can be processed directly from styling clay models. In these cases, models should be prepared with the greatest possible care.

This also holds true with models that are developed for master model purposes. Negatives and positives made with a high degree of precision can become tooling master models. They can be used to process steel tools for high production. Therefore, models finalized for casting master models must be prepared with the greatest possible accuracy.

Examples of items or parts requiring master models for processing steel tools include mass produced stamped or die cast metal parts and plastic parts that are formed or injected. Steel tooling surface is made by Kellering the surface of master models.

Kellering machines are highly accurate and stable copy milling machines that mill steel. Production tools are also machined by computer controlled mills using cutter paths processed from surface data.

Support for Negatives

Prior to commencing a negative, a frame or some type of support should be prepared to attach to the negative before it is removed from the model. The size, weight, type, and precision required of the negative determines the type of support to be used.

When a negative is pulled and inverted, it is highly desirable to have not only a stable base supporting the mold but also to have the mold orthogonal (right-angled) to the set up of the design model. Likewise, handles should be provided for lifting the mold. They can be built into the support structure or attached separately.

A negative that is constructed without adequate support or frame reinforcing structure may become warped and is more difficult to clean up, sand, and finish. In addition, changes or adjustments to the negative can be very inconvenient. Therefore, supports that will provide automatic positioning, easy access, and good work height should always be considered.

The type of support prepared for a negative can range from simple wooden legs to a highly accurate tooling dock. In each case, the support will facilitate cleaning up the negative and casting a positive. However, care must be taken when supporting FRP negatives to avoid "print through" of reinforcing members in positive casts. A strong perimeter support is good, whereas support members running through the FRP buildup would print through.

A small negative can have wooden legs or feet, made from wooden dowels or some other type of standard stock material and bonded into the reinforcing coat of the molding material. If the negative is being constructed on a surface table, legs can be aligned by using an angle block. The feet can be leveled with a surface gauge, a height gauge, or a level. Be sure to provide nails or screws or flanging of some type to the wooden dowels or other stock material to assure a good bond to the negative.

Larger negatives may use legs, cross members, and braces that attach to each other and become a support base. The pieces can be cut and preassembled as a unit ready to attach to the negative.

Very large negatives need a supporting structure that reinforces the mold. These frames are bonded to the negative with the molding material. The frames can be metal or wooden structures preassembled, or they may be assembled as they are attached. Also, they can be mounted on casters depending on their use and need for mobility of the negative.

A large piece mold negative requires special support. A system sometimes used for a large model involves the attachment of the various molded parts to a steel or aluminum fixture. This type of fixture is made so that it disassembles with the separate parts of the piece mold. These include the sides, front, rear, and top sections. The various parts of the piece mold are constructed with thin separator dams left in place. The fixture is assembled around the model after the piece mold has been cast but not pulled. Each part of the piece mold is bonded to structural members that are bolted to the fixture. The fixture is then disassembled with the top being lifted off first. This may require a chain hoist. The various other parts of the fixture are then disassembled, each with a part of the negative of the model.

When laid open, each part of the negative is supported by a section of the fixture. When the various parts are cleaned up, the fixture is reassembled preparatory to making a positive cast. This type of structure is made as a rollover fixture to facilitate inverting the finished positive cast. When all positive casts are completed, the parts of the piece mold can be unbolted and stored so the fixture can be used over-and-over again.

Such an elaborate system, of course, is not essential. Instead of using a fixture, each individual part of a large piece mold negative may have its own frame and support. Each separate part, with its mold and frame support, can be pinned and bolted to its adjacent part. These frames are unique to the particular negative for which they are made. They can be constructed from wood or metal.

Small piece molds can have the various parts cradled into one of the larger mold parts. When constructing this type of negative, the larger mold part would cap the other parts. The smaller parts of the piece mold must be made with draft so the cap can be pulled off from the smaller molded parts as well as the model.

A tooling dock is used to process highly accurate master negative and positive models. Depending on type, size, and complexity of a model; a tooling dock may be composed of angle blocks, cubes, and parallel bars assembled on a surface plate or table. A master negative constructed from such a set up is orthogonal when inverted or when stood on its sides. This is accomplished by bonding prefinished base pads to the supporting structure in precisely orthogonal vertical and horizontal alignment by the various members of the tooling dock.

A tooling dock in its ultimate form is a specially designed and constructed fixture used to attach and locate piece molds. Each part maintains absolute orthogonality in all three axes in both assembled and disassembled conditions. It differs from the rollover fixture previously mentioned in that it is very precise, and it permits individual parts of a piece mold to be positioned orthogonally in several positions; that is, tipped back 90 degrees, 90 degrees to either side or inverted 180 degrees.

This system was developed by Rainier Kersting and supervised by Paul Metz.

Joint lines between the parts of the piece mold for the negative of this large styling clay model have been carefully chosen. Shim stock has been inserted along these joint lines to form a separator dam. Four air hose fittings for quick release of the negative have been positioned on the model. The grill, lights, and ornamentation will be removed before commencing with construction of the negative. This is a see-through styling clay model. Windows have been formed, finished, and set in place. The roof armature is supported by four adjustable tubes, 1963. (Photograph: Design Office, Ford Werke A.G., West Germany)

When the styling clay model is finished, a parting agent is sprayed on to the clay surface and it is waxed. An epoxy surface coat is applied next. The surface is then built up with several layers of fiberglass cloth and epoxy resin. (Photograph: Design Office, Ford Werke A.G., West Germany)

Pre-cut plywood framing members are assembled together and to individual piece molds. The plywood members from one mold part contacting plywood members from bordering molds are bolted to each other, 1963. (Photograph: Design Office, Ford Werke A.G., West Germany)

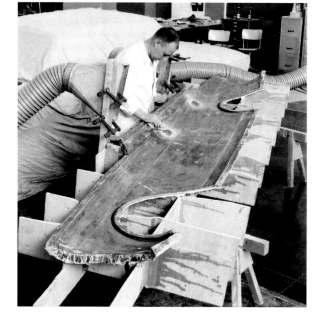

Each part of the negative is disassembled and laid open. The surface of the many molds are cleaned and epoxy fiberglass parts are cast into each mold. Photograph: Design Office, Ford Werke A.G., West Germany 1963)

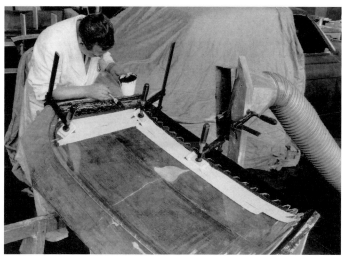

The acrylic windshield is bonded into the cowl, A-pillars, and header. Notice the serrated acrylic edge at the header for a better bond. (Photograph: Design Office, Ford Werke A.G., West Germany)

The various sections of this large piece mold together with their cast parts are reassembled. The various castings are bonded together, filled, and reinforced. (Photograph: Design Office, Ford Werke A.G., West Germany)

Notice the built up flanges for the hood and fender openings and the 10 millimeter steel rod reinforcing members. All of this cast assembly work is done inside the inverted negative mold and positive cast. (Photograph: Design Office, Ford Werke A.G., West Germany)

The cast is completed and the mold is returned to an upright position. A manifold is used to connect the compressed air line to the air hose fittings, one part at a time, 1963. (Photograph: Design Office, Ford Werke A.G., West Germany)

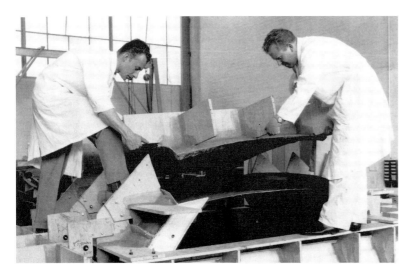

Each piece mold part is unbolted from its bordering molds and released by turning on the compressed air. Each mold with its reinforcing framework is removed, 1963. (Photograph: Design Office, Ford Werke A.G., West Germany)

The unitized body cast is removed from the negative, and lowered onto a prepared chassis. (Photograph: Design Office, Ford Werke A.G., West Germany)

The doors, hood, and trunk lid are all functional. The chrome plated grill, bumpers, and head lamp frames are plated cast polyester parts. (Photograph: Design Office, Ford Werke A.G., West Germany)

The completed exterior body is ready for the installation of interior parts and assemblies, 1963. (Photograph: Design Office, Ford Werke A.G., West Germany)

CHAPTER 13 Making a Plaster Cast

Model Preparation

Making a negative of a styling clay model for record purposes requires very little preparation when plaster or gypsum cement compounds are used. This assumes that the conditions outlined in the previous chapters have been met and the clay surface has been refinished.

Styling clay contains wax and oil as two of its ingredients. Therefore, a parting agent is not required when making plaster negatives off models constructed from styling clay. Nevertheless, to protect the clay surface and aid the release of a plaster negative, the model may be sprayed with either polyvinyl alcohol (PVA) or strippable vinyl. This finish, however, should have a parting agent applied. Also, a parting agent is required on the work surface around the model if that is to be cast as a reference surface. In addition, any blockoffs or separator dams require an application of a parting agent unless they are made from styling clay.

Using Block Offs & Separator Dams

Block offs are required to cover openings and undercuts or any area that is not a part of the surface of the model. They are also constructed to outline flanges and thus provide a line for trimming positive casts. An example of this is the flange or the material thickness around the edge of a model. Block offs may be made from styling clay or wood, or from metal or plastic sheet.

Separator dams are used to separate the various parts of a piece mold. They may be made from clay extrusions or from pieces of shim stock, strips of light weight aluminum sheet, or strips of thin plastic sheet. Separator dams made from thin materials may be left in place when making the mold. Clay extrusion dams must be removed after each section of the negative separated by them has been completed. The plaster edges exposed after removal of the clay extrusions must have an application of parting agent before constructing the adjacent sections.

Considerable care is required when locating the parting line for positioning separator dams. For instance, a parting line may cut across a sculptured line or a highlight or run parallel to them but should not run directly on them. Always check each area separated by parting lines to assure adequate draw angle from side-to-side and top to bottom.

The clay surface around blockoffs and separator dams must be cleaned up after they are constructed. Also, the pieces of a separator dam may need to be taped together.

Use of Parting Agents

A parting agent must be applied where plaster will be cast against any material other than styling clay. Oils, wax mixtures, or other specially prepared materials are used as a parting agent or mold release when making plaster negatives. These same materials may also be used when casting positives from properly prepared plaster negatives.

A parting agent commonly used in plaster model work can be made from a mixture of stearic acid, kerosene, and bees wax. Heat and mix these ingredients into a heavy liquid or thin paste. The mixture can be applied with a brush and any excess can be wiped away with a soft absorbent cloth. This release agent can also be applied to the container used for mixing and the tools used for applying the plaster. This will allow an easier release of hard plaster when cleaning the tools and the container.

Sources of Material for Casting Negatives

Many types of plaster and gypsum cement materials are manufactured by United States Gypsum Company (USG). Several of these have been especially formulated for use in model making and tooling. Some of the materials used are:

1. USG Moulding Plaster; a soft workable, low expansion material.

2. HYDROCAL B-11 Gypsum Cement; a lower expansion and harder material.

3. ULTRACAL 30 Gypsum Cement; a very low expansion, hard, and strong material.

A new two part plaster base system has been co-developed by United States Gypsum Company in conjunction with Chavant, Inc. This two part system is primarily to cast negatives from styling clay models.

4. RAYITE™ MDM (Model Duplicating Material):
    a. Surface Coat; a very smooth workable material.
    b. Reinforcing Coat; a very strong, lighter weight material.

Also, United States Gypsum Company has developed an entirely new material that works like plaster but can be machined and polished to a "Class A" finish. This non-combustible and non-toxic mineral based media is "self lubricating" and results in dust free milling.

5. RAYITE™ 100 Machinable Media; a hard smooth material that is super-tough and has excellent stability.

Information concerning the many types and uses of US Gypsum products can be obtained from: United States Gypsum Company, Industrial Gypsum Division, P. O. Box 803871, 125 South Franklin Street, Chicago, Illinois 60680-3871.

Another company, Guilini Chemie of Germany developed a series of gypsum base materials especially for the aircraft industry. These materials, under the trade name Ludur, have also been used by the automobile industry in Europe.

6. Ludur Process Materials:
    a. Ludur 500M surface coat; a smooth and low expansion material.
    b. Ludur SPM; a bonding coat.
    c. Ludur 500L reinforcing coat; a low expansion, hard, and strong material.

Making A Plaster Negative

To mix plaster use a clean plastic bowl, bucket or a rubber bowl especially made for mixing plaster. The manufacturer of the casting compound you wish to use will recommend a certain ratio of water and dry material by weight. To mix the plaster, clean cold water is added to the bowl first, then dry plaster is slowly poured into the water. The plaster can be sifted through the fingers to remove any lumps that may be found as it is poured. The water will soak up through the plaster and wet all of the dry material. Once this has taken place, start to mix the ingredients from the bottom of the bowl with an upward motion.

The classical way of mixing plaster of Paris is as follows: Pour the plaster into the water until it stands above the center of the water as a small cone or mound. The plaster of paris may be sifted and mixed same as above. However this "sift, soak, and mound" method of mixing is not recommended especially when mixing larger batches.

Mixing can be done with the hand or with a wooden or plastic spatula, a whisk, a unimixer drill attachment, or a Jiffy® mechanical mixer. A mechanical mixer is used when mixing larger amounts of plaster. The US Gypsum Company recommends that when using a mechanical mixer, the shaft of the mixer should be held at an angle of 15° to 25° from vertical for better mixing results. When mixed, the plaster should be the consistency of latex paint. It should be thin enough to brush on easily and thick enough not to run off when applied to the side of a model. Work life of each of the materials listed earlier is approximately 30 minutes.

The first layer of plaster may be applied to the model using a "lay on" technique with a brush or may be brushed on. A China bristle brush or a coarse throwaway brush can be used. The plaster mixture should be applied evenly and care should be taken to assure that all areas of the surface are covered. Be careful not to over brush which may cause air bubbles resulting in voids or pinholes on the negative surface.

As the first layer of plaster begins to set up, apply more plaster with a brush, a spatula, or with a trowel. The negative can be reinforced with strips and pieces of burlap, scrim, or with sisal. Cheesecloth may be used on small models or details. Dip the material into the liquid plaster in the bowl and then lay it onto the first layers of plaster on the negative. Pat it down and lay successive layers of the plaster soaked material onto the negative. Make sure you overlap previous layers of the reinforcing material. The plaster should be built up to a thickness of approximately 1/2 to 1 inch (12mm to 25mm). The thickness depends on the size of the model and whether a hard or soft plaster is being used.

If the RAYITE™ MDM surface coat mixture is used, it should be applied and built up to a thickness of approximately 1/16 to 1/8 inch (1-1/2mm to 3mm). After the surface coat starts to set up, the RAYITE™ MDM reinforcing coat mixture must be prepared. Before it is applied, the surface coat may be wet down so that it doesn't absorb water from the reinforcing coat. The reinforcing coat can be applied in balls and patted down, or it may be applied with a spatula, a trowel, or a brush and patted down so there is no air between the two coats. The reinforcing coat should be built up an additional amount of approximately 1/4 to 3/4 inch (7mm to 20mm). This again depends on the size of the model. It is not necessary to add additional reinforcing material with this reinforcing coat. The RAYITE™ MDM materials combine to make a plaster negative that is lighter than molds made from other plaster materials. This is because the reinforcing coat has a strengthening fiber added.

The support frame and any reinforcing members previously prepared for the negative should be positioned next. This may require angle blocks, cubes, height gauges, levels or some type of fixture arrangement. After these are positioned, they should be bonded in with the same plaster used to build up the mold.

In some situations, plaster negatives from styling clay models are faced with epoxy resin backed by a layer of fiberglass mat. These negatives have certain advantages over those made entirely from epoxy fiberglass. Advantages include lower cost, reduced processing time, and structural stability. There will be more information on this in the next chapter.

A plaster surface coat is applied to the center piece of the glass lamp model. The surface of the table around the model is waxed to provide a parting agent for the plaster negatives of the other two pieces. (Photograph: T. A. Hoadley)

A plaster reinforcing coat is added after the surface coat has set up approximately 30 minutes. The surface coat is wet down before applying the reinforcing coat. (Photograph: T. A. Hoadley)

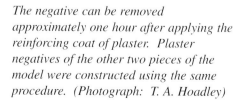

The reinforcing coat is completed and feet are added to the negative and are leveled. (Photograph: T. A. Hoadley)

The negative can be removed approximately one hour after applying the reinforcing coat of plaster. Plaster negatives of the other two pieces of the model were constructed using the same procedure. (Photograph: T. A. Hoadley)

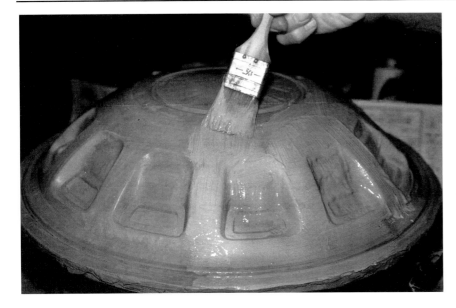

A plaster surface coat is brushed on the clay model of the motor home wheel cover. Care is taken to make sure all small corners and recessed areas are covered. Styling clay contains wax so no parting agent is required. (Photograph: T. A. Hoadley)

The plaster surface coat sets up in approximately 30 minutes. It should be wet down before applying the plaster reinforcing coat. This is done so it does not absorb water from the reinforcing plaster mix. (Photograph: T. A. Hoadley)

The negative may be pulled from the model within two hours. If the plaster sets overnight or for a longer period than two hours, it should be covered with a damp cloth and watered down. Here we see the plaster negative and the undisturbed surface of the clay model. (Photograph: T. A. Hoadley)

Removing The Plaster Negative

Plaster negatives can be removed soon after the plaster has set up. The time is somewhat flexible. If you are in a hurry, and again depending on the size and complexity of the negative, it may be removed after the plaster reaches its highest exotherm temperature.

If a negative is removed from a model soon after the plaster sets up, you will see a lot of water on the surface of the clay. This moisture acts as a lubricant and aids in separating the mold from the model. After the plaster sets up and cools down, the moisture on the surface of the model is reabsorbed by the plaster. As the mold continues to cool down, it starts to dry out and it could become difficult to remove. Therefore, keep the mold damp. If it sits over night, cover it with a cloth and wet it down with water.

Ambient air temperature and humidity can also affect the successful construction of a plaster negative. High ambient temperature may extend the normal set up time of the plaster mix. Ideally, ambient air temperature should be 68 degrees F (20 degrees C). Low humidity will dry out the wet plaster more quickly. A combination of the two, or any situation where the plaster mold is permitted to dry out before it is removed, can cause a condition where the plaster could adhere to the clay surface. If this happens, the clay model may be pulled apart when the negative is removed. If these situations exist, keep the mold wet down with water until it is removed.

To loosen and raise the negative, drive some wooden or plastic wedges in around the edges. Go all the way around the perimeter of the negative tapping in wedges until it releases. Handles provided with the support or cast in can be used to lift the mold. If it is very large and heavy, it can be lifted by using one or more chain hoists.

Negatives constructed on a surface plate or work table can be released by casting in nuts and long bolts screwed together. The nuts with the bolts can be attached to the work surface with double sided tape and positioned around the model in well-planned locations. Parting agent should only be applied to the bolts. When making the negative, these locations should be strengthened with an extra layer of reinforced plaster built up around the bolts and nuts leaving the bolt heads exposed. After the plaster has set up, the negative is released by turning in the bolts against the table surface.

To lift the model, wedges can be used in a similar manner. Wedges can be positioned around the model and attached to the work surface with double sided tape. Parting agent must be applied to the exposed surfaces of the wedges. When making the negative, plaster is built up over the pointed end of the wedges. After the plaster has set up, the negative can be lifted by tapping in the wedges around the model.

Preparing Negatives To Cast Positives

The plaster negative will be damp when first pulled from the model, and the surface layer will be soft and easily cleaned up at this time. The surface must be scraped and smoothed where obvious high places (low places in the positive) exist. This can be done with steels similar to those used on styling clay. Scrape off any high places on the surface but be careful not to gouge into the plaster. Do not remove the reference lines that were scribed onto the model. Point up any voids or holes that the surface layer did not fill. This can be done by mixing a small amount of the surface plaster material in a small plastic or rubber cup. Special plaster tools are available for this work.

The plaster negative should be dried thoroughly before starting a positive cast. Smaller negatives may be put into a convection type oven that circulates heated air. This will reduce the time required for drying. Large negatives can be put into a warm room where fans may be used to move a large volume of air over the mold to accelerate drying. Temperature should be below 120 degrees F (49 degrees C).

When a support or frame is required for the positive cast, it can be fabricated and fitted at this time. This is relatively simple if the negative is set up orthogonally in relation to the model and all reference lines are exposed on the inside surface of the mold. Reference lines must be scribed onto the frame to properly accomplish this task. When positioning the frame in the mold, adequate clearance must be provided between it and the mold surface for the build up of the positive cast. Some type of fixturing can be used to accurately reposition the support or frame back in the mold after the positive cast has been built up.

When the plaster negative is dry, all final clean up or pointing must be completed. Obvious low places in the surface can be overlooked at this time. They will be more easily cleaned up when they become high places in the positive cast.

When all clean up work is completed, the surface of the negative is sealed with two or three coats of shellac, a quick drying lacquer, or a low viscosity polyester resin. Reduce the first coat of sealer for better absorption into the surface of the plaster.

Preparing Negatives to Cast Positives (cont.)

Let each coat dry before adding the next. The sealer can either be brushed on or sprayed. Make sure the surface is evenly covered and avoid a build-up in pockets or hollows. When dry, the surface should be shiny but should not show a build-up of sealer. The surface must then be covered with a suitable parting compound or separator. Apply the separator with a brush or a clean soft cloth. Go over the surface in different directions until all of the surface has been evenly covered. You may need to use a stiff bristle brush on heavily textured surface and in grilles or louvers. To avoid excessive build-up of the parting compound it may be necessary to wipe the surface with a dry soft cloth after application, but take care not to wipe the separator completely away.

Making A Plaster Positive

Fabrication of a positive plaster cast is similar to casting a negative. A surface layer or surface coat of plaster is brushed on first. Care must be taken to assure that the whole surface has been coated. This is followed by further layers of plaster or by a reinforcing coat of plaster and built up to a desired thickness.

Plaster casts can also be reinforced with burlap, sisal, hemp, or bleeder cloth. Very thin casts can be reinforced with several layers of cheesecloth soaked in plaster. Strips of the fabric used for reinforcing the cast should be precut to fit into the cast that is being built-up. These should be dipped into a fresh mixture of plaster, then removed, opened up, and applied to the cast one layer at a time. The fabric, soaked in plaster, should be patted down over the brushed on layers of plaster in the mold. Make sure these reinforcing strips overlap previous reinforcing strips. Build up the plaster or gypsum cement to a shell thickness that can carry the load of the model. Depending on the size of the model and the materials used, the thickness can vary from 1/8 to 3/8 inch (3mm to 10mm).

This is now the proper time to position and attach a support or frame to the positive cast. If the framework has been previously fitted and located in the mold, it becomes a simple task to set it in place and tie it into the cast with reinforced plaster.

When the plaster has set up, the cast can be removed. Wedges or compressed air can be forced in around the edges of the cast. Framework or handles cast into the positive may be used to lift the cast out of the mold after it has been released. It may be necessary in some cases to invert the mold to release the cast. If it is a piece mold, each piece must be removed separately starting with the cap mold piece.

The cast is now ready for final clean up. Any high places can be scraped off and small openings or voids can be pointed up. The cast must be thoroughly dried after which it can be lightly sanded with fine sandpaper.

Any loose pieces or ornamentation should now be fitted and the surface around these parts should be cleaned up. If there are any working parts to be assembled to the finished cast, they should also be fitted and tried out.

When all of this has taken place, the cast is ready to seal, fill, and paint.

Plaster & Gypsum Cement Information

This information has been supplied by Ray Kaligian, New Products and Systems Development Marketing Manager, United States Gypsum Company, Industrial Gypsum Division, P. O. Box 803871, Chicago, Illinois 60680-3871.

One of the most asked questions from users of United States Gypsum Company (USG) products is "what is plaster?". This question really infers "is plaster safe to use". Plaster and gypsum cements are made from calcining gypsum rock. Gypsum rock is a naturally occurring mineral composed of calcium, sulfate and water ($CaSO_4$ •$2H_2O$, or gypsum dihydrate). Calcining is simply "cooking" the mineral until 75% of the water has been driven out. The resultant product is represented by $CaSO_4$ •$1/2H_2O$, or hemihydrate. The end user, when adding water to plaster powder is in reality returning the hemihydrate form back to the dihydrate.

How safe is plaster and gypsum cement products? The dihydrate form is used as soil amendments and as fillers and performance promoters in foodstuffs! Remember, the building blocks of plaster: calcium, sulfur (in the form of sulfate) and water! Several product brochures, available from U.S.Gypsum Company illustrates the safety and versatility of gypsum.

The cooking (or calcining) process determines whether the hemihydrate crystal is a plaster (beta hemihydrate) or gypsum cement (alpha hemihydrate). With plaster products (plaster of Paris, Casting Plaster, etc.), the gypsum is calcined in an atmospheric kettle. The resultant crystals are coarse and rough. Alpha hemihydrate (such as ULTRACAL 30, HYDROCAL B-11) are calcined in a pressure calciner. The resultant crystals are geometric in shape. Translation: plaster products require more water for conversion than gypsum cement products, thus gypsum cement casts are stronger and typically are more dense. It is important to stress the difference between plaster products and gypsum cement products.

USG never recommends using the "sift, soak and mound" approach to determine water and powder relationships. This method has significant flaws. For one, not all products "soak out" the same. Second, high strength gypsum cement products require such a significantly less amount of water than plaster products that it would be impractical to properly soak these products.

Another mistake is that users try to volumetrically measure water and powder. This also creates errors. Simply put, the density of powder can easily change by "packing". Therefore it is always recommended by USG that the user weigh the water and the plaster or gypsum cement.

Plaster reinforcing aids include sisal, hemp, and bleeder cloth (like the type used on vacuum bag lay-ups). Regarding fiberglass mat, woven products (like those used with polyester resin) are usually water resistant. Using water resistant cloth will repel plaster and gypsum cement slurries and can actually weaken the cast. Also, please be aware that some gypsum cement products are slightly alkaline. Some fiberglass mat, not protected against alkaline products will be negatively affected by long-term exposure to these products.

USG Technical Bulletin IG-515, *"Sealers and Parting Compounds"* for Gypsum Cements suggests several release agents and sealers that work well with these products.

USG Technical Bulletin IG-503, *"Plasters Mixing Procedures"*. Like using the correct water-to-plaster ratio, using the correct mixing procedure is also critical to the performance of any plaster product. Proper mixing energy provides maximum performance to the product. This is especially true for larger batches. Using a stick or spatula to mix 10 or 20 pounds of HYDROCAL B-11 is difficult. The user tends to over-water the mix which translates to a weak casting. Also, the type of mixer is important to a good, uniform mix. Using a hardware store paint mixer is not appropriate as this type can actually pump air into the slurry. A prop or Jiffy®mixer is recommended.

USG Technical Bulletin IG-502, *"Drying Plaster Casts"* describes efficient drying systems depending on how much plaster is required to be dried in a specific amount of time. The degree of dryness is also a major factor. There are a few simple "rules of thumb" that can be used here. First, air temperatures should never exceed 120°F. Sustained plaster temperatures above 120°F will actually calcine the surface. Secondly, air movement is as important to the efficiency of drying as air temperature. Plaster casts will not dry in hot, humid environments.

The finished hanging glass lamp.
(Photograph: Author)

CHAPTER 14 - Using Plastics To Cast Models

Types of Plastics Used

Several types of plastics are used for making negative molds and positive casts from styling clay models. Each particular plastic has certain advantages for its application.

For instance, silicone rubber and urethane elastomer are used to make flexible molds from models that otherwise would require very complicated piece molds. The materials are expensive but their use results in an exact duplicate without showing any piece mold joint lines.

Another example is the use of quick cast tooling plastics to cast tools. These rapid curing plastic materials result in an exact reproduction of the model. Casts become tools for various uses including vacuum forming sheet thermoplastic materials such as ABS (acrylonitrile-butadiene-styrene).

Polyester resin is a high performance, lower cost material that is used in FRP (fiber-reinforced plastic) parts. It is the primary material used in fabricating parts for recreational vehicles, boats, and many after market product items.

Epoxy resin is a high strength, high heat resistant, low shrink material also used in fabricating FRP parts. In addition, it is the principle material used in producing high quality tooling aids, and for other applications where high performance is required. Epoxy resin is more expensive than polyester resin.

The preparation of the styling clay surface and the use of each of these plastic systems will be reviewed in this chapter.

For more information on this subject see: The Complete Guide to *SCULPTURE, MODELING, and CERAMICS, Techniques and Materials*, by Barry Midgley, John Calcutt, Trevor Crabtree, Andrew Fyvie, and Dave Harper, published by Chartwell Books 1982.

Testing Materials

Once again it is important to emphasize that you should test materials and processes with which you may not be thoroughly familiar. If you do not have confidence in the use of a material or if a material is new to you, try it out first on small clay test samples. Be sure to follow all of the directions and give proper heed to cautions and health hazards.

Room Temperature Vulcanizing (RTV) Materials

Silicone rubber is a flexible cold cure compound used to construct negatives from styling clay models that have unusual molding problems. These could be situations where there are undercuts in the modeled surface, or interlocking sections, or areas with negative draft. The compound is a two-part system consisting of a silicone elastomer and a catalyst. The two liquid materials are mixed and then poured over the model. Since this is a liquid compound, there must be special preparation for its use on a design model.

To make a RTV negative requires constructing a dam or a jacket around the model. In some situations only a portion of a model requires a flexible mold. In these cases, the RTV molded area becomes a part of a larger piece mold.

If the surface of the model to be molded is in a horizontal position, or if the model can be positioned horizontally, then it may be dammed off. The dam can be constructed from styling clay extrusions or other materials but it must be well sealed. Also, since the RTV mixture is in a liquid state, it will seek a natural level. The top edge of the dam, therefore, must be level and above the top surface of the area to be molded.

If the model cannot be positioned horizontally, then it becomes necessary to construct a jacket or core box. The purpose for the jacket is to form a cavity or matrix to retain the liquid when it is poured. A jacket can be temporary or permanent and may be made from styling clay extrusions, wood, metal, sheet plastic, or a combination of materials.

Silicone rubber has a tendency to seep through the smallest opening, therefore, the jacket must be well sealed. A release agent is required on the jacket, but normally not on the styling clay surface.

Construct the jacket with draft around the mold so it can be easily removed. If the area to be molded is on a rounded surface or a surface that extends beyond the limitation of a single jacket, then the jacket must be constructed with a seam. In such situations, the flexible mold may also have to be constructed as a piece mold with a seam or a break. Sometimes it may be necessary to cut the silicone mold to release it from the model or to release a cast from the mold. An example of this would be a surface with a formed-in handle attached at both ends.

When the dam or jacket has been prepared around the surface to be molded, then the silicone material and catalyst can be mixed. Mix the two parts well together. Make sure all of the silicone base material is mixed in. If you are using a slow curing agent as a catalyst, then you may let the compound stand for several minutes so entrapped air can rise out of it. Pour the compound over the modeled surface or into the cavity of the jacket until the surface is well covered. Tap the jacket several times to help release air that may be trapped. The mixture must stand undisturbed overnight or until it has set up.

The compound should be poured into one end of a dammed off model so the liquid flows from one end to the other to force out the air. Likewise, pour the compound into one side of the cavity of a model that has been jacketed so that the air will be forced out as the liquid travels. Continue pouring until the surface is covered. Pour the liquid along the work surface at the edge of the model or down the edge of the jacket, if you are concerned that the force of the liquid might deface the model. Watch for bubbles forming along valleys on the model and try to remove them with a tongue depressor, but do not touch the clay. Avoid multi-mix pours because different curing times can cause warping or deforming of the mold.

If a fast curing agent is being used as a catalyst, then the compound must be poured immediately after mixing, since the silicone and catalyst mixture will set up in five to fifteen minutes.

There is also another variable in using silicone mold making materials. If the styling clay being used has sulfur as a filler, there can be a chemical reaction between the silicone compound and the sulfur, thus blocking the mold surface of the negative from setting up. Using a fast curing agent with the silicone may overcome this problem since there is not time for the chemical reaction to occur between the two materials.

If a slow curing agent is used in the silicone compound when forming a negative from a sulfur base clay model, then it will be necessary to seal the clay surface. The model may be sealed by spraying the surface with several light coats of PVA or strippable vinyl, or spraying the surface with shellac or other sealers. Do not brush shellac on the clay surface because the clay may not be properly sealed.

More information about silicone mold making materials can be obtained from the following sources: General Electric Company, Silicone Products Division, Marketing Department, Waterford, New York 12188 and Dow Corning Corporation, Midland, Michigan 48640.

Urethane elastomer is also used as a RTV material. The use of urethane mold making materials will also require sealing the surface of the clay model. After sealing, the surface of the model and the dam or jacket around the model must be waxed or sprayed with a wax solution. When this is dry, the urethane and catalyst may be mixed and poured.

Before removing the mold, if the jacket around the model is a temporary arrangement or if a dam has been used to retain the liquid, then this must be removed and replaced by a permanent covering. A casing or backing must be built up over the mold to maintain its shape when it is removed. The casing can be a simple plaster splash with legs or a support attached as needed.

If the RTV mold is a portion of a larger piece mold, the negative of the larger surface can encase the flexible mold after the jacket or dam has been removed. For this, you can use either plaster or FRP construction. However, it is necessary to clean up the clay surface around the silicone mold where the temporary jacket or the dam had been built up.

To remove the RTV mold from the model, the jacket or casing must first be removed. This permits the flexible mold to be carefully folded and lifted away from the modeled surface. Compressed air around the edges of the mold may be used to aid in the removal. However, do not remove the rubber mold from the model until the permanent jacket or casting (or a larger overall negative) has been completed.

A variety of materials can be used to cast parts from silicone rubber molds including metals with low temperature melt points. To assure the original shape of the model, the mold must be returned to its permanent jacket or casing before parts are cast. Also, to retain the original shape of the mold when it is in storage, cast an extra part and leave it in the mold with the mold in its jacket.

An approved instrument panel design model is mounted in the tilting fixture to facilitate fabricating a master negative. The negative is keyed to the tilting fixture through the use of brackets molded into the negative. Numerous holes are provided in the tilting fixture to accept armatures and brackets for various size instrument panels, 1970. (Photograph: Ford Design Center)

The master negative as it looks when it is just removed from the styling clay model. This is a piece mold consisting of four parts: top, face, and two sides. Note the keying brackets molded into each of the side pieces, 1970. This is a silicone rubber mold backed-up with plaster. (Photograph: Ford Design Center)

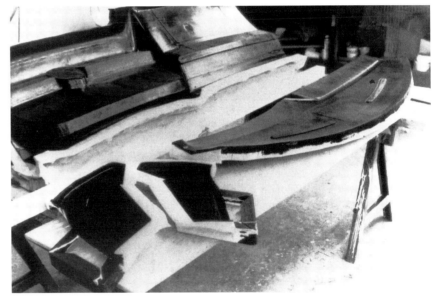

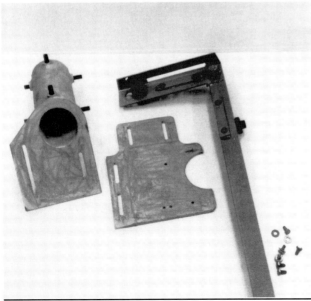

A light weight welded angle iron frame is fabricated for FRP instrument panel models. Locating pins are mounted loosely in over size holes on the frame. The adjustable steering column mount must be assembled. (Photograph: Ford Design Center)

The light weight frame assembly is mounted onto the tilting fixture. The frame is centered and the locator nuts are tightened and locked up. The steering column mount is set at the proper angles and tightened. Mounting brackets to bond to the instrument panel fiberglass cast are loosely attached to the frame, 1970. (Photograph: Ford Design Center)

The master negative is reassembled and a FRP cast is laid up in the mold. The assembled and adjusted angle iron frame is mounted and locked to the portable magnesium fixture. The master negative with the positive cast inside is next attached to the portable fixture through the same brackets and key holes as on the tilting fixture. The mounting brackets loosely assembled to the frame are adjusted to fit to the inside surface of the fiberglass cast and are bonded in place. The master negative is loosened and removed from the portable fixture, 1970.
(Photograph: Ford Design Center)

The FRP cast with the frame is removed from the portable fixture and mounted to the tilting fixture for final clean up and finish, 1970. Note, all holes in all fixtures are accurately jig bored to a small tolerance. The clay instrument panel models and the fiberglass casts are in the exact same position relative to reference lines on any instrument panel fixture. (Photograph: Ford Design Center)

Quick Cast Tooling Plastics

Tooling plastics are used to cast tools for specific purposes such as vacuum forming. Tooling plastics are composed of a base plastic compound in a suspended system filled with various other materials for strength. Cure cycle time for polyolefin and polyurethane base plastics used in quick cure systems is 30 minutes or less. Various fillers are used including silicon dioxide, powdered aluminum, iron oxide, and glass beads. Certain combinations of these materials create plastics having special qualities suitable for particular types of tools.

Tools made from these plastic materials can be processed directly from design models constructed from styling clay. This process is ideal for producing vacuum forming tools. Other types of tools cast from tooling plastics include patterns, autoclave tools, compression dies, injection molding dies, and many types of fixtures.

Quick cure tooling plastic can be used to make the negative off a styling clay model. It is fast, accurate, and simple to use. Either a surface casting technique or a mass casting technique may be used to produce the negative mold and the positive tool. Compared to mass casting, the cross sectional area of casting material in surface casting is kept to a minimum and therefore shrinkage is minimized. The surface casting technique is used where there is a large void that would otherwise be filled with the casting material. Mass casting does not require a core since the entire void is filled with the casting material. However, surface casting requires a core to fill the void and to allow the desired thickness of casting material between the model and the core.

Because tooling plastics are liquid two part systems, a dam must be constructed around the model to retain the material when it is poured. The dam should be level at a uniform height above the model since it also provides the support and set up height for the negative when it is inverted.

If a core is to be used, it should be made to the rough shape of the model minus the desired tooling plastic thickness. A core can be made from blocks of polyurethane foam or wood. The core is suspended over the model and supported by the dam surrounding it.

A wax release agent is sprayed onto all surfaces other than the core. Good adhesion of the plastic resin to the core must be assured. If desired, the styling clay surface may be sprayed with several light coats of PVA (polyvinyl alcohol). Each coat of PVA must dry thoroughly before applying the next coat. When it is dry, the wax release agent is sprayed over this surface.

A sprue or opening should be provided in the core so that the surface casting material will enter at the lowest point of the model. Risers or holes may be drilled into the core at the high points of the model to release air that otherwise might be entrapped.

When all of this is prepared and the core is fixed in place, the model is ready to mold. First, each of the two parts of the casting system should be thoroughly mixed independently. The two parts then can be combined and mixed immediately. This mixture is poured at a fast rate into the sprue opening or openings. Allow it to set undisturbed during the cure cycle. Remember, the tooling plastic resin is in a liquid state and it will seek a natural level. Pouring should be done on a leveled surface. Unmold the negative within 30 minutes and do any minor clean up that is necessary.

The same general procedure will be followed in casting a positive tool off the negative. The wax release agent is applied to the entire negative surface. If a core is used, it is again prepared to provide the desired thickness of casting resin. A dam may or may not be required depending on the base for the tool, but normally, the negative itself forms the dam. Sprue and riser openings are cut into the core and it is positioned and supported over the negative.

The mixing and pouring procedure is the same as before. Cure cycle is again within 30 minutes. Remove the cast and do any minor clean up. For vacuum forming, the cast will have to be attached to a platen and drilled for venting on the vacuum table. The person doing the vacuum forming may wish to drill the venting holes himself.

The significance of this procedure for producing vacuum forming tools, and other tools, is the short interval between an approved completed model and a finished tool or finished parts. When vacuum formed parts are required in a hurry, tools can be cast from a styling clay model and parts can be formed, trimmed, and ready for use, all within one day.

A Coachmen travel trailer fender design model is developed from a design illustration and a surface layout proposed by John Dunlap. (Photograph: John Dunlap)

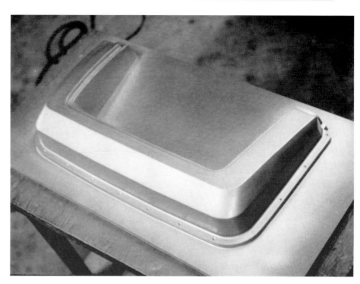

The finished styling clay model is sprayed with several light coats of PVA and when that is thoroughly dry the surface is waxed. (Photograph: John Dunlap)

From the finished and prepared design model, a negative master model is constructed using a quick setting polyurethane tooling plastic. Set up time is 20 minutes. (Photograph: John Dunlap)

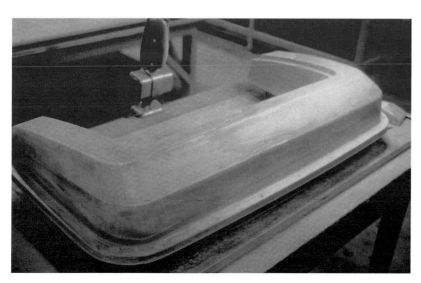

A positive master vacuum forming tool is cast out of the negative using the same polyurethane tooling plastic. The negative is sprayed with a wax parting agent and the cast is backed out with polyurethane foam blocks. Set up time is 20 minutes. This positive master cast is cleaned up, mounted to a sub plate and drilled for vacuum forming venting. (Photograph: John Dunlap)

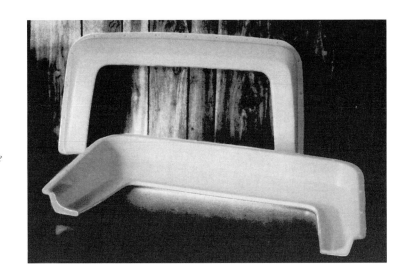

Finished vacuum formed parts are drawn from the tool. (Photograph: John Dunlap)

Finished fenders are installed on the Coachmen Travel Trailer. This process from clay model, to production tool, to installed production parts is accomplished in one day. (Photograph: John Dunlap)

A pick up cap louvered window cover design model is developed in styling clay from a design illustration by Joe Pappi and engineering information, lower left.
A negative master is cast from the clay model using quick setting polyurethane tooling plastic, upper left.
A positive vacuum forming tool is cast from the negative master using the same quick setting polyurethane tooling plastic. The positive cast is cleaned up and mounted on to a sub plate and drilled for venting, upper right.   Finished, textured ABS vacuum formed parts ready for trimming are made from this tool for Viking Formed Products, lower right. This process from clay model to finished parts is accomplished in one day. (Photograph: John Dunlap)

Preparing Vacuum Forming Tools

There are several restrictions that control the development of styling clay models to be used to process vacuum forming tools. For instance, models developed for vacuum forming normally require a minimum draft angle of 2 degrees around the model. This is necessary so the negative can be removed from the model and parts can be removed from the tool.

If the trim line for a vacuum formed part is in a flat plane and parallel to the platen, a circular cutter can be utilized in a table that has been set up to trim parts. But if the trim line varies from a flat plane or is not parallel to the platen, a flange can be developed on the model to be used as a guide for a routing tool attachment to follow when trimming the part.

It is advisable before you commence a vacuum forming tool, or any tool that may be constructed, to discuss the situation with the person who will be using the tool to produce parts. In the case of vacuum forming, you need to determine the proper draw angle for the tool to be set up on the vacuum table. The model may have to be tipped to produce the tool with the proper draw angle, in which case the draft angle will be relative to the draw angle. In a situation like this, the model would be tipped relative to the tool base. (Draw angle is the set up position of a die or tool relative to the direction of draw of the material formed over it. This can be a compound angle differing from the design coordinates of the model.)

You must also determine the draw depth and the amount of extra material needed for trimming and for part fasteners in order to establish the sheet size. Always keep in mind that the finished surface of the material is the surface away from the tool. The surface finish may be smooth or textured and can be ABS or other similar thermoplastic sheet material. (Draw depth is the vertical depth of the tool relative to the platen or the base of the tool.)

The plastic sheet thickness will be partially controlled by the limitations in radii and draw depth of the material. Finished parts will be larger than the tool by the amount of the material thickness. Consequently, if parts must meet certain dimensional criteria, the tool must be material thickness smaller. Also, the model must be adjusted dimensionally according to the shrinkage of the sheet plastic material.

Therefore, when a model is developed to produce a tool for vacuum formed parts it is necessary to know:

1. The trim line of the part relative to the platen.
2. The draw angle of the tool.
3. The draw depth of the part plus additional material required for trimming.
4. The plastic sheet thickness and limitations.
5. The shrink factor of the vacuum forming thermoplastic material.

These points must be known so that when the model is cleaned up and finished, it will be ready to process the vacuum forming tool.

More information can be obtained from plastic material distributors and companies' sales offices; The Modern Plastics Encyclopedia; and the Society of the Plastics Industry, 355 Lexington Ave., New York, N.Y. 10017.

The sheet material thickness may greatly alter the form of the tool relative to the surface of the finished part. It may be necessary to first rough in the model to the desired form of the finished part to obtain design approval. When the form has been approved, a depth cutter (a tool used to cut an exact depth into the surface of a clay model) can be used to remove the thickness of clay representing the plastic sheet material. The model can then be cleaned up for processing the tool. An alternative is to develop a design model for appearance and a separate model for tooling purposes.

Vacuum forming tools may be produced through the use of epoxy and polyester FRP casting techniques, or by using quick cast tooling plastics and epoxy tooling plastics.

Epoxy Tooling Plastics

Epoxy tooling plastics are used to produce prototype tools and for various other tooling requirements. They too can be cast from negatives made from styling clay models. However, a design model developed for this purpose must satisfy the requirements and constraints of the manufacturing process in which the tool will be used and the material from which parts will be made.

To keep expansion to a minimum, cure cycle time for cast epoxy systems range from 8 hours to 10 days. Surface casting is also recommended for these tools to reduce the resin thickness, and thus the amount of resin and the exotherm (a chemical reaction that produces heat and expansion).

Epoxy systems are used in developing vacuum forming tools, various metal forming tools including draw dies for stamping steel parts, RIM (reaction injection molding) and RTM (resin transfer molding) tools, and other plastic part tooling. Tubes can be cast into the plastic wall of these tools and used for circulating water for cooling and controlling tool temperature during production cycles.

Negatives made off of models to be used for processing these tools, are usually made with FRP construction.

There are limitations in the size and use of cast epoxy tools due to the weight of the plastic compound, heat removal problems, and structural integrity of tools.

Epoxy FRP Negatives

Making epoxy FRP negatives off of styling clay models, requires a barrier coat between the styling clay surface and the plastic resin. The reason for this is that the plastic resin will not cure properly if the clay surface is not well sealed.

When a negative from a styling clay model is to be used to cast parts that will be further cleaned-up and painted, a simple system for sealing the clay surface is used. Several light coats of PVA are sprayed on to the surface of the model. Each coat of PVA must be allowed to thoroughly dry before the next coat is sprayed on. When four or five coats have been added and well dried, a mold release wax must be applied over the PVA. Using a soft cloth, the surface should be well waxed and it should be applied with considerable care so that the PVA will not be disturbed. When the wax has been lightly buffed, normal FRP casting techniques are utilized.

The PVA may be available under other names, such as Partall, on distributors' labels. It is normally light green in color with a strong alcohol odor. When dry, the PVA forms a thin acetate shell over the model. When the mold is removed from the model, the acetate can be washed off the mold surface with water.

There are variations to this procedure and there are other materials that can be used as a barrier coat. One of these materials is Dow Corning's 1890 strippable coating. You may wish to develop your own system. Just remember to try out any new process on a styling clay sample before applying the materials to a finished design model.

Epoxy Faced Negatives

Negatives are sometimes made with an epoxy FRP face but backed up with plaster. This combination will provide a quick rigid mold having the advantages of an FRP surface but with lower cost and reduced processing time.

To accomplish this, the clay surface must be perfectly sealed from the plastic resin with a barrier coat. One solution is to first spray the clay surface with a strippable vinyl paint. When this is dry, the surface is covered with a mold release wax applied with a clean soft cloth. Next, several very light coats of PVA are sprayed over the surface. Each of these coats must dry thoroughly before the next one is sprayed on. When these are dry, the mold release wax is again applied to the surface but with great care so the PVA will not be disturbed. This is an alternative to spraying PVA directly over the clay surface.

To build up the negative, a surface coat of epoxy is brushed on the prepared surface of the model. This should be allowed to cure to a jelled or very tacky state. The second coat is then applied. Immediately lay on precut fiberglass cloth and pat it down into the soft second coat.

While this is still wet, a plaster mix is applied against the second surface coat and fiberglass cloth. For best results, the plaster should not be overly wet. Work the plaster into the wet epoxy and the surface of the mat. A good bond will result. Build up the plaster to a desired thickness for structural integrity. Attach some type of legs or support to provide a stable and orthogonal negative, as required.

Epoxy Faced Negatives (Cont.)

Some epoxy surface coats have been developed with the ability to cure in contact with and bond to freshly poured wet plaster. Thermoset 267 and 270 have this ability, also United Resin Unigel SC90 together with United Resin TP-41F hardener.

After the negative is removed from the model, the strippable vinyl can be cut and removed, leaving the clay surface undisturbed. The model is therefore ready for further development work, if necessary.

Normal procedures are used to clean up, polish, and wax the negative for casting purposes.

Using Tooling Foam

Materials other than plaster can be used to back up the epoxy surface coat such as Ad-Tech's Tooling Foam, United Resin's Tooling Foam or Blehm's Epoxy Clay. These two part systems are mixed together, rolled out in sheets, and applied to the second fiberglass cloth layer and epoxy surface coat. One or two more layers of epoxy resin and fiberglass cloth should be laid down on top of the epoxy foam to form a sandwich construction. This produces a negative that is lighter in weight in a much reduced time frame compared with conventional fiberglass buildup.

As discussed above, the tooling foam process can be very valuable. This is particularly so when it is necessary to develop tooling in a very short period of time and where high precision is not a requisite. It is particularly important that the process can also be used to produce a quick strong positive cast.

Tooling foam can be thinned by adding United Resin UNIBOND-WG to the two part system. With this thinned mixture it is possible to squeeze cast prototype parts such as air deflectors and spoilers that can emulate properties of a structural foam part. For this type of application, the epoxy surface coat need not be backed-up with fiberglass.

Tooling foam (syntactic foam) can be made by mixing glass beads with epoxy resin and hardener in separate containers. The two parts are then mixed when they are to be used.

Polyester FRP Negatives

The same system used for preparing the styling clay surface when making epoxy FRP negatives can be used when making FRP negatives with polyester resin. A barrier coat must be applied between the clay surface and the polyester resin. As previously outlined, several light coats of PVA are sprayed onto the surface of the model. Each coat of PVA must dry thoroughly before the next coat is sprayed on. After these have dried, mold release wax is applied over the PVA. The wax must be applied with care so the PVA is not disturbed. The difficulty with this surface preparation system is that it does not produce a class "A" finish.

Industries that use polyester resins prefer a class "A" polyester gel coat finish on the model. Negatives made from models with a class "A" finish will be able to produce positive casts with a class "A" finish.

For a good basic book on polyester/fiberglass work covering materials, chemistry, uses, and finishes see: Paul J. Petrick, *Fiberglass Repairs*, 1986, Cornell Maritime Press, Inc.

Industries using polyester FRP negative molds and positive casts include companies producing recreational vehicles, boats, pick-up caps, running boards, air spoilers, and many other after market items. Models for these products are usually made from wood, fiberglass, and Bondo. A model constructed with these materials may have a wood frame and a plywood shell or it may be built on a reinforced fiberglass part cast from a previous production tool. The shell is modified and the surface is built up, formed, and modeled with Bondo. The Bondo surface is sanded, smoothed, built-up, sanded, and smoothed until the model receives client approval.

When a client's approval is received, the surface is sprayed with several layers of polyester tooling gel coat or polyester enamel type primers and topcoats. This surface is finished with medium to fine sand paper, rubbed out, and buffed to a beautiful high luster. A negative off a model so finished will produce parts with a mirror-like, beautiful high luster finish. It is this class "A", beautiful high luster finish that is desired by the industries using polyester FRP construction in their products.

This same beautiful finish is also possible on models constructed with styling clay. To accomplish this, the following system is used. The surface of the finished and approved styling clay model is first sprayed with two coats of R-M Undercoat 811 Clear Adhesion Promoter or with shellac.

Polyester FRP Negatives (cont.)

When this is thoroughly dry, spray four or five coats of R-M Undercoat HP 100 Gray Acrylic Hydrosol Waterborne Primer Surfacer onto the surface. Each of these coats should be allowed to flash-off only long enough to prevent sagging. This barrier coat must thoroughly dry before proceeding. These materials may be obtained from your dealer or from BASF Corporation, 3301 Bourke Ave., Detroit, Michigan 48238. Telephone (313) 861-1000.

The surface may then be sprayed and built-up to the desired thickness with several coat layers of polyester sandable primer. When dry, this surface is sanded with a medium grit sandpaper, 180-320 grit. Care must be taken to assure that the R-M barrier coat is not sanded through. For this system to work, this seal must not be broken.

Polyester tooling gel or polyester enamel type primers and topcoats are then sprayed on the surface. This surface is dry sanded starting with a medium grit sandpaper and ending with 400 grit. Do not go to the next finer grit sandpaper until all the scratches are removed from the previous sanding. The finer the grit the longer it will take to remove the previous scratches. Always use the largest sanding block possible to avoid sanding holes or low areas into the surface.

The surface is next wet sanded with 600 grit sandpaper. Even, bi-directional diagonal or transverse strokes will aid in controlling the surface preparation and in avoiding distortions.

Machine buff the surface starting with a coarse rouge buffing compound. Buff the whole area evenly and with light pressure. Do not heat the surface with the buffing wheel. Switch to finer buffing compounds and either clean off the buffing pad or run off the compound completely before applying a finer compound. Continue buffing until a satisfactory high luster is obtained.

If the clay model was steeled properly and the sanding block was used correctly, there will be no distortions in the reflections and highlights from the surface of the model's polyester gel coat finish.

Making a negative off a styling clay model finished with this system is similar to making a negative off a wood and Bondo polyester gel coat finished model. The buffed surface of the model should be cleaned with mold presealer glaze. Wax the surface with a good mold release wax. Multiple coats of wax are generally recommended to assure complete surface coverage.

The negative can be vented, if so desired, to facilitate its removal from the model. This can be accomplished by attaching an air hose fitting (or a small cork or small tube) with double sided tape to the surface. (See photographs under, Support for Negatives, Chapter 12.)

Normal FRP casting techniques are used in making the negative. Spray or brush tooling gel onto the waxed surface. Preferably two coats of two different tooling gel colors should be used. Apply resin and 1-1/2 ounce fiberglass mat in successive layers.

Roll out each layer and allow sufficient time between layers to avoid excessive exothermic heat. Build up seven to twelve layers of resin and fiberglass, depending on the size of the negative. Baltex (cubes of balsa wood bonded to an open weave cloth) or other similar honeycomb materials can be used to reduce the numbers of layers of fiberglass and the processing time. The Baltex must be sandwiched in with at least two layers of resin and fiberglass mat. For more information on this process see, "Sandwich Construction", Fabrication News, March 1991, pages 15 through 27, and -Composites Fabrication, February 1996, pages 8 through 12.

When the resin has cured, attach an air hose to the air hose fitting, if one has been cast into the negative, and apply compressed air through the vent to aid in releasing the negative from the model.

Carefully remove the negative. If the negative has been vented, fill and finish the surface around the air vent hole. Clean, buff, and wax the surface. This is now a master negative and can be used with the normal FRP technique in casting parts having polyester FRP construction. Parts will have a beautiful high luster finish. In addition to parts, a reinforced master positive cast may also be constructed from this master negative to be used as a plug in processing production tools. (A plug is a master model used to produce production tools.)

There may be other products that can be used as a barrier coat to seal the clay. The R-M Undercoat HP 100 is a water-borne primer surfacer and not a solvent based material. Therefore, there is no solvent sensitivity to undercoats or top coats since it is water-borne, and there is no reaction to the styling clay.

There are variations on this surface preparation system, and there is an additional step which can be quite valuable. Following the application of the R-M Undercoat HP 100 on the clay model, the surface can be laminated with polyester resin and a very fine fiberglass such as surfacing veil or surfacing mat (sometimes called angel hair). When this has set up, sand off any high points of this laminate but do not sand through the fiberglass veil. Spray the surface with several coats of polyester sandable primer. Build up with the polyester tooling gel coat, sand and buff to a high luster. This thin fiberglass shell will protect the clay surface, provide a harder surface for sanding and buffing, and assure a crack free polyester gel coat finish.

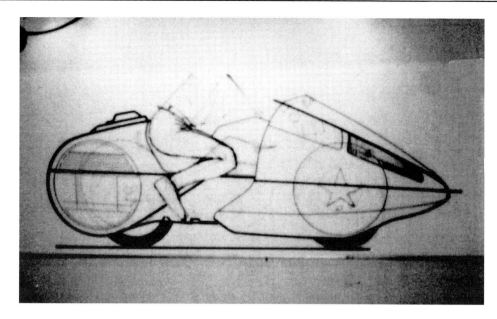

A motion picture special vehicle proposal is illustrated in a full size black tape drawing. (Photograph: Tom Stone)

A full size styling clay model of the special movie vehicle is developed. (Photograph: Tom Stone)

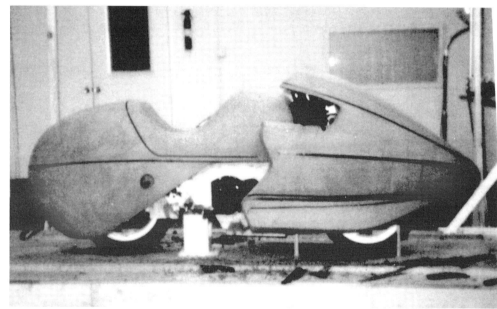

A negative of the left hand half of the movie prop has been completed. Note the points being cast into the negative to key and locate the two halves of the piece mold. (Photograph: Tom Stone)

The negative is built up as a piece mold separating on the centerline. Two layers of epoxy fiberglass have been applied to the right hand half of the model. Tooling foam is being applied over this initial lay up. Two more layers of epoxy fiberglass will be laid over the completed tooling foam build-up. (Photograph: Tom Stone)

The negative is completed in two halves and is boxed in and stabilized. (Photograph: Tom Stone)

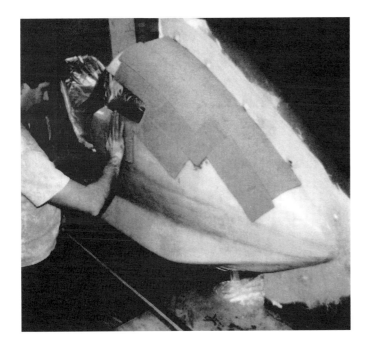

Two special vehicles are completed for "BACK TO THE FUTURE II". (Photograph: Tom Stone)

Why Molds Stick

The reason molds stick is due to surface reactivity. In a new mold, 4-6% of the polymer molecules exposed on the surface have not interconnected with other polyester polymer molecules, thus the surface has not completely cured.

In response to a survey by Fiberglass Fabrication Association, Technical Services Director, Bob Lacovara, the sticking rate of molds/initial parts was much greater than molds/plugs, Bob Lacovara, "Why Molds Stick", <u>Fabrication News</u>, February 1991.

It was also found that a certain number of all new molds stick regardless of the type or brand of mold release used. Wax or semi-permanent release agents do not form an impervious barrier.

Molds from plugs stick less than parts from molds. This is because the plug surface, by a large percentage, consists of polyester enamel type primers and topcoats. These primers and topcoats usually consist of a polyester polymer dissolved in a solvent vehicle. The hardening process is a combination of curing and drying.

Tooling gel coats do not contain a solvent. Very little evaporation takes place during the cure of these materials. The implication is that primer/topcoat materials react differently from tooling gel coat under similar circumstances and conditions. Parts from molds stick more often because molds are built-up with tooling gel coats.

The problem does not exist with molds that have been broken in because they have an inert surface. So it is important in keeping surface reactivity to a minimum to reduce the time required to break in or stabilize the surface of a mold. The key factors for maximum cure of tooling gel coat materials include:

1. Accurate catalyzation, follow the manufacturer's recommendations exactly.
2. Complete mixing, catalyst must be evenly and completely dispersed throughout the tooling gel coat material.
3. Ambient air temperature should never be lower than 60°- 65°F.
4. A reasonably fast cure with the first few part applications of production gel coat is desirable to reduce the time on the mold.

There is a foolproof method to avoid the chance of parts sticking on mold break-in. This is to use PVA as a parting film to form a barrier coat in the mold. The procedure is as follows:

1. Prep the mold with a PVA compatible mold release agent.
2. Apply PVA.
3. Apply production gel coat and an optional laminate.
4. Fully cure the gel coat.
5. Pull the gel coat and clean the mold.
6. Repeat steps 1 through 5.
7. Once 2 pulls with PVA are completed, prep the mold with a production release agent and run the first production part without PVA.

This procedure reduced sticking to 0.1% according to the survey.

Proper application of PVA is essential; gradually build up a number of thin layers to form a continuous thick film.

CHAPTER 15 - 3-D Engineering and Master Modeling

A Cost and Time Reduction System

Through the use of the cost saving system known as 3-D Engineering and Master Modeling, master models can be produced at much less than the cost of other methods. Styling clay is the material used in these developments together with stable armatures, precision positioning, accurate dimensional control of the models and unique processing.

This system can be used to develop and reconcile master models of all components of any item requiring multiple pieces for assembly. Furthermore, these master models can be constructed so they can be cubed together to assure engineering and design integrity.

The reduction in time span and man-hours utilizing this system, also results in a similar reduction in cost. Conventional machining is nonexistent in these techniques.

Use of 3-D Engineering and Master Modeling also brings to reality, programs and projects that previously were not possible due to excessive time and costs.

This system was originally developed by Wallace A. Stanley for automobile body design, engineering, and tooling. In 1956, Stanley presented a paper to The Society of the Plastics Industry, titled, "Master Modeling and Reconciliation of Inner Models With Plastic". Following this presentation, the aircraft industry picked up and utilized this master modeling system in air frame design and development. This technique has also been used successfully in the construction of master models and tools for other products as well. Five examples of the use of these techniques and principles follow:

1. One-Piece Roof Inner Panel

The 3-D Engineering and Master Modeling system was utilized to develop an Advance Engineering one-piece roof inner panel proposal to be used for engineering testing and appearance evaluation. This project exemplified the great savings in span time and man-hours made possible with these techniques.

The significance of the results of this project were two-fold:

First

3-D Engineering and Master Modeling was the only alternative possible because of the unavailability of man-power and surface drafts, and the cost involved in conventional die model development.

Second

This system provided a low-budget, fast, and accurate design development method for making concept and prototype parts for testing and evaluation.

The importance of these results encompasses several vital aspects which should be pointed out:

• *Design and engineering development was done in three dimensions directly in clay.*

• *Continuous modifications for appearance and feasibility were incorporated in the model as it developed.*

• *Only an advance engineering drawing of master lines and sections, and a previous picture model, were available and used in developing this model.*

• *All surfaces were made symmetrical about the centerline and verified accurate to the surface plate and base rails.*

• *Perfect mating or reconciliation of this structural inner panel to the carryover roof panel was accomplished by construction. The mating surfaces were "zero tolerance" reconciled. This was possible since the mating surface was the inside surface of the existing roof outer panel.*

• *There were no new untried technologies or techniques used.*

• *Precision equipment was used to achieve the end results.*

• *There was no machining of any kind.*

• *The setup, from clay model through the finished plastic female model, was not disturbed.*

• *The resulting high quality model was well within master model dimensional tolerances.*

• *From this master control model, prototype draw dies and tools were processed, followed by actual sheet metal stampings. These parts were bonded and welded into roof panels, assembled into experimental vehicles, and tested.*

• *A complete and uninterrupted cycle from clay model to tools was demonstrated to be feasible and economical.*

The following photos are a condensation of the actual steps involved in the project:

A steel roof outer panel is cradled in exact orthogonal position relative to the surface plate and the base rails. The cradled supports are bonded to the roof and to the surface plate. Styling clay is built-up to sections taken from the advance design engineering drawing. The development is modified to design preference and engineering requirements. (Photograph: W. A. Stanley)

This picture shows the design development of the roof inner panel in an advance stage during a study of different sun visors and alternative roof trim schemes. (Photograph: W. A. Stanley)

Sun visor swing and movements are checked. (Photograph: W. A. Stanley)

The 3-D master development is completed and ready for constructing the master negative. (Photograph: W. A. Stanley)

A PVA separator film is applied to the clay surface. The film surface is waxed and then covered with an epoxy surface coat. Several layers of fiberglass cloth and epoxy resin are built-up. (Photograph: W. A. Stanley)

A base structure is built up from reinforced aluminum honeycomb cut to fit the surface of the fiberglass lamination. The top edges of the honeycomb cross members are cut on a horizontal reference line. They are assembled in an egg crate pattern and reinforced with fiberglass cloth and epoxy resin. (Photograph: W. A. Stanley)

Square fiberglass tubing, sub-frame members, are laminated to the egg crate base. A "tooling dock" made of parallels and angles is used to position the aluminum base pads as they are bonded to the sub-frame. The tooling dock assures that the base pads are located and potted exactly parallel to, and square with the surface plate and the base rails. (Photograph: W. A. Stanley)

The roof inner panel master negative is removed from the clay model and inverted to true car position. Kirksite tools are processed from this master negative and several steel roof inner panels are stamped. The master model and the master negative meet all engineering and manufacturing requirements. Two of these panels are bonded and welded to roof outer panels and assembled into prototype vehicles for evaluation and testing. (Photograph: W. A. Stanley)

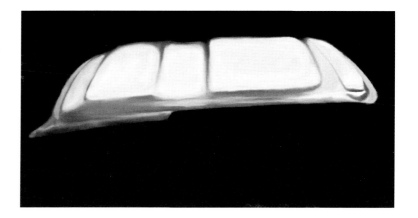

2. *Precision Styling Clay Model Replication*

A parallel exercise was conducted to study three methods for producing cubed master die models: the Ford Numerical Control method, the Visioneering Optical Construction method, and the 3-D Engineering and Master Modeling method.

Cubed master die models are models of adjacent parts brought together on a leveled precision base to display and demonstrate a complete assembly of parts for continuity of surfaces.

All three methods started from either data or negative molds taken from a final feasibility model (final design model including all engineering requirements). The 3-D Master Modeling Method had by far the fewest labor hours, the fewest span time hours, and the least cost.

With 3-D Engineering and Master Modeling, final data is obtained from the cubed master die model. Opposite hand masters are either copy milled or milled from data. Some of the important steps for producing cubed plastic master die models from released clay models are shown in the photographs that follow.

This example of precision replication showed the following benefits:

. *The plastic male model was well within .004" of original clay surface.*

. *Excellent quality of all styled character lines, highlights, and surfaces was evident.*

. *The fender master model was completed in five days with a total of 140 man-hours and weighed 78 lbs. Material costs were minimal.*

. *Plastic model surfaces can be carved, machined, and reworked if changes are required.*

. *Master models developed by this system may also be used for prototype tooling, design aids and other advance tooling aids.*

Pre-fabricated base structures are built from aluminum honeycomb materials, assembled on a surface plate in an egg crate pattern, bonded together, and reinforced. Side and end pads are positioned square to the bottom base pads and each pad is bonded to its sub-frame member.
The hood and side base structures are pre-assembled on the surface plate in their correct relative position to each other.
(Photograph: Ford Design Center)

When the styling clay model is finished, a parting agent is sprayed on to the clay surface and it is waxed. An epoxy surface coat is applied next. The surface is then built-up with several layers of fiberglass cloth and epoxy resin. The pre-fabricated hood base assembly is positioned above the fiberglass hood laminate and located in proper reference to the surface plate and square to the styling bridge. The hood base is bonded to the fiberglass laminate and reinforced.
(Photograph: Ford Design Center)

Next, the side base structure is accurately positioned and aligned to the hood structure and assembled with dowel pins and bolts. It is bonded to the fiberglass laminate and reinforced with fiberglass cloth and epoxy resin.
(Photograph: Ford Design Center)

The two completed master model negatives are ready to be disassembled and separated from the clay model. (Photograph: Ford Design Center)

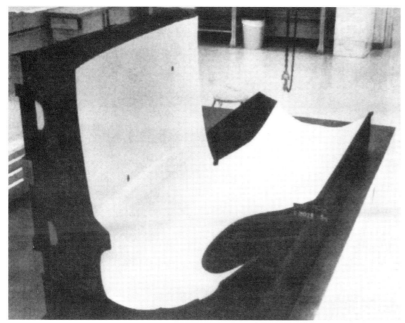

The plastic female masters are reassembled, bolted and doweled, and are ready for processing a male master model of the front fender. Notice that this assembly is set up on a surface plate in a correct orthogonal position on its own base pads. (Photograph: Ford Design Center)

The front fender surfaces are "blocked off" with clay in the female master model to provide edge definition of the fender. A parting agent is applied to the clay and the surface is waxed. A carveable epoxy surface coat is applied and reinforced with one half inch open cell aluminum honeycomb sandwiched between several layers of cross-biased fiberglass and epoxy resin. This results in a one inch thick, stable, and strong shell. (Photograph: W. A. Stanley)

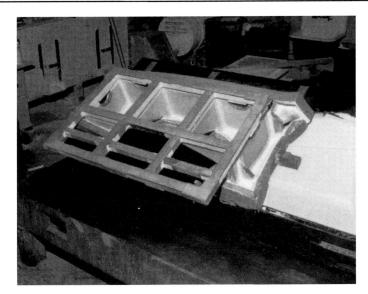

After the fender cast has cured, a prefabricated base structure, made from reinforced aluminum honey comb and square fiberglass tubing, is potted in place and reinforced with fiberglass cloth and epoxy resin. In this situation, oversize aluminum base pads have been bonded onto the base structure and these are machined in all three axes. (Photograph: W. A. Stanley)

This composite male master model was processed from the feasibility styling clay model. It was cubed with impreg hood and door models made by Visioneering, Inc. The highlights and surface continuity were true and flawless. This method for producing master die models has been proven feasible. Total development time took 140 labor hours, 5 days time, and minimal material costs. The model weighed only 78 pounds. (Photograph: W. A. Stanley)

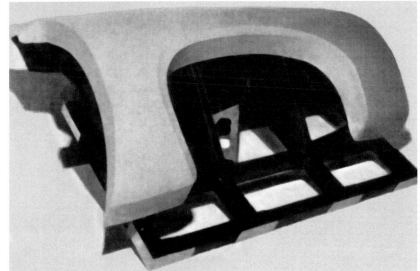

A master model for the 1974 Ford Mustang II fender was the result of this 3-D Master Modeling study. (Photograph: Public Relations, Ford Motor Company)

3. Motorhome Hood and Front Panel

While other work was progressing, the hood for this motor home was developed through 3-D Engineering and Master Modeling.

The motorhome front panel and hood surface was first completed in styling clay and approved. Hood sections were developed on a surface layout drawing and hinges were engineered to swing the hood through its proper arc. Precision templates were made from Lexan and the hood opening was laid out on the clay surface. Hood flanges were dragged into the model by working from the completed clay surface and a horizontal work surface. Steel tape (feeler gauge stock) was laid onto the clay surface for dragging. The completed hood model was sealed and primed and an FRP female control master model was constructed.

Next, the proper depth for the flange on the front panel around the hood was dragged into the clay surface. Tapered strips of wood were used to represent the hood opening and these were mounted flush to the clay hood flange. Clay was then built-up to the other side of the wood strips and the surface was refinished. The edge of the hood clay model, from which the mold had been made, was then cut away to the length of the flange on the front panel under the hood edge. This was shown on the surface layout drawing. Removing the wood strips exposed the proper front panel flange and hood opening in perfect alignment with the hood. This flange surface was then cleaned-up for sealing and priming prior to mold construction of the motor home front panel.

Since the hood and front panel surfaces were developed as one surface and the opening was developed from the hood flange, perfect alignment resulted.

The apron behind the bumper and in front of the radiator was also processed through 3-D Engineering and Master Modeling, to provide a removable part for passage when removing the engine.

In this close up, notice the horizontal work surface, the shiny steel tapes, and the Lexan template being dragged against these surfaces. (Photograph: T. A. Hoadley)

The Rockwood motorhome hood is developed through the "Three Dimensional Engineering and Master Modeling System".
The cap and hood surfaces are first completed and approved. Hood sections are developed on surface drawings and hinges are designed to swing the hood through its proper arc.
Precision templates are made from Lexan. The hood flange is dragged into the surface of the model, by the author. The template rides over steel tape (feeler gauge stock) bonded to the clay surface and a horizontal work surface supported by wedge shaped clay columns. Just one side of the hood is developed at a time. (Photograph: T. A. Hoadley)

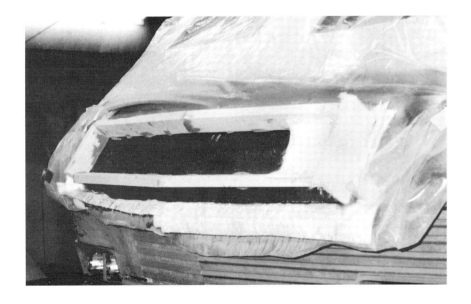

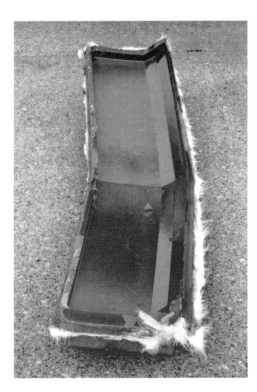

The completed hood and hood flange is sealed, painted, and sprayed with PVA. A fiberglass master negative is constructed. (Photograph: T. A. Hoadley)

The master negative of the hood, including the hood flange, is shown immediately after it is released from the model and before the surface has been touched. The PVA, which can be seen peeling here and there, will be washed off the surface with water. (Photograph: T. A. Hoadley)

After the master negative of the hood is pulled, the proper depth for the flange on the surrounding cap surface is dragged in around the edge of the hood. (Photograph: T. A. Hoadley)

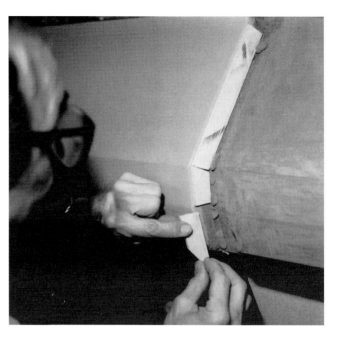

Tapered strips of wood are used to represent the hood opening and these are mounted next to the hood flange. The hood opening will be the two sides of the wood strips. (Photograph: T. A. Hoadley)

A tapered clay extrusion is used for the corner. (Photograph: T. A. Hoadley)

Clay is then built-up to the outside of the wood strips which is the cap side hood opening. (Photograph: T. A. Hoadley)

The cap surface is then cleaned-up. (Photograph: T. A. Hoadley)

The hood side of the wood strips is cut back to the dimension of the flange under the hood edge. The wood strips are removed leaving the opening in perfect alignment with the hood. The hood opening and flange is cleaned-up with a Lexan drag template.
After final clean-up, the front cap is ready to be sealed and primed prior to construction of a front cap negative. (Photograph: T. A. Hoadley)

Surface continuity between the hood and the surrounding panel is excellent. (Photograph; Rockwood, Inc.)

4. Multi Piece Tractor Roof

The development of this tractor roof utilized 3-D Engineering and Master Modeling. The roof consisted of an outer panel with a flush mounted escape hatch, a hatch headliner, instrument pod, and a multiple piece roof inner frame. The tractor roof was developed from design illustrations and advance structures drawings. Construction of this model was made on a tractor cab frame.

The roof outer surface was developed in styling clay. Lights were installed and the model was completed for a presentation. After changes were made, escape hatch hinge pads were laid out on the clay surface and modeled. Aluminum foil was laid down around the escape hatch area so that a negative master FRP epoxy mold could be made. Paper was also laid down to protect the surface during the time of mold construction. The 3-D Engineering and Master Modeling system was first utilized to develop the escape hatch and then the roof opening flange. Female masters were made for the escape hatch and the roof outer panel with escape hatch opening.

The roof outer panel was then revised for the roof version without the escape hatch. A female master was then constructed from this revised full roof outer panel form. Three different master negatives were fabricated from this same roof outer surface styling clay model.

This precisely replicated full roof outer female master was inverted, leveled, and used to develop the roof inner rails, hatch headliner, and instrument pod in styling clay. Side rails and end rails were dragged in hot clay on straight edge tubes and radius sweeps. Drag templates were made from Lexan from sections developed on the surface draft. Where possible, the inner surface areas were dragged with a template. Surfaces between templates were modeled free hand on one side and then duplicated with section templates to the opposite side.

This tractor roof development was completed and parts were cast from female control masters. These parts were cleaned, painted, assembled, and tested on prototype tractors. The speed, accuracy, low cost, and minimal manpower required to construct these models could not be approached by any other system.

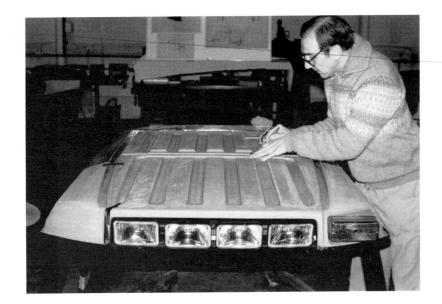

A tractor roof design model is developed for J. I. Case. A tractor cab frame is utilized to construct an armature upon which to build the styling clay model. The model is developed with an escape hatch. Aluminum foil is laid down beyond the escape hatch flange to protect the adjacent area of the model. (Photograph: T. A. Hoadley)

Paper is laid down around the hatch cover to protect the surface of the model. An epoxy fiberglass master negative of the escape hatch outer is constructed. The hatch model includes the hatch flanges and hinge pads. The negative is reinforced and provided with a stand. The perimeter of the hatch is then cut back the amount of the hatch overlap. Next, the roof opening and drain for the opening is modeled and cleaned-up. A master negative tool of the entire roof outer with hatch opening is then constructed, reinforced, and pulled. (Photograph: T. A. Hoadley)

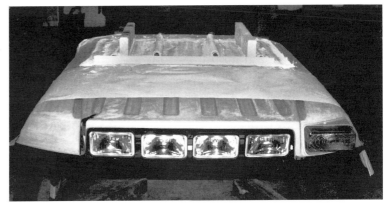

This view shows the roof outer master negative inverted and leveled. Aluminum tubing straight edges are aligned and leveled and bonded in place on each side of the roof inner surface. These aluminum tubes are used for dimensional control of the model. (Photograph: T. A. Hoadley)

The tractor roof inner frames, headliner, and instrument pod are developed as one part. The hatch inner surface and instrument pod cover are separate parts. All are developed inside the roof outer master negative.
Here we see the hatch inner and the headliner inner being dragged in clay as a compound surface by the author and Robert Doehler. (Photograph: T. A. Hoadley)

Side rails are dragged in hot clay on straight edge tubes. The drag template is made from Lexan. To make the template, a copy of the master section was bonded to a sheet of Lexan with spray adhesive. After the template was cut out to the line and cleaned-up, the paper copy was cut back away from the line. Therefore, the actual template outline in clear Lexan is difficult to discern in the photograph. (Photograph: T. A. Hoadley).

The rear roof rail is dragged with a template riding on two straight edge tubes. (Photograph: T. A. Hoadley)

The front rail is dragged as a compound curved surface. The Lexan template is riding against an angled true sweep and on flat surfaces set at the same angle. As the template rides toward the center of the sweep, it cuts deeper into the clay. (Photograph: T. A. Hoadley)

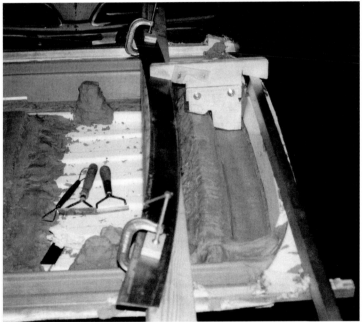

Another view of the front rail set-up showing the compound sweep arrangement. The roof corners are modeled on one side, templated, and duplicated on the opposite side. (Photograph: T. A. Hoadley)

A prototype of the tractor roof proposal is made from an assembly of composite parts cast from the master negatives taken off the model. Parts fit together with zero design tolerance because they are all processed from the same surface of the same model. This is a front three quarter view of the roof from above with the hatch opened. (Photograph: Dennis Otto)

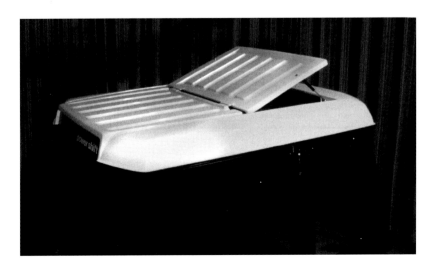

This view is looking up through the rear window at the roof console, the hatch is closed. Composite parts are processed directly from master negatives taken from the styling clay models. (Photograph: Dennis Otto)

Here the view is up through the front window, the hatch is open. (Photograph: Dennis Otto)

The view here is looking up at the roof through an open cab side door. (Photograph: Dennis Otto)

5. Minivan Flush Mounted Side Door

Male master models were cast from molds that were taken off a styling clay design model. These molds had been inverted, accurately reassembled, and reinforced. Each of these male master models had a plywood inner structure that was bonded to the inside of its FRP polyester skin while each mold was in this accurate reassembled position. The structure of each master model was pinned and bolted to its adjoining master model structure. Included were the left-and-right sides with the cab seal and the rear end cap with the door opening. These casts were unbolted and removed from the molds, inverted, reassembled, repinned and rebolted, and set on a preconstructed leveled platform. Through this process a stable master model was constructed. From these three cleaned-up male masters or plugs, production FRP tools were fabricated.

The 3-D Engineering and Master Modeling system was utilized to develop a flush mounted side door version of the minivan. First of all, templates were cut from lines laid out on the master model in the area where the door would be installed. Next, a surface layout drawing was drafted. The door and all parts relating to it were engineered, drawn, and laid out as details of the surface development.

The FRP right side tool was set up 90 degrees from vertical and leveled, and lines from the surface layout drawing were laid out on the tool. The flange for the door was then developed from a clay extrusion and located by the lines laid out on the tool. The clay extrusion die template section came from an engineering drawing.

Frederick (Fritz) Wagner, retired master modeler from Ford Design Center and GM Design, is finishing the front corner of the minivan styling clay model. (Photograph: Dennis Otto)

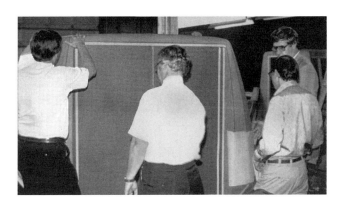

Final development of the flat rear door version of the minivan design model. At the right behind the author is Vernon R. Wamsley, Vice President, Coachmen Industries, Inc., responsible for design and engineering at the time of this development. (Photograph: Dennis Otto)

The minivan design development model is finished and is prepared for the construction of the master negative. The styling clay model was completed in two weeks. (Photograph: Dennis Otto)

The master model of the Duke, is in three sections, two halves and a rear section panel. This first development had a rear mounted flat door. (Photograph: John Dunlap)

The door surface, obtained from the side panel tool surface, and the flange, obtained from the clay build-up, were cast and stabilized. This became the FRP male master model of the door outer.

Second, the side panel flanging or jamb for the door opening was developed in styling clay with template sections derived from the engineering drawings and laid out on the tool to the same reference lines used for the door. This side panel, with the door opening built-up in styling clay, was cast and stabilized and became the new FRP male master side panel model.

Third, the door inner panel was developed in the door opening of the new male master side panel model. This was built to engineering drawings from clay and plywood. A mold was made from this model, stabilized, and became the female FRP master door inner panel model.

The door and side panel surface was not flat but had a compound curved surface. Constructing these master models successfully by conventional means would have been very time consuming and expensive.

A door assembly fixture was then designed on the surface layout drawing. Simple brackets were engineered and fabricated and tubular steel frames were engineered and preassembled.

The fixture halves were developed utilizing clay extrusion moldings to locate the steel brackets. The brackets were bonded to the tubular steel frames with epoxy and fiberglass. The bracket positioning on the outer half fixture was reconciled by mating with and casting to the door opening of the FRP male side panel master model. The door inner half fixture was cast to the FRP male door inner master model.

Production door FRP inner panels had a tubular steel welded frame assembled and bonded into the panel, producing a stable panel assembly. This stable panel was then placed on the door inner half fixture. A bead of acrylic adhesive was applied around the edge of this inner door panel. The flexible door outer panel was then mounted onto the door inner panel, and the door outer panel half fixture was placed onto the door outer panel. The fixture halves brought the two parts of the door into their proper position.

This resulted in exact door thickness and alignment

This production minivan flat rear door model, 1980, was a Datsun Conversion built by Coachmen Industries, Inc., and sold through Datsun Dealers as the Duke DV 170. It was designed by Dennis Otto under the direction of Vern Wamsley. (Photograph: Dennis Otto)

This illustration is for the Coachmen (Duke) side hinged flush door show model. Designed by Dennis Otto. (Photograph: Author)

of the two parts, and the acrylic adhesive bonded these parts into one assembly.

Wheel house styling clay models were developed in car position on a partial minivan buck that was built-up on a steel table with correct side panel and floor. The right wheel house also enclosed the gasoline filler tube to tank. Casts of the two wheel houses were assembled into one tool for vacuum forming production parts.

The entrance step was also developed in styling clay on this same car position buck and a tool was fabricated for vacuum forming steps for production.

The minivan side mounted door development was completed and went into production. The door fit the compound surface perfectly; the step and wheel house parts met engineering and manufacturing requirements. It was said that this polyester door had a better, tighter fit than many of the steel doors of the truck cabs on which the assembly was mounted.

To develop the flush side door, all parts relating to it were engineered, drawn, and laid out as details of a surface development drawing. A right hand side reinforced negative was set up 90 degrees from vertical and leveled. A door flange was developed in clay to lines laid out in the negative. This door surface and the flange was molded and stabilized. This becomes the positive master of the door outer. (Photograph: John Dunlap)

Second, the side panel flange for the door opening was developed in clay to the same reference lines used for the door. This side panel with door opening is molded and stabilized with a frame and becomes the new positive master side panel. (Photograph: John Dunlap)

Third, the door inner panel was developed in the door opening of the new master side panel. (Photograph: John Dunlap)

The negative surface of the door inner panel is molded and a prewelded tubular frame is bonded to the mold. This becomes the negative master door inner panel. (Photograph: John Dunlap)

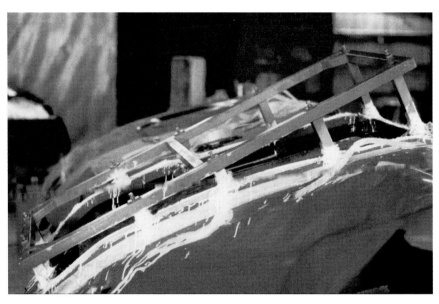

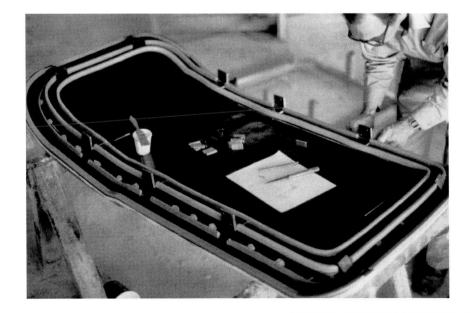

A flush side mounted door assembly fixture is designed on the surface layout drawing by the author. Brackets to accomplish the construction of this fixture are fabricated and epoxyed to the build-up of the fixture. (Photograph: John Dunlap)

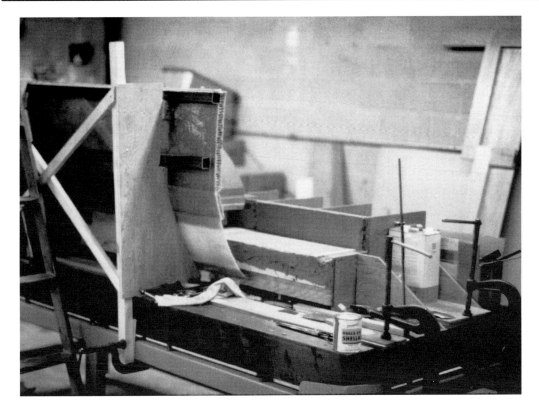

Wheel house models are developed in car position on a surface plate utilizing a production side panel and built-up floor. (Photograph: John Dunlap)

The wheel house model was developed with a flange below the floor. This view shows the floor removed and the model and negative with the floor flange. (Photograph: John Dunlap)

A view of the wheel house model with side panel and floor in proper position. (Photograph: John Dunlap)

The entrance step was also developed in styling clay on the same car position mock-up model. The model was developed to accept a rubber seal. (Photograph: John Dunlap)

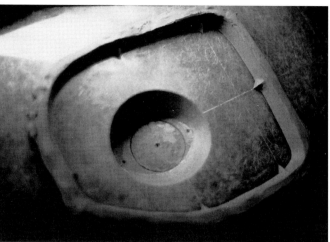

A depression in the right hand side panel was required to accommodate the gas filler. The filler pipe passes through the wheel house opening. A replication of this depression was cut into the positive master of the side panel. Note the reference lines on the model and method for putting them into the cast. (Photograph: John Dunlap)

A view of the finished styling clay model with the rubber seal in place. (Photograph: John Dunlap)

The finished show model of the flush side door Coachmen Duke minivan. (Photograph: Author)

The production Duke side hinged door minivan is completed. The door fits the compound surface perfectly. The development is successful and attractive. (Photograph: Author)

This view shows the door opening flange, door hinges, and inner door finish. (Photograph: Author)

This shows the minivan entrance, the thin door, and the lock mechanism. (Photograph: Author)

This is the vacuum formed entrance step and the gasoline filler to the left. (Photograph: Author)

CHAPTER 16 - Forming Plexiglas ®

Twelve Steps in Forming Acrylic Sheet

Fascias or clear coverings for many items can be made from formed clear or tinted acrylic sheet. In automotive design, clear or tinted acrylic sheet is used to represent safety glass windshields, backlights, and side windows having a compound form. To successfully develop these acrylic sheet forms for design models requires several steps of preparation.

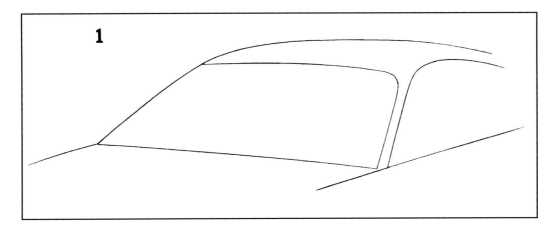

1. The clay surface of the fascia or window is modeled to be the outside or primary surface so that the proper surrounding surface conditions can be developed and evaluated.

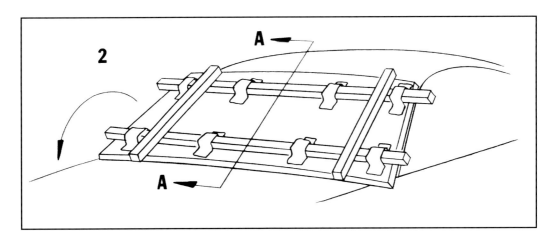

2. When this surface has been finished and approved for forming the acrylic sheet, any molding or frame surrounding the surface should be removed.
A plaster negative of the surface must then be constructed. The negative should be reinforced and a base that lays in one plane should be attached. This is necessary to prevent the surface from warping when the negative is supported by its base. After the plaster negative is removed and has dried, the negative surface and its perimeter edges should be shellacked.

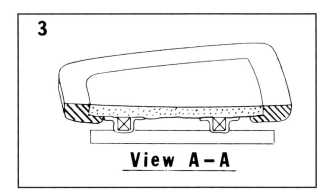

3. The edges around the negative of the surface need to be extended with styling clay to a width of approximately 3 or 4 inches (75 to 100mm). This extended clay surface must be cleaned-up and steeled.

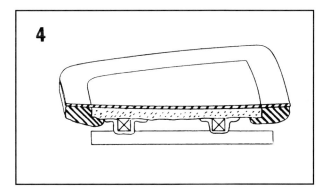

4. The entire surface must then be built-up with clay extrusions the thickness of the acrylic sheet that will be formed. When doing this, outline the actual edge of the plaster surface with the first extruded clay molding. Transpose this plaster edge as a line on the new surface of clay extrusions. This clay extrusion surface needs to be cleaned-up and steeled, but the edge outline of the original surface must be retained.

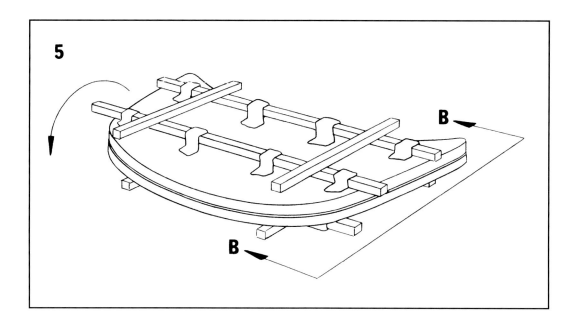

5. Next, construct a high strength gypsum cast of this new surface. The cast should be reinforced. Some materials used for reinforcement such as burlap, sisal or hemp absorb moisture and are unsatisfactory. Depending on the size and contour of the surface, you may use fiberglass mat (preferably fiberglass protected against alkaline products), wire mesh, expanded metal, or steel rods. Attach a base that lays in one plane.
 After the cast has been removed and dried, it should also be shellacked. Make sure the edge outline of the original surface is retained.

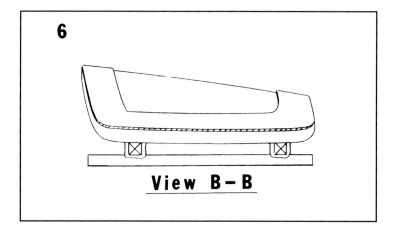

6. This plaster cast represents the inside surface of the acrylic sheet to be formed. It has been extended around its perimeter to support a hold-down ring. This form will be used to drape the heated acrylic sheet, but before doing this, you must construct the hold-down ring.
The actual size of the formed acrylic piece that is needed is known because the outline of the surface is on the positive cast. The holddown ring will therefore lay on the extended surface that was built up beyond the edge of the original surface. However, it must lay on the acrylic sheet outer surface and not the inner surface.
Clay extrusions the thickness of the acrylic sheet must again be laid down but only on the extended surface outside of the line on the positive cast. This ring of extrusion clay surface must be cleaned-up and steeled.

7. When this is completed, other clay extrusions can be used to frame in both edges of the ring surrounding the surface. This forms a circular dam in which to cast the hold-down ring.

The hold-down ring should also be cast in high strength gypsum and be reinforced. If the acrylic piece to be formed is very large, then steel rod can be used for reinforcement. The rod can be formed to fit into the plaster hold-down ring and hoops of steel rod can run from one side to the other. These pieces of steel rod must be welded together and prepared before the plaster ring is cast.

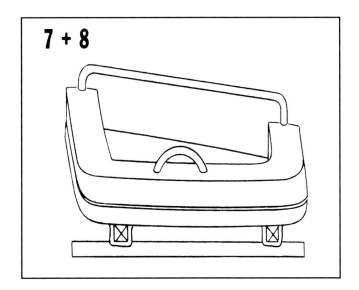

8. Construct the plaster ring and add reinforcing material or the welded rod if it is prepared.

Weight is important to hold-down the heated acrylic sheet so the hold-down plaster ring, depending on size, should be 2 or 3 inches (50 or 75mm) thick.

Add handles of reinforcing material soaked in plaster as the hold-down ring is being constructed. If welded rod is placed into the ring, then the hoops or rod will serve as handles.

When the plaster has set, remove the ring cast and set it aside to dry thoroughly and clean-off the clay form from which it was made.

9. The result is a positive form of the inner surface to be used for drape forming the heated acrylic sheet and a holddown ring of the outer surface to maintain the form of the acrylic sheet as it cools.
The positive cast should now be covered with soft flannel cloth, flannelette, velvet, or billiard felt.
Transpose the positive line on the cast to the top surface of the flannel with a marker.

10. The acrylic sheet to be formed should be cut somewhat oversize and stripped of masking paper. The sheet should be clean, dry, and free from any specks of adhesive or dust. Soft cotton gloves should be worn to avoid fingerprinting or scratching the surface.
The acrylic sheet can now be heated in an appropriate oven prior to draping it over the prepared form. In general, acrylic sheet 0.25 inches (6.35mm) thick should be heated for 25 minutes. Recommended sheet temperatures for forming Plexiglas will vary due to the type of plastic and the thickness of the sheet. Temperatures range from approximately 240°F (115°C) to 340°F (170°C).

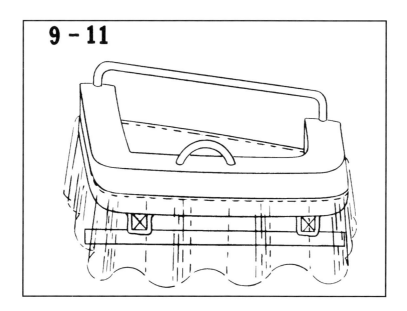

11. When the acrylic sheet has been heated the proper length of time, it must be removed from the oven and draped over the prepared form. The edges of the acrylic sheet should be pulled down and the ring must then be put in place on the draped material. This must be done quickly because of the limited time available for forming. Care in handling this heated acrylic material is necessary because it is like a sheet of rubber.

12. Plexiglas should be cooled slowly and uniformly. During the cooling process, a heavy blanket may be used to cover the material, the form, and the hold-down ring. The various acrylic materials will all be stable below 140°F (60°C). Remove the hold-down ring but before removing the formed acrylic sheet, trace the trim line on the surface from the line that will show through from the flannel covering. Remove the formed acrylic sheet and make a cut outside of the line to allow for shrinkage of 1/16 to 3/32 inch (0.0625 to 0.0938mm) per foot. Do whatever fitting and trimming is necessary.

There are other methods for forming acrylic sheet. The system described is satisfactory for forming one or for a few pieces, but if a series of parts are needed, then a more permanent arrangement should be considered. A hanging device to handle and travel the acrylic sheet into and out of the oven and to the forming fixture could be used. In addition the fixture could be equipped with a clamping ring along with other improvements.

If a scan/mill system is available, the outside surface of the fascia or the window of the design model may be recorded digitally and the inside surface may be obtained through a computer program. The inside surface could be milled either in the negative and a positive cast made from it, or the positive can be milled, cleaned up and replicated. This would eliminate or modify steps 2, 3, and 4.

Information concerning the specifications and suggested uses of Plexiglas acrylic sheet products can be obtained from: Auto Elf Chem Phone: (215) 826-2608.

PART THREE

INFORMATION

CHAPTER 17 - Business Considerations

Administrative Concerns

Let's look at some of the administrative concerns and how these affect a design project. These concerns exist whether the project is only a model, or a design development including a model and engineering from sketches to tools.

A design project usually starts when the client meets with the designer and provides a list of design objectives. These objectives may include design sketches or illustrations, pictures of similar or competitive products, basic package dimensions, and other information. The client may be an individual such as the owner or the representative of a company, or even a committee from a company. While the size of design projects will differ from client to client, the stages in the design development process will remain generally the same.

Work on a design project should not commence until costs have been reviewed, a cost quotation, payment arrangement, and timing have been agreed upon, a contractual agreement has been signed, and an initial payment has been received.

For additional information in administrative and legal matters see: *The Artist's Friendly Legal Guide*, by Floyd Conner, Rodger Gilcrest, Peter Karlen, Jean Perwin and David Spatt, published by North Light Books, Cincinnati, Ohio.

How To Charge For Your Services

Ways in which you may charge for your services might include one or more of the following:

1. Straight project basis
2. Retainer fee
3. Royalty
4. Cost plus
5. Consultation fee

1. Straight project basis requires that a price be set to cover all time and expenses. The cost quotation must be acceptable to a client, yet large enough to assure a profit.

2. A retainer fee could be the most satisfactory for both parties when service is provided on a continuing basis.

A retainer fee is usually paid in advance a month at a time. The fee must be agreed upon and would be paid at an equal amount over a fixed period of time; (i.e. three months, six months, one year). It is advisable to review the retainer fee at the end of each agreed upon period and adjust as required.

Additional cost for expenses over and above those normally part of the retainer fee should be approved by the client and charged on the next billing.

Additional costs for parts, services or labor for which you have negotiated, should have an appropriate percentage added for your time.

3. On a royalty basis, negotiate an arrangement for payment to cover costs with a royalty percentage to provide a profit.

Royalty arrangements are infrequent and are applicable on special projects or specialty items where you will have considerable input in design and development. Be sure to have a carefully prepared contract with an agreement for royalty to be paid throughout the life of the product.

4. Cost plus should be applicable only on certain projects and possibly with clients for whom you have provided service for some time.

Cost plus is ideal on projects where cost estimates, for various reasons, are difficult to determine. Some projects extend over a long period of time and require continuing design development work. In such cases, a reasonable profit should be determined by you and agreed to by your client. Charges will cover actual cost plus profit and are billed monthly.

5. Consultation fees are the most suitable for those times when a manufacturer requires the services of a consultant for artistic or technical reasons. A consultant is chosen for his background experience and reputation.

The fee charged by a consultant may cover work for only a few hours or for a few days. In some cases, a consultant's services are for work on an annual basis. The fee depends on the consultant's ability and how critically a company needs the advice.

Payment Arrangement

In setting up a payment arrangement for work to be charged on the straight project basis, it is advisable to agree to a partial payment arrangement. The client should be billed and a payment should be made following the completion and approval of certain phases or stages of the development. The work may extend over a long period of time and capital will be needed to proceed with the development.

Design development work falls into several logical phases requiring directional approval or final approval by the client. These phases could include (1) preliminary visualizations, (2) development of finished illustrations and models, (3) dimensional drawings, layouts and casts of models, and (4) development of tooling, engineering and prototype models. The initial payment will start the design development process; each succeeding payment will continue the work into the next phase. Final payment is made after the work is finished and final approval is given by the client.

Payment for each phase, or a percentage of the cost of each phase, should be made by the client prior to commencing work on each successive phase. This method of payment protects the designer and the client. The client may decide on a major change in the development or to stop the project altogether. Decisions such as this would limit the liability of the client and the losses for the designer.

Cost Control - Profit

Small changes in an ongoing design project are to be expected. However, the additional cost overrun of a larger change, requested by the client, should be approved prior to making the change.

Cost control is most important to complete a design development project successfully. Without a satisfactory level of profit, you cannot expect to stay in business.

Your position in a design organization may not include the responsibility for contractual agreements. However, an estimate of the hours required by each person on a project should be prorated into the overall cost of a project. The performance of each person in a design organization is therefore very important to the success of every project.

If you are a model maker and operate a modeling shop, the scenario above would apply to your situation even though you may not have full design responsibility. You should explain to your client the steps involved in building a styling clay model and clearly identify the stages or phases of model development. Progress approvals would be needed and payments would be required at the completion of each of these phases.

This outline does not pretend to be a primer on establishing successful business practices. It is simply an attempt to provide some basic principles to follow, especially to anyone just entering this profession.

CHAPTER 18 - Tables and Charts

Millimeters to Decimals

mm	Decimal	mm	Decimal	mm	Decimal	mm	Decimal	mm	Decimal
0.01	.00039	0.41	.01614	0.81	.03189	21	.82677	61	2.40157
0.02	.00079	0.42	.01654	0.82	.03228	22	.86614	62	2.44094
0.03	.00118	0.43	.01693	0.83	.03268	23	.90551	63	2.48031
0.04	.00157	0.44	.01732	0.84	.03307	24	.94488	64	2.51969
0.05	.00197	0.45	.01772	0.85	.03346	25	.98425	65	2.55906
0.06	.00236	0.46	.01811	0.86	.03386	26	1.02362	66	2.59843
0.07	.00276	0.47	.01850	0.87	.03425	27	1.06299	67	2.63780
0.08	.00315	0.48	.01890	0.88	.03465	28	1.10236	68	2.67717
0.09	.00354	0.49	.01929	0.89	.03504	29	1.14173	69	2.71654
0.10	.00394	0.50	.01969	0.90	.03543	30	1.18110	70	2.75591
0.11	.00433	0.51	.02008	0.91	.03583	31	1.22047	71	2.79528
0.12	.00472	0.52	.02047	0.92	.03622	32	1.25984	72	2.83465
0.13	.00512	0.53	.02087	0.93	.03661	33	1.29921	73	2.87402
0.14	.00551	0.54	.02126	0.94	.03701	34	1.33858	74	2.91339
0.15	.00591	0.55	.02165	0.95	.03740	35	1.37795	75	2.95276
0.16	.00630	0.56	.02205	0.96	.03780	36	1.41732	76	2.99213
0.17	.00669	0.57	.02244	0.97	.03819	37	1.45669	77	3.03150
0.18	.00709	0.58	.02283	0.98	.03858	38	1.49606	78	3.07087
0.19	.00748	0.59	.02323	0.99	.03898	39	1.53543	79	3.11024
0.20	.00787	0.60	.02362	1.00	.03937	40	1.57480	80	3.14961
0.21	.00827	0.61	.02402	1	.03937	41	1.61417	81	3.18898
0.22	.00866	0.62	.02441	2	.07874	42	1.65354	82	3.22835
0.23	.00906	0.63	.02480	3	.11811	43	1.69291	83	3.26772
0.24	.00945	0.64	.02520	4	.15748	44	1.73228	84	3.30709
0.25	.00984	0.65	.02559	5	.19685	45	1.77165	85	3.34646
0.26	.01024	0.66	.02598	6	.23622	46	1.81102	86	3.38583
0.27	.01063	0.67	.02638	7	.27559	47	1.85039	87	3.42520
0.28	.01102	0.68	.02677	8	.31496	48	1.88976	88	3.46457
0.29	.01142	0.69	.02717	9	.35433	49	1.92913	89	3.50394
0.30	.01181	0.70	.02756	10	.39370	50	1.96850	90	3.54331
0.31	.01220	0.71	.02795	11	.43307	51	2.00787	91	3.58268
0.32	.01260	0.72	.02835	12	.47244	52	2.04724	92	3.62205
0.33	.01299	0.73	.02874	13	.51181	53	2.08661	93	3.66142
0.34	.01339	0.74	.02913	14	.55118	54	2.12598	94	3.70079
0.35	.01378	0.75	.02953	15	.59055	55	2.16535	95	3.74016
0.36	.01417	0.76	.02992	16	.62992	56	2.20472	96	3.77953
0.37	.01457	0.77	.03032	17	.66929	57	2.24409	97	3.81890
0.38	.01496	0.78	.03071	18	.70866	58	2.28346	98	3.85827
0.39	.01535	0.79	.03110	19	.74803	59	2.32283	99	3.89764
0.40	.01575	0.80	.03150	20	.78740	60	2.36220	100	3.93701

Decimals to Millimeters

Decimal	mm	Decimal	mm
0.001	0.0254	0.500	12.7000
0.002	0.0508	0.510	12.9540
0.003	0.0762	0.520	13.2080
0.004	0.1016	0.530	13.4620
0.005	0.1270	0.540	13.7160
0.006	0.1524	0.550	13.9700
0.007	0.1778	0.560	14.2240
0.008	0.2032	0.570	14.4780
0.009	0.2286	0.580	14.7320
		0.590	14.9860
0.010	0.2540		
0.020	0.5080		
0.030	0.7620		
0.040	1.0160	0.600	15.2400
0.050	1.2700	0.610	15.4940
0.060	1.5240	0.620	15.7480
0.070	1.7780	0.630	16.0020
0.080	2.0320	0.640	16.2560
0.090	2.2860	0.650	16.5100
		0.660	16.7640
0.100	2.5400	0.670	17.0180
0.110	2.7940	0.680	17.2720
0.120	3.0480	0.690	17.5260
0.130	3.3020		
0.140	3.5560		
0.150	3.8100		
0.160	4.0640	0.700	17.7800
0.170	4.3180	0.710	18.0340
0.180	4.5720	0.720	18.2880
0.190	4.8260	0.730	18.5420
		0.740	18.7960
0.200	5.0800	0.750	19.0500
0.210	5.3340	0.760	19.3040
0.220	5.5880	0.770	19.5580
0.230	5.8420	0.780	19.8120
0.240	6.0960	0.790	20.0660
0.250	6.3500		
0.260	6.6040		
0.270	6.8580	0.800	20.3200
0.280	7.1120	0.810	20.5740
0.290	7.3660	0.820	20.8280
		0.830	21.0820
0.300	7.6200	0.840	21.3360
0.310	7.8740	0.850	21.5900
0.320	8.1280	0.860	21.8440
0.330	8.3820	0.870	22.0980
0.340	8.6360	0.880	22.3520
0.350	8.8900	0.890	22.6060
0.360	9.1440		
0.370	9.3980		
0.380	9.6520		
0.390	9.9060	0.900	22.8600
0.400	10.1600	0.910	23.1140
0.410	10.4140	0.920	23.3680
0.420	10.6680	0.930	23.6220
0.430	10.9220	0.940	23.8760
0.440	11.1760	0.950	24.1300
0.450	11.4300	0.960	24.3840
0.460	11.6840	0.970	24.6380
0.470	11.9380	0.980	24.8920
0.480	12.1920	0.990	25.1460
0.490	12.4460	1.000	25.4000

Fractions to Decimals to Millimeters

Fraction	Decimal	mm	Fraction	Decimal	mm
1/64	0.0156	0.3969	33/64	0.5156	13.0969
1/32	0.0312	0.7938	17/32	0.5312	13.4938
3/64	0.0469	1.1906	35/64	0.5469	13.8906
1/16	0.0625	1.5875	9/16	0.5625	14.2875
5/64	0.0781	1.9844	37/64	0.5781	14.6844
3/32	0.0938	2.3812	19/32	0.5938	15.0812
7/64	0.1094	2.7781	39/64	0.6094	15.4781
1/8	0.1250	3.1750	5/8	0.6250	15.8750
9/64	0.1406	3.5719	41/64	0.6406	16.2719
5/32	0.1562	3.9688	21/32	0.6562	16.6688
11/64	0.1719	4.3656	43/64	0.6719	17.0656
3/16	0.1875	4.7625	11/16	0.6875	17.4625
13/64	0.2031	5.1594	45/64	0.7031	17.8594
7/32	0.2188	5.5562	23/32	0.7188	18.2562
15/64	0.2344	5.9531	47/64	0.7344	18.6531
1/4	0.2500	6.3500	3/4	0.7500	19.0500
17/64	0.2656	6.7469	49/64	0.7656	19.4469
9/32	0.2812	7.1438	25/32	0.7812	19.8438
19/64	0.2969	7.5406	51/64	0.7969	20.2406
5/16	0.3125	7.9375	13/16	0.8125	20.6375
21/64	0.3281	8.3344	53/64	0.8281	21.0344
11/32	0.3438	8.7312	27/32	0.8438	21.4312
23/64	0.3594	9.1281	55/64	0.8594	21.8281
3/8	0.3750	9.5250	7/8	0.8750	22.2250
25/64	0.3906	9.9219	57/64	0.8906	22.6219
13/32	0.4062	10.3188	29/32	0.9062	23.0188
27/64	0.4219	10.7156	59/64	0.9219	23.4156
7/16	0.4375	11.1125	15/16	0.9375	23.8125
29/64	0.4531	11.5094	61/64	0.9531	24.2094
15/32	0.4688	11.9062	31/32	0.9688	24.6062
31/64	0.4844	12.3031	63/64	0.9844	25.0031
1/2	0.5000	12.7000	1	1.0000	25.4000

English Sweep Chart 1-50

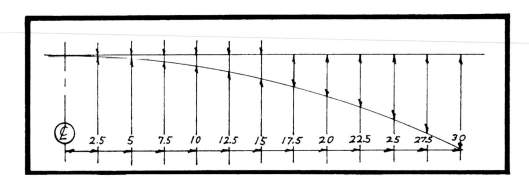

| Sweep Number | One half Chord Lengths, in | | | | | | | | | | | | Radius |
	2.5	5.0	7.5	10.0	12.5	15.0	17.5	20.0	22.5	25.0	27.5	30.0	
1	0.001	0.003	0.008	0.014	0.022	0.031	0.043	0.056	0.070	0.087	0.105	0.125	3600.063
2	0.002	0.007	0.016	0.028	0.043	0.062	0.085	0.111	0.141	0.174	0.210	0.250	1800.125
3	0.003	0.010	0.023	0.042	0.065	0.094	0.128	0.167	0.211	0.260	0.315	0.375	1200.188
4	0.003	0.014	0.031	0.056	0.087	0.125	0.170	0.222	0.281	0.347	0.420	0.500	900.250
5	0.004	0.017	0.039	0.069	0.108	0.156	0.213	0.278	0.351	0.434	0.525	0.625	720.313
6	0.005	0.021	0.047	0.083	0.130	0.187	0.255	0.333	0.422	0.521	0.630	0.750	600.375
7	0.006	0.024	0.055	0.097	0.152	0.219	0.298	0.389	0.492	0.607	0.735	0.875	514.723
8	0.007	0.028	0.062	0.111	0.173	0.250	0.340	0.444	0.562	0.694	0.840	1.000	450.500
9	0.008	0.031	0.070	0.125	0.195	0.281	0.382	0.500	0.632	0.781	0.945	1.125	400.563
10	0.009	0.035	0.078	0.139	0.217	0.312	0.425	0.555	0.703	0.868	1.050	1.250	360.625
11	0.010	0.038	0.086	0.152	0.238	0.343	0.467	0.610	0.773	0.954	1.155	1.375	327.960
12	0.010	0.042	0.094	0.166	0.260	0.374	0.510	0.666	0.843	1.041	1.260	1.500	300.750
13	0.011	0.045	0.101	0.180	0.281	0.405	0.552	0.721	0.913	1.127	1.365	1.625	277.736
14	0.012	0.048	0.109	0.194	0.303	0.436	0.594	0.776	0.983	1.214	1.470	1.750	258.018
15	0.013	0.052	0.117	0.208	0.324	0.467	0.636	0.832	1.053	1.301	1.575	1.875	240.938
16	0.014	0.055	0.124	0.221	0.346	0.498	0.679	0.887	1.123	1.387	1.679	2.000	226.000
17	0.015	0.059	0.132	0.235	0.367	0.529	0.721	0.942	1.193	1.473	1.784	2.125	212.827
18	0.016	0.062	0.140	0.249	0.389	0.560	0.763	0.997	1.263	1.560	1.889	2.250	201.125
19	0.016	0.066	0.148	0.262	0.410	0.591	0.805	1.052	1.332	1.646	1.994	2.375	190.661
20	0.017	0.069	0.155	0.276	0.432	0.622	0.847	1.107	1.402	1.732	2.098	2.500	181.250
21	0.018	0.072	0.163	0.290	0.453	0.652	0.889	1.162	1.472	1.819	2.203	2.625	172.741
22	0.019	0.076	0.171	0.303	0.474	0.683	0.931	1.217	1.541	1.905	2.308	2.750	165.011
23	0.020	0.079	0.178	0.317	0.495	0.714	0.972	1.271	1.611	1.991	2.412	2.875	157.959
24	0.021	0.083	0.186	0.330	0.517	0.744	1.014	1.326	1.680	2.077	2.517	3.000	151.500
25	0.021	0.086	0.193	0.344	0.538	0.775	1.056	1.381	1.749	2.163	2.621	3.125	145.563
26	0.022	0.089	0.201	0.357	0.559	0.805	1.097	1.435	1.819	2.249	2.726	3.250	140.087
27	0.023	0.093	0.208	0.371	0.580	0.836	1.139	1.489	1.888	2.335	2.830	3.375	135.021
28	0.024	0.096	0.216	0.384	0.601	0.866	1.180	1.544	1.957	2.420	2.935	3.500	130.321
29	0.025	0.099	0.224	0.398	0.622	0.896	1.222	1.598	2.026	2.506	3.039	3.625	125.950
30	0.026	0.103	0.231	0.411	0.643	0.927	1.263	1.652	2.095	2.592	3.143	3.750	121.875
31	0.026	0.106	0.238	0.424	0.664	0.957	1.304	1.706	2.164	2.677	3.247	3.875	118.067
32	0.027	0.109	0.246	0.438	0.684	0.987	1.345	1.760	2.232	2.763	3.351	4.000	114.500
33	0.028	0.113	0.253	0.451	0.705	1.017	1.386	1.814	2.301	2.848	3.456	4.125	111.153
34	0.029	0.116	0.261	0.464	0.726	1.047	1.427	1.868	2.370	2.933	3.560	4.250	108.007
35	0.030	0.119	0.268	0.477	0.746	1.076	1.468	1.922	2.438	3.018	3.664	4.375	105.045
36	0.031	0.122	0.275	0.490	0.767	1.106	1.509	1.975	2.506	3.103	3.767	4.500	102.250
37	0.031	0.126	0.283	0.503	0.787	1.136	1.549	2.028	2.574	3.188	3.871	4.625	99.610
38	0.032	0.129	0.290	0.516	0.808	1.165	1.590	2.082	2.642	3.273	3.975	4.750	97.112
39	0.033	0.132	0.297	0.529	0.828	1.195	1.630	2.135	2.710	3.358	4.079	4.875	94.745
40	0.034	0.135	0.305	0.542	0.848	1.224	1.670	2.188	2.778	3.442	4.182	5.000	92.500
41	0.035	0.138	0.312	0.555	0.869	1.254	1.711	2.241	2.846	3.527	4.286	5.125	90.367
42	0.035	0.142	0.319	0.568	0.889	1.283	1.751	2.294	2.913	3.611	4.389	5.250	88.339
43	0.036	0.145	0.326	0.581	0.909	1.312	1.791	2.346	2.981	3.696	4.493	5.375	86.408
44	0.037	0.148	0.333	0.593	0.929	1.341	1.830	2.399	3.048	3.780	4.596	5.500	84.568
45	0.038	0.151	0.340	0.606	0.949	1.370	1.870	2.451	3.115	3.864	4.699	5.625	82.813
46	0.039	0.154	0.347	0.619	0.969	1.399	1.910	2.504	3.182	3.948	4.803	5.750	81.136
47	0.039	0.157	0.354	0.631	0.988	1.427	1.949	2.556	3.249	4.031	4.906	5.875	79.533
48	0.040	0.160	0.361	0.644	1.008	1.456	1.988	2.608	3.316	4.115	5.009	6.000	78.000
49	0.041	0.164	0.368	0.656	1.028	1.484	2.028	2.659	3.382	4.198	5.111	6.125	76.532
50	0.042	0.167	0.375	0.669	1.047	1.513	2.067	2.711	3.449	4.282	5.214	6.250	75.125

English Sweep Chart 51-100

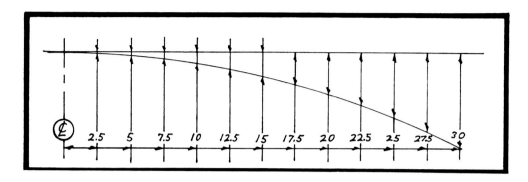

Sweep Number	One half Chord Lengths, in												Radius
	2.5	5.0	7.5	10.0	12.5	15.0	17.5	20.0	22.5	25.0	27.5	30.0	
51	0.042	0.170	0.382	0.681	1.067	1.541	2.106	2.763	3.515	4.365	5.317	6.375	73.776
52	0.043	0.173	0.389	0.693	1.086	1.569	2.144	2.814	3.581	4.448	5.420	6.500	72.481
53	0.044	0.176	0.396	0.705	1.105	1.597	2.183	2.865	3.647	4.531	5.522	6.625	71.237
54	0.045	0.179	0.403	0.718	1.124	1.625	2.221	2.916	3.712	4.614	5.624	6.750	70.042
55	0.045	0.182	0.409	0.730	1.144	1.653	2.260	2.967	3.778	4.696	5.727	6.875	68.892
56	0.046	0.185	0.416	0.742	1.162	1.680	2.298	3.018	3.843	4.779	5.829	7.000	67.786
57	0.047	0.188	0.423	0.754	1.181	1.708	2.336	3.068	3.908	4.861	5.931	7.125	66.720
58	0.048	0.191	0.430	0.766	1.200	1.735	2.374	3.118	3.973	4.943	6.033	7.250	65.694
59	0.048	0.193	0.436	0.777	1.219	1.763	2.411	3.169	4.038	5.025	6.135	7.375	64.704
60	0.049	0.196	0.443	0.789	1.238	1.790	2.449	3.218	4.103	5.106	6.236	7.500	63.750
61	0.050	0.199	0.449	0.801	1.256	1.817	2.486	3.268	4.167	5.188	6.338	7.625	62.829
62	0.050	0.202	0.456	0.813	1.274	1.844	2.524	3.318	4.231	5.269	6.439	7.750	61.940
63	0.051	0.205	0.462	0.824	1.293	1.870	2.561	3.367	4.295	5.351	6.541	7.875	61.080
64	0.052	0.208	0.469	0.836	1.311	1.897	2.597	3.416	4.359	5.432	6.642	8.000	60.250
65	0.053	0.211	0.475	0.847	1.329	1.924	2.634	3.465	4.422	5.512	6.743	8.125	59.447
66	0.053	0.213	0.481	0.858	1.347	1.950	2.671	3.514	4.486	5.593	6.844	8.250	58.670
67	0.054	0.216	0.488	0.870	1.365	1.976	2.707	3.563	4.549	5.673	6.945	8.375	57.919
68	0.055	0.219	0.494	0.881	1.383	2.002	2.743	3.611	4.612	5.754	7.046	8.500	57.191
69	0.055	0.222	0.500	0.892	1.400	2.028	2.779	3.659	4.675	5.834	7.146	8.625	56.486
70	0.056	0.224	0.506	0.903	1.418	2.054	2.815	3.707	4.737	5.913	7.247	8.750	55.804
71	0.057	0.227	0.512	0.914	1.435	2.079	2.851	3.755	4.799	5.993	7.347	8.875	55.142
72	0.057	0.230	0.519	0.925	1.453	2.105	2.886	3.802	4.861	6.072	7.447	9.000	54.500
73	0.058	0.233	0.525	0.936	1.470	2.130	2.921	3.850	4.923	6.151	7.547	9.125	53.878
74	0.059	0.235	0.531	0.947	1.487	2.155	2.956	3.897	4.985	6.230	7.647	9.250	53.274
75	0.059	0.238	0.537	0.958	1.504	2.180	2.991	3.944	5.046	6.309	7.746	9.375	52.688
76	0.060	0.240	0.542	0.968	1.521	2.205	3.026	3.990	5.107	6.387	7.846	9.500	52.118
77	0.061	0.243	0.548	0.979	1.538	2.230	3.060	4.037	5.168	6.466	7.945	9.625	51.566
78	0.061	0.246	0.554	0.989	1.555	2.254	3.095	4.083	5.228	6.544	8.044	9.750	51.029
79	0.062	0.248	0.560	1.000	1.571	2.279	3.129	4.129	5.289	6.621	8.143	9.875	50.507
80	0.063	0.251	0.566	1.010	1.588	2.303	3.163	4.174	5.349	6.699	8.242	10.000	50.000
81	0.063	0.253	0.571	1.020	1.604	2.327	3.196	4.220	5.408	6.776	8.340	10.125	49.507
82	0.064	0.256	0.577	1.031	1.620	2.351	3.230	4.265	5.468	6.853	8.439	10.250	49.027
83	0.064	0.258	0.583	1.041	1.636	2.375	3.263	4.310	5.527	6.930	8.537	10.375	48.561
84	0.065	0.261	0.588	1.051	1.652	2.398	3.296	4.354	5.586	7.006	8.635	10.500	48.107
85	0.066	0.263	0.594	1.061	1.668	2.422	3.329	4.399	5.645	7.082	8.733	10.625	47.665
86	0.066	0.265	0.599	1.071	1.684	2.445	3.361	4.443	5.703	7.158	8.831	10.750	47.235
87	0.067	0.268	0.605	1.080	1.700	2.468	3.394	4.487	5.761	7.234	8.928	10.875	46.817
88	0.067	0.270	0.610	1.090	1.715	2.491	3.426	4.531	5.819	7.309	9.025	11.000	46.409
89	0.068	0.272	0.615	1.100	1.730	2.514	3.458	4.574	5.877	7.384	9.122	11.125	46.012
90	0.069	0.275	0.621	1.109	1.746	2.536	3.490	4.617	5.934	7.459	9.219	11.250	45.625
91	0.069	0.277	0.626	1.119	1.761	2.559	3.521	4.660	5.991	7.534	9.316	11.375	45.248
92	0.070	0.279	0.631	1.128	1.776	2.581	3.552	4.703	6.047	7.608	9.412	11.500	44.880
93	0.070	0.282	0.636	1.138	1.791	2.603	3.584	4.745	6.104	7.682	9.508	11.625	44.522
94	0.071	0.284	0.641	1.147	1.806	2.625	3.614	4.787	6.160	7.755	9.604	11.750	44.173
95	0.071	0.286	0.646	1.156	1.820	2.646	3.645	4.829	6.216	7.829	9.700	11.875	43.832
96	0.072	0.288	0.651	1.165	1.835	2.668	3.675	4.870	6.271	7.902	9.795	12.000	43.500
97	0.072	0.290	0.656	1.174	1.849	2.689	3.706	4.912	6.326	7.974	9.891	12.125	43.176
98	0.073	0.293	0.661	1.183	1.863	2.711	3.735	4.953	6.381	8.047	9.986	12.250	42.860
99	0.074	0.295	0.666	1.192	1.877	2.732	3.765	4.993	6.435	8.119	10.080	12.375	42.551
100	0.074	0.297	0.671	1.200	1.891	2.752	3.795	5.034	6.490	8.190	10.175	12.500	42.250

Metric Sweep Chart 1-50

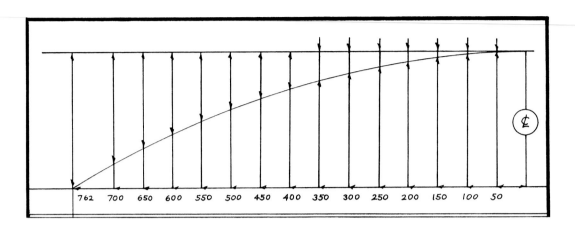

Sweep Number	Radius	One half Chord Lengths, mm 762	700	650	600	550	500	450	400	350	300	250	200	150	100	50
1	91441.59	3.18	2.68	2.31	1.97	1.65	1.37	1.11	0.87	0.67	0.49	0.34	0.22	0.12	0.05	0.01
2	45723.18	6.35	5.36	4.62	3.94	3.31	2.73	2.21	1.75	1.34	0.98	0.68	0.44	0.25	0.11	0.03
3	30484.76	9.53	8.04	6.93	5.91	4.96	4.10	3.32	2.62	2.01	1.48	1.03	0.66	0.37	0.16	0.04
4	22866.35	12.70	10.72	9.24	7.87	6.62	5.47	4.43	3.50	2.68	1.97	1.37	0.87	0.49	0.22	0.05
5	18295.94	15.88	13.40	11.55	9.84	8.27	6.83	5.53	4.37	3.35	2.46	1.71	1.09	0.61	0.27	0.07
6	15249.53	19.05	16.07	13.86	11.81	9.92	8.20	6.64	5.25	4.02	2.95	2.05	1.31	0.74	0.33	0.08
7	13073.97	22.23	18.75	16.17	13.78	11.57	9.56	7.75	6.12	4.69	3.44	2.39	1.53	0.86	0.38	0.10
8	11442.70	25.40	21.43	18.48	15.74	13.23	10.93	8.85	6.99	5.35	3.93	2.73	1.75	0.98	0.44	0.11
9	10174.29	28.57	24.11	20.78	17.71	14.88	12.29	9.96	7.87	6.02	4.42	3.07	1.97	1.11	0.49	0.12
10	9159.88	31.75	26.79	23.09	19.67	16.53	13.66	11.06	8.74	6.69	4.91	3.41	2.18	1.23	0.55	0.14
11	8330.19	34.93	29.46	25.40	21.64	18.18	15.02	12.16	9.61	7.36	5.40	3.75	2.40	1.35	0.60	0.15
12	7639.05	38.10	32.14	27.70	23.60	19.83	16.38	13.27	10.48	8.02	5.89	4.09	2.62	1.47	0.65	0.16
13	7054.48	41.28	34.82	30.01	25.56	21.47	17.74	14.37	11.35	8.69	6.38	4.43	2.84	1.59	0.71	0.18
14	6553.65	44.45	37.49	32.31	27.52	23.12	19.10	15.47	12.22	9.35	6.87	4.77	3.05	1.72	0.76	0.19
15	6119.81	47.63	40.17	34.62	29.48	24.76	20.46	16.57	13.09	10.02	7.36	5.11	3.27	1.84	0.82	0.20
16	5740.40	50.80	42.84	36.92	31.44	26.41	21.82	17.67	13.95	10.68	7.84	5.45	3.49	1.96	0.87	0.22
17	5405.81	53.98	45.51	39.22	33.40	28.05	23.17	18.76	14.82	11.34	8.33	5.78	3.70	2.08	0.93	0.23
18	5108.58	57.15	48.19	41.52	35.36	29.69	24.53	19.86	15.68	12.00	8.82	6.12	3.92	2.20	0.98	0.24
19	4842.79	60.32	50.86	43.82	37.31	31.33	25.88	20.95	16.55	12.66	9.30	6.46	4.13	2.32	1.03	0.26
20	4603.75	63.50	53.53	46.12	39.27	32.97	27.23	22.05	17.41	13.32	9.79	6.79	4.35	2.44	1.09	0.27
21	4387.62	66.68	56.20	48.41	41.22	34.61	28.58	23.14	18.27	13.98	10.27	7.13	4.56	2.56	1.14	0.28
22	4191.29	69.85	58.87	50.71	43.17	36.24	29.93	24.23	19.13	14.64	10.75	7.46	4.77	2.68	1.19	0.30
23	4012.16	73.03	61.54	53.00	45.12	37.88	31.28	25.32	19.99	15.30	11.23	7.80	4.99	2.80	1.25	0.31
24	3848.10	76.20	64.20	55.29	47.06	39.51	32.62	26.40	20.85	15.95	11.71	8.13	5.20	2.92	1.30	0.32
25	3697.29	79.38	66.87	57.58	49.01	41.14	33.96	27.49	21.70	16.60	12.19	8.46	5.41	3.04	1.35	0.34
26	3558.20	82.55	69.53	59.87	50.95	42.76	35.31	28.57	22.55	17.26	12.67	8.79	5.63	3.16	1.41	0.35
27	3429.53	85.72	72.20	62.16	52.89	44.39	36.64	29.65	23.41	17.91	13.15	9.12	5.84	3.28	1.46	0.36
28	3310.16	88.90	74.86	64.45	54.83	46.01	37.98	30.73	24.26	18.56	13.62	9.45	6.05	3.40	1.51	0.38
29	3199.14	92.07	77.52	66.73	56.77	47.63	39.31	31.81	25.11	19.20	14.10	9.78	6.26	3.52	1.56	0.39
30	3095.63	95.25	80.18	69.01	58.70	49.25	40.65	32.88	25.95	19.85	14.57	10.11	6.47	3.64	1.62	0.40
31	2998.89	98.43	82.84	71.29	60.64	50.87	41.98	33.95	26.80	20.49	15.04	10.44	6.68	3.75	1.67	0.42
32	2908.30	101.60	85.50	73.57	62.56	52.48	43.30	35.03	27.64	21.14	15.51	10.77	6.89	3.87	1.72	0.43
33	2823.30	104.78	88.15	75.84	64.49	54.09	44.63	36.09	28.48	21.78	15.98	11.09	7.09	3.99	1.77	0.44
34	2743.39	107.95	90.81	78.12	66.42	55.70	45.95	37.16	29.32	22.42	16.45	11.41	7.30	4.10	1.82	0.46
35	2668.13	111.13	93.46	80.39	68.34	57.30	47.27	38.22	30.15	23.06	16.92	11.74	7.51	4.22	1.87	0.47
36	2597.15	114.30	96.11	82.65	70.26	58.90	48.58	39.28	30.99	23.69	17.38	12.06	7.71	4.34	1.93	0.48
37	2530.00	117.47	98.76	84.92	72.17	60.50	49.90	40.34	31.82	24.33	17.85	12.38	7.92	4.45	1.98	0.49
38	2466.64	120.65	101.41	87.18	74.09	62.10	51.21	41.40	32.65	24.96	18.31	12.70	8.12	4.57	2.03	0.51
39	2406.53	123.83	104.06	89.44	76.00	63.69	52.52	42.45	33.48	25.59	18.77	13.02	8.33	4.68	2.08	0.52
40	2349.50	127.00	106.70	91.70	77.90	65.28	53.82	43.50	34.30	26.22	19.23	13.34	8.53	4.79	2.13	0.53
41	2295.33	130.17	109.34	93.96	79.81	66.87	55.12	44.54	35.12	26.84	19.69	13.66	8.73	4.91	2.18	0.54
42	2243.82	133.35	111.98	96.21	81.71	68.45	56.42	45.59	35.94	27.47	20.15	13.97	8.93	5.02	2.23	0.56
43	2194.77	136.53	114.62	98.46	83.61	70.03	57.71	46.63	36.76	28.09	20.60	14.28	9.13	5.13	2.28	0.57
44	2148.03	139.70	117.26	100.71	85.50	71.61	59.00	47.67	37.57	28.71	21.05	14.60	9.33	5.24	2.33	0.58
45	2103.44	142.88	119.89	102.95	87.39	73.18	60.29	48.70	38.38	29.32	21.50	14.91	9.53	5.36	2.38	0.59
46	2060.85	146.05	122.53	105.19	89.28	74.75	61.57	49.73	39.19	29.94	21.95	15.22	9.73	5.47	2.43	0.61
47	2020.14	149.22	125.16	107.43	91.16	76.31	62.85	50.76	40.00	30.55	22.40	15.53	9.92	5.58	2.48	0.62
48	1981.20	152.40	127.78	109.66	93.04	77.87	64.13	51.78	40.80	31.16	22.85	15.84	10.12	5.69	2.53	0.63
49	1943.91	155.58	130.41	111.89	94.91	79.43	65.40	52.80	41.60	31.77	23.29	16.14	10.32	5.80	2.57	0.64
50	1908.18	158.75	133.03	114.12	96.79	80.98	66.67	53.82	42.40	32.37	23.73	16.45	10.51	5.90	2.62	0.66

Metric Sweep Chart 51-100

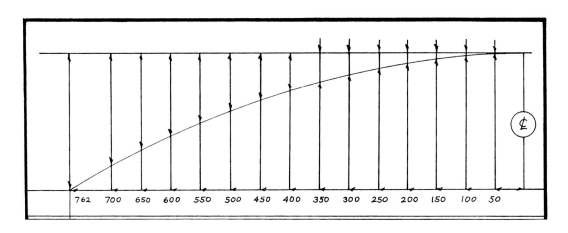

Sweep Number	Radius	One half Chord Lengths, mm														
		762	700	650	600	550	500	450	400	350	300	250	200	150	100	50
51	1873.90	161.93	135.65	116.34	98.65	82.53	67.94	54.83	43.19	32.98	24.17	16.75	10.70	6.01	2.67	0.67
52	1841.01	165.10	138.27	118.56	100.52	84.08	69.20	55.84	43.98	33.58	24.61	17.05	10.90	6.12	2.72	0.68
53	1809.42	168.27	140.89	120.78	102.38	85.62	70.45	56.85	44.77	34.17	25.04	17.35	11.09	6.23	2.77	0.69
54	1779.06	171.45	143.50	122.99	104.23	87.15	71.71	57.85	45.55	34.77	25.48	17.65	11.28	6.33	2.81	0.70
55	1749.86	174.63	146.11	125.20	106.08	88.68	72.96	58.85	46.33	35.36	25.91	17.95	11.47	6.44	2.86	0.71
56	1721.76	177.80	148.72	127.41	107.93	90.21	74.20	59.85	47.11	35.95	26.34	18.25	11.66	6.55	2.91	0.73
57	1694.70	180.97	151.32	129.61	109.77	91.73	75.44	60.84	47.88	36.54	26.76	18.54	11.84	6.65	2.95	0.74
58	1668.63	184.15	153.93	131.81	111.61	93.25	76.67	61.82	48.65	37.12	27.19	18.83	12.03	6.76	3.00	0.75
59	1643.49	187.32	156.53	134.00	113.44	94.76	77.90	62.81	49.42	37.70	27.61	19.13	12.21	6.86	3.05	0.76
60	1619.25	190.50	159.12	136.19	115.27	96.27	79.13	63.79	50.18	38.28	28.03	19.42	12.40	6.96	3.09	0.77
61	1595.85	193.67	161.72	138.37	117.09	97.77	80.35	64.76	50.94	38.85	28.45	19.70	12.58	7.07	3.14	0.78
62	1573.26	196.85	164.31	140.55	118.91	99.27	81.57	65.73	51.70	39.43	28.87	19.99	12.76	7.17	3.18	0.79
63	1551.44	200.03	166.89	142.73	120.72	100.76	82.78	66.70	52.45	39.99	29.28	20.28	12.95	7.27	3.23	0.81
64	1530.35	203.20	169.48	144.90	122.53	102.25	83.99	67.66	53.20	40.56	29.69	20.56	13.13	7.37	3.27	0.82
65	1509.96	206.38	172.06	147.07	124.33	103.73	85.19	68.61	53.95	41.12	30.10	20.84	13.30	7.47	3.31	0.83
66	1490.23	209.55	174.64	149.23	126.12	105.21	86.38	69.57	54.69	41.68	30.51	21.12	13.48	7.57	3.36	0.84
67	1471.14	212.72	177.21	151.39	127.92	106.68	87.57	70.51	55.42	42.24	30.91	21.40	13.66	7.67	3.40	0.85
68	1452.66	215.90	179.78	153.54	129.70	108.15	88.76	71.46	56.16	42.79	31.32	21.67	13.83	7.77	3.45	0.86
69	1434.75	219.08	182.35	155.68	131.48	109.61	89.94	72.40	56.89	43.34	31.71	21.95	14.01	7.86	3.49	0.87
70	1417.41	222.25	184.91	157.83	133.26	111.06	91.12	73.33	57.61	43.89	32.11	22.22	14.18	7.96	3.53	0.88
71	1400.60	225.42	187.47	159.96	135.02	112.51	92.29	74.26	58.33	44.44	32.51	22.49	14.35	8.06	3.57	0.89
72	1384.30	228.60	190.03	162.09	136.79	113.95	93.45	75.18	59.05	44.98	32.90	22.76	14.52	8.15	3.62	0.90
73	1368.49	231.78	192.58	164.22	138.54	115.39	94.61	76.10	59.76	45.51	33.29	23.03	14.69	8.25	3.66	0.91
74	1353.15	234.95	195.13	166.34	140.30	116.82	95.77	77.02	60.47	46.05	33.67	23.29	14.86	8.34	3.70	0.92
75	1338.26	238.13	197.67	168.46	142.04	118.24	96.91	77.93	61.18	46.58	34.06	23.56	15.03	8.43	3.74	0.93
76	1323.81	241.30	200.21	170.57	143.78	119.66	98.06	78.83	61.88	47.11	34.44	23.82	15.20	8.53	3.78	0.94
77	1309.77	244.47	202.75	172.67	145.51	121.07	99.19	79.73	62.57	47.63	34.82	24.08	15.36	8.62	3.82	0.95
78	1296.13	247.65	205.28	174.77	147.24	122.48	100.32	80.62	63.27	48.15	35.20	24.34	15.52	8.71	3.86	0.96
79	1282.88	250.82	207.81	176.86	148.96	123.88	101.45	81.51	63.95	48.67	35.57	24.60	15.69	8.80	3.90	0.97
80	1270.00	254.00	210.33	178.95	150.67	125.27	102.57	82.40	64.64	49.18	35.94	24.85	15.85	8.89	3.94	0.98
81	1257.48	257.18	212.85	181.03	152.38	126.66	103.68	83.28	65.32	49.69	36.31	25.10	16.01	8.98	3.98	0.99
82	1245.30	260.35	215.36	183.10	154.08	128.04	104.79	84.15	65.99	50.20	36.68	25.35	16.17	9.07	4.02	1.00
83	1233.45	263.53	217.87	185.17	155.77	129.41	105.89	85.02	66.66	50.70	37.04	25.60	16.32	9.15	4.06	1.01
84	1221.92	266.70	220.38	187.23	157.45	130.78	106.98	85.88	67.33	51.20	37.40	25.85	16.48	9.24	4.10	1.02
85	1210.70	269.88	222.88	189.28	159.13	132.14	108.07	86.74	67.99	51.69	37.76	26.09	16.63	9.33	4.14	1.03
86	1199.78	273.05	225.37	191.33	160.80	133.49	109.15	87.59	68.64	52.19	38.11	26.34	16.79	9.41	4.17	1.04
87	1189.15	276.22	227.86	193.37	162.47	134.84	110.23	88.43	69.29	52.67	38.46	26.58	16.94	9.50	4.21	1.05
88	1178.79	279.40	230.35	195.40	164.12	136.17	111.29	89.27	69.94	53.16	38.81	26.82	17.09	9.58	4.25	1.06
89	1168.70	282.58	232.83	197.43	165.77	137.51	112.36	90.11	70.58	53.64	39.16	27.05	17.24	9.67	4.29	1.07
90	1158.88	285.75	235.30	199.45	167.42	138.83	113.41	90.94	71.22	54.12	39.50	27.29	17.39	9.75	4.32	1.08
91	1149.30	288.93	237.77	201.47	169.05	140.15	114.46	91.76	71.85	54.59	39.85	27.52	17.54	9.83	4.36	1.09
92	1139.96	292.10	240.23	203.47	170.68	141.46	115.50	92.58	72.48	55.06	40.18	27.75	17.68	9.91	4.39	1.10
93	1130.86	295.28	242.69	205.47	172.30	142.76	116.54	93.39	73.11	55.53	40.52	27.98	17.83	9.99	4.43	1.11
94	1121.99	298.45	245.14	207.46	173.91	144.05	117.57	94.20	73.72	55.99	40.85	28.21	17.97	10.07	4.47	1.11
95	1113.34	301.63	247.59	209.45	175.51	145.34	118.59	95.00	74.34	56.45	41.18	28.43	18.11	10.15	4.50	1.12
96	1104.90	304.80	250.03	211.42	177.10	146.62	119.61	95.79	74.95	56.90	41.51	28.65	18.25	10.23	4.53	1.13
97	1096.67	307.98	252.46	213.39	178.69	147.89	120.61	96.58	75.55	57.35	41.83	28.88	18.39	10.31	4.57	1.14
98	1088.64	311.15	254.89	215.35	180.27	149.15	121.62	97.36	76.15	57.80	42.15	29.09	18.53	10.38	4.60	1.15
99	1080.80	314.33	257.31	217.30	181.84	150.41	122.61	98.14	76.74	58.24	42.47	29.31	18.67	10.46	4.64	1.16
100	1073.15	317.50	259.73	219.25	183.40	151.66	123.60	98.91	77.33	58.68	42.79	29.53	18.80	10.53	4.67	1.17

Metric/English Unit Equivalents

Multiply:	by:	to get:	Multiply:	by:	to get:

LINEAR

inches	X 25.4	= millimetres (mm)	X 0.03937	= inches	
feet	X 0.3048	= metres (m)	X 3.281	= feet	
yards	X 0.9144	= metres (m)	X 1.0936	= yards	
miles	X 1.6093	= kilometres (km)	X 0.6214	= miles	
inches	X 2.54	= centimetres (cm)	X 0.3937	= inches	
microinches	X 0.0254	= micrometres (μm)	X 39.37	= microinches	

AREA

inches^2	X 645.16	= millimetres^2 (mm^2)	X 0.00155	= inches^2	
inches^2	X 6.452	= centimetres^2 (cm^2)	X 0.155	= inches^2	
feet^2	X 0.0929	= metres^2 (m^2)	X 10.764	= feet^2	
yards^2	X 0.8361	= metres^2 (m^2)	X 1.196	= yards^2	
acres	X 0.4047	= hectares (10^{4}m^2)			
		(ha)	X 2.471	= acres	
miles^2	X 2.590	= kilometres^2 (km^2)	X 0.3861	= miles^2	

VOLUME

inches^3	X 16387	= millimetres^3 (mm^3)	X 0.000061	= inches^3	
inches^3	X 16.387	= centimetres^3 (cm^3)	X 0.06102	= inches^3	
inches^3	X 0.01639	= litres (l)	X 61.024	= inches^3	
quarts	X 0.94635	= litres (l)	X 1.0567	= quarts	
gallons	X 3.7854	= litres (l)	X 0.2642	= gallons	
feet^3	X 28.317	= litres (l)	X 0.03531	= feet^3	
feet^3	X 0.02832	= metres^3 (m^3)	X 35.315	= feet^3	
fluid oz	X 29.57	= millilitres (ml)	X 0.03381	= fluid oz	
yards^3	X 0.7646	= metres^3 (m^3)	X 1.3080	= yards^3	
teaspoons	X 4.929	= millilitres (ml)	X 0.2029	= teaspoons	
cups	X 0.2366	= litres (l)	X 4.227	= cups	

MASS

ounces (av)	X 28.35	= grams (g)	X 0.03527	= ounces (av)	
pounds (av)	X 0.4536	= kilograms (kg)	X 2.2046	= pounds (av)	
tons (2000 lb)	X 907.18	= kilograms (kg)	X 0.001102	= tons (2000 lb)	
tons (2000 lb)	X 0.90718	= tonne (t)	X 1.1023	= tons (2000 lb)	

FORCE

ounces — f (av)	X 0.278	= newtons (N)	X 3.597	= ounces — f (av)	
pounds — f (av)	X 4.448	= newtons (N)	X 0.2248	= pounds — f (av)	
kilograms — f	X 9.807	= newtons (N)	X 0.10197	= kilograms — f	

TEMPERATURE

$$°\text{Celsius} = 0.556 \, (°F - 32) \qquad °F = (1.8°C) + 32$$

Metric/English Unit Equivalents

Multiply:	by:	to get:	Multiply:	by:	to get:

ACCELERATION

| feet/sec^2 | X 0.3048 | = metres/sec^2 (m/s^2) | X 3.281 | = feet/sec^2 |
| inches/sec^2 | X 0.0254 | = metres/sec^2 (m/s^2) | X 39.37 | = inches/sec^2 |

ENERGY OR WORK (watts X seconds = joules)

foot–pounds	X 1.3558	= joules (J)	X 0.7376	= foot–pounds
calories	X 4.187	= joules (J)	X 0.2388	= calories
Btu	X 1055	= joules (J)	X 0.000948	= Btu
watt–hours	X 3600	= joules (J)	X 0.0002778	= watt–hours
kilowatt — hrs	X 3.600	= megajoules (MJ)	X 0.2778	= kilowatt — hrs

FUEL ECONOMY

miles/gal	X 0.42514	= kilometres/litre (km/l)	X 2.3522	= miles/gal
gal/mile	X 2.3522	= litres/kilometre (l/km)	X 0.42514	= gal/mile
gal/mile	X 235.22	= litres/100 kilometres (l/100 km)	X 0.004251	= gal/mile

LIGHT

| footcandles | X 10.76 | = lumens/metre^2 (lm/m^2) | X 0.0929 | = footcandles |

PRESSURE OR STRESS (newton/sq metre = pascal)

inches Hg	X 3.368	= kilopascals (kPa)	X 0.2953	= inches Hg
pounds/sq in	X 6.895	= kilopascals (kPa)	X 0.145	= pounds/sq in
inches H$_2$O	X 0.2491	= kilopascals (kPa)	X 4.014	= inches H$_2$O
bars	X 0.1	= megapascals (MPa)	X 10.0	= bars
pounds/sq ft	X 47.88	= pascals (Pa)	X 0.02088	= pounds/sq ft

POWER

| horsepower | X 0.746 | = kilowatts (kW) | X 1.34 | = horsepower |
| ft–lbf/min | X 0.0226 | = watts (W) | X 44.25 | = ft–lbf/min |

TORQUE

| pound–inches | X 0.11298 | = newton–metres (N·m) | X 8.851 | = pound–inches |
| pound–feet | X 1.3558 | = newton–metres (N·m) | X 0.7376 | = pound–feet |

VELOCITY

miles/hour	X 1.6093	= kilometres/hour (km/h)	X 0.6214	= miles/hour
feet/sec	X 0.3048	= metres /sec (m/s)	X 3.281	= feet/sec
kilometres/hr	X 0.27778	= metres/sec (m/s)	X 3.600	= kilometres/hr
miles/hour	X 0.4470	= metres/sec (m/s)	X 2.237	= miles/hour

COMMON METRIC PREFIXES

mega	(M) = 1 000 000	or 10^6	centi	(c) = 0.01	or 10^{-2}
kilo	(k) = 1 000	or 10^3	milli	(m) = 0.001	or 10^{-3}
hecto	(h) = 100	or 10^2	micro	(μ) = 0.000 001	or 10^{-6}

CHAPTER 19 - Modeling Tools

Tool Information and Specifications

Plaster and Ceramic Tools

Tools used in plaster model making and ceramic work are sometimes valuable in design modeling. Sources for fine steel tools, chisels of various sizes and shapes, mold knives, small scrapers,etc. can be found under *Clay Modeling Tools - Other* listed under *Resource Directory*.

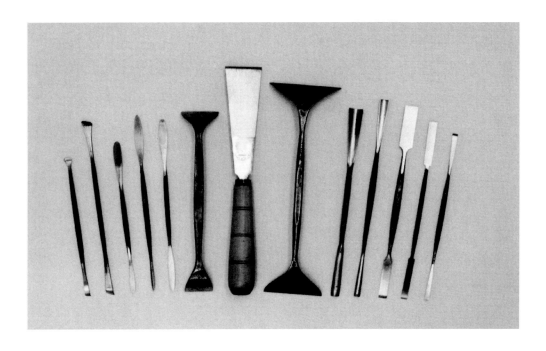

Plaster and ceramic steel tools are also useful in styling clay detail modeling.

Plastic Tools and Slicks

Plastic tools are used on styling clay models having fine detail work. They are also used to form aluminum foil. Plastic slicks are used to smooth or slick styling clay after it has been steeled and to smooth aluminum foil and squeegee Dinoc. These tools must have a very smooth finish. All scratches must be polished out and tools for this purpose should be protected when they are not being used.

Plastic tools can be made from Plexiglass or Lucite or other similar materials. Each one is made for a specific use such as folding in aluminum foil or stretching foil into depressed areas. The shape and smoothness of the tool finish is very important.

Plastic slicks may be made from any flexible thin plastic sheet. You will need slicks of various sizes and shapes. There are times when a small strip of 0.005" to 0.010" plastic is very useful in smoothing out a corner. However, most slicks have a thickness ranging from 0.050" to 0.100". The thickness usually depends on the flexibility and size of the slick.

You will need to make most plastic tools yourself although some standard slicks are available; see *Clay Modeling Tools* under *Resource Directory*.

Plastic Tools and Slicks (Cont.)

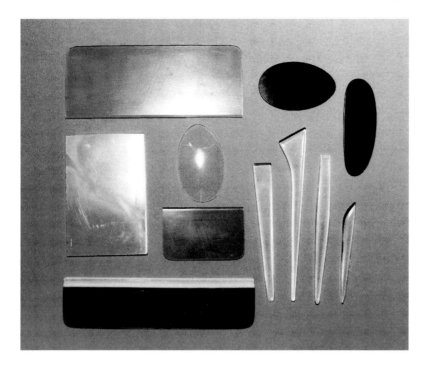

Plastic tools and slicks are used to apply aluminum foil to styling clay models and models cast in plaster or plastic. Plastic slicks are also used to smooth clay surface when checking highlights, and to apply sheets of Dinoc to a surface.

Styling Clay Knives

Knives for use on styling clay models should have a comfortable handle and a good balance. Knives of various sizes and shapes will be useful for specific purposes. Teeth should be filed into knife blades for better control on the clay surface. It may be necessary to make your own knives to the forms you prefer, although some knives are available where plaster and ceramic steel tools are sold.

Styling Clay Scrapers

Perhaps the most valuable tool in design modeling is the styling clay scraper. It is an essential tool for forming and shaping surface when roughing in a model. The texture developed by a tooth scraper is also very helpful in reading a quickly roughed in surface.

The weight and length of the scraper blade, the section of the blade, and the angle of the cutting edges are the most important details concerning scraper design. A scraper with a hefty blade and the proper angle of the cutting edge can be a joy to use. A light weight scraper with a poor angle on the cutting edge makes for a lot of hard work.

The dimensions of the scrapers that follow are quite important but you may wish to adjust dimensions or add other size scrapers. The size of scrapers in this chart should be adequate for most styling clay work.

Styling Clay Scraper Specifications

Blade Length	Blade Width	Blade Thickness
1.5"	0.375"	0.10"
2.3"	0.5"	0.125"
3.6"	0.75"	0.20"
4.2"	1.0"	0.25"

These tools have been especially developed for fast roughing in and cleaning up the styling clay surface. Scrapers having similar length of blades but narrower and thinner section of blades are best suited for clean up and surface finishing. Scrapers having very thin blades are used for fine detail work.

A source for clay scrapers may be found under *Clay Modeling Tools* listed under *Resource Directory*.

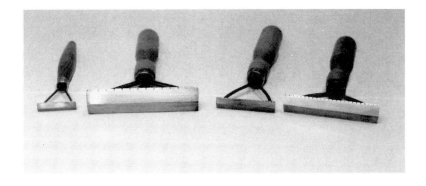

Clay scrapers are the principle tools used in roughing in a clay model's surface. A tooth scraper develops a pleasing texture which allows the surface to be easily read. Also, a tooth scraper cuts more easily into the clay surface. However, the tools shown here have teeth on only one edge of each blade since there are times when it is desirable to have a plain edge scraper.

Styling Clay Steels

Steels for use in design modeling come in many sizes and shapes. They are cut from a variety of thicknesses of blue spring steel. Steels of standard size and shape may be used on most surfaces, however, special shaped steels may be required for some situations. If a number of steels are to be made the same size or shape, they can be stacked and milled or ground. Individual steels can be cut with shears but care must be taken to keep the steel from deforming from the force of the shears.

A smooth mill file is used to sharpen steels. To aid in sharpening straight edged steels, an appropriate fixture can be made to hold a 12 inch mill file with a separate fixture to hold and align the steel.

Styling Clay Steel Specifications

Material: Spring Steel

Dimensional tolerances of the following steel sizes are not critical:

Length	Width	Thickness
2-3/4"	1-3/8"	0.003"
2-7/8"	1-3/16"	0.006"
12"	1-1/2"	0.012"
4-3/8"	1-1/2"	0.015"
8-3/4"	1-1/2"	0.020"
11"	3"	0.030"
18"	3"	0.060"

Smaller shaped steels are made from 0.006" spring steel stock. Larger shaped steels are made from 0.012", 0.015", and 0.020" spring steel.

It is necessary to find a metal supply house, metal shop, or hardware store that has spring steel or that can order the material that is needed. Some standard steels are available, see *Clay Modeling Tools* under *Resource Directory*.

Steel scrapers are used for final clean up of clay surface. They are cut from blue spring steel of various thicknesses. They may have a straight edge or they may be formed to any shape the design modeler desires. The steels shown here are those I have found most useful.

Surform Blade Tools

There are several Surform blade tools that can be used as planes to speedily form styling clay. These tools have several advantages: they take a very smooth cut, the handles or frames that hold the blades are open so that clay is easily removed from the tool, and there are many shapes to choose from. Since Surform blade tools are mass produced, they are not expensive and they can be purchased from most hardware stores.

Surform blades are excellent tools for forming styling clay. They are used as clay planes in roughing in ideas, trimming edges, cutting in valleys, and forming catwalks. They may be purchased at hardware stores and come in a variety of shapes and sizes. Frames or holders are available to attach and hold the blades.

True Sweeps (Radius Sweeps)

Anodized aluminum sweeps are available in six lengths: 20", 24", 30", 36", 48", and 60"; two thicknesses: 1/8" and 3/16"; and two styles: STANDARD - two numbers on each sweep, and PARALLEL - one number on each sweep (both sides with the same sweep number).

Sweeps are available in: #1/4, 1/2, 3/4, 1, 1-1/2, 2, 2-1/2, 3, 3-1/2, 4, 4-1/2, 5, 5-1/2, 6, 6-1/2, 7, 7-1/2, 8, 9, 10, etc. up to #50 in all lengths. From #50 to #100 sweeps are available in even numbers only. Because of the greatness of the arc, #52 to #78 are only available in lengths up to 48". Also, because of a greater arc, sweeps #80 through #100 are only available in lengths up to 36".

In addition, these sweeps are available in 1/8" green plexiglas.

All sweeps and all curves, including sets of curves, and all drafting instruments and furniture may be purchased from Du-All Instrument Service, see *Drafting Supplies* listed under *Resource Directory*.

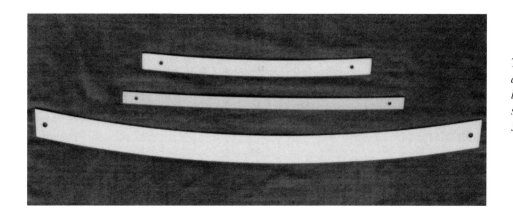

True Sweeps are available in six lengths. Shown are sweeps that are 24", 30", and 60".

Wire Tools

Wire tools are available in many sizes and shapes but seldom will you need more than a few of these standard tools. Many wire tools are made for soft sculpturing clay but they bend and deform when used on hard styling clay. Wire tools for design models should have a stiff larger gauge wire that will not deform, flex, or spring back when a cut is taken in styling clay.

The list of wire tools that follows represents a standard set of these tools, however many more sizes could be added:

Wire Tool Specifications

Material: Piano Wire

Blade Size	Wire Diameter	Type
1/2"	3/32"	Straight
1/2"	3/32"	Round
3/4"	3/32"	Straight
3/4"	3/32"	Round
1-1/4"	1/8"	Gouge

A source for wire tools may be found under Clay Modeling Tools *listed under Resource Directory*.

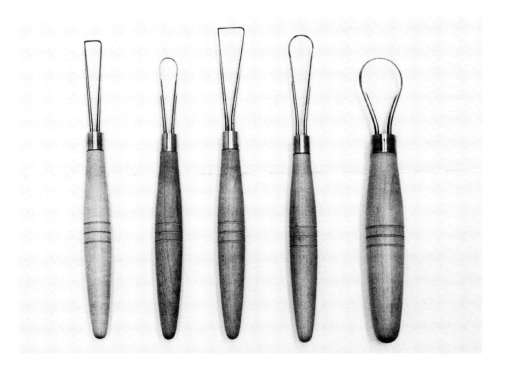

Notice that the straight bladed wire tools have a sharp corner on one side of the blade and a small radius on the other side. These alternate type corners are very useful when trimming the inside edge of a model. (Photograph: T. A. Hoadley)

Wood Battens (and Metal Splines)

Battens or wood splines are usually made from clear, straight grain, well seasoned maple. While a slight curve is acceptable in a batten, it should not have an ogee or long S-shaped curve. The edge of a batten should be finished with a sharp right angle cut made with a jointer. Battens can be resharpened by taking a very fine cut off the edge with a jointer.

Laminates of maple-mahogany-maple are used especially on larger battens. The maple should be used on the outside edges and the alternating mahogany/maple inside of the edges. The width of each laminate should be approximately 3/8 of an inch.

Dimensional tolerances of the batten sizes that follows are not critical:

Wood Batten Specifications

Length	Width	Thickness	Material
15"	1"	1/8"	Maple
16"	1-1/4"	5/32"	Maple
18"	1-1/4"	3/16"	Maple
29"	1-7/8"	5/32"	Maple-Mahogany
39"	2"	1/4"	Maple-Mahogany
48"	3-3/8"	3/8"	Maple-Mahogany

Wood battens may be procured from certain model and pattern shops and some wood furniture and cabinet shops. You may decide to make them yourself, however, no matter who makes them, not every batten that is cut in a batch will be satisfactory because of variations in woodgrain.

Wood battens, sometimes referred to as splines, are usually made from well seasoned maple. Heavier battens are made from laminated maple and mahogany. Long wood splines, 6 to 12 feet long, are milled from straight grained wood. They have a ½ to 1 inch square section and are used to check large surface areas that have a minor contour. Standard molding section from a lumber supply may also be used for this purpose if they are straight.

Metal Splines

Metal splines are made from hard aluminum, 70-75T9, and are used for the same purpose as wood battens. Since they are made from a material much harder than maple, they will maintain their sharp edge for a much longer time and their use will result in a smoother finish.

Metal Spline Specifications

Material: Aluminum 70-75T9

Length	Width	Thickness
18"	1-3/8"	1/8"
24"	1-7/8"	1/8"
30"	2-3/8"	1/8"

Metal splines may be purchased from Lamerson,U.S.A., see *Modeling Equipment* listed under *Resource Directory.*

Metal splines are used like wood battens to check and clean up roughed in surface by filling low areas and scraping off high areas. Aluminum extrusions in ½ x ½ x 1/8 inch angle and channel sections are available in six and eight foot lengths. These and other extrusion sections work quite well as splines for checking surfaces.

Wood Tools

Small wood tools are very useful in detail modeling. Some wood tools become a part of a design modelers standard set of tools.

Wood tools are sometimes made especially for a specific task, these you have to make yourself. Sculpture House, Inc. has a very large variety of wood tools and American Art Clay Co., Inc. have a few tools. See *Clay Modeling Tools - Other* under *Resource Directory* for addresses. Art and craft stores and artist supply stores may have some wood tools for use in styling clay work.

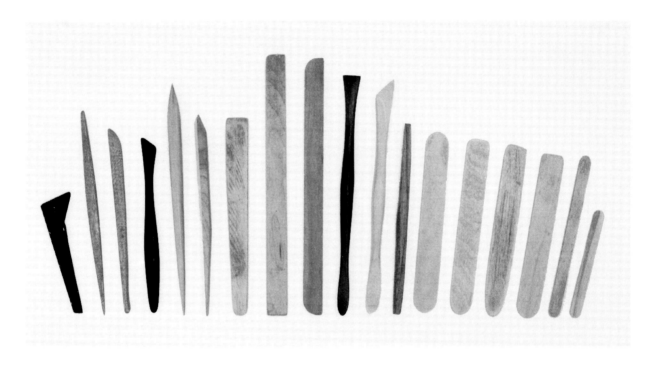

Small wood tools are one of the design modelers most useful tools. They are made from lemon wood, maple, ebony, birch, boxwood, or other tight grained woods. Many of these tools were made on the job or reformed to meet a particular need. Note the especially finished tongue depressors and frozen sucker sticks. My most useful wood tool is number four from the left.

CHAPTER 20 - Resource Directory

Schools and Associations

Schools Teaching Product Design

There are many excellent design schools. Check with your local or preferred school. Clay modeling is taught in the transportation design curriculum at several design colleges.

Art Center College of Design
1700 Lida Street
Pasadena, California 91102

Center for Creative Studies
College of Art and Design
245 East Kirby
Detroit, Michigan 48202

Cleveland Institute of Art
11141 East Boulevard
Cleveland, Ohio 44106

Cranbrook Academy of Art
P. O. Box 801
500 Lone Pine Road
Bloomfield Hills, Michigan 48013

Pratt Institute
200 Willoughby Avenue
Brooklyn, New York 11205

Rhode Island School of Design
Two College Street
Providence, Rhode Island 02903

Milwaukee Institute of Art and Design
273 East Erie Street
Milwaukee, Wisconsin 53202

Schools of Engineering using Styling Clay

Dartmouth College
Thayer School of Engineering
Cummings Building
Hanover, New Hampshire 03755

ITT Technical Institute
630 E. Brier Dr., #150
San Bernardino, California 92408

Purdue University
Mechanical Engineering
1288 ME/Room 42
West Lafayette, Indiana 47907-1288

University of Delaware
104 Spencer Lab
Mechanical Engineering Dept.
Newark, Delaware 19716

Associations Providing Information and Seminars

Association of Professional Model Makers
118 King Street, Suite 540
San Francisco, California 94107

Industrial Designers Society of America
1142 Walker Rd..
Great Falls, Virginia 22066

Composites Fabricators Association
1655 North Fort Myer Drive, Suite 510
Arlington, Virginia 22209-2022

Society of Automotive Engineers, Inc.
400 Commonwealth Drive
Warrendale, Pennsylvania 15096-0001

Supplies and Equipment

Aluminum Foil

Especially processed aluminum foil is used on styling clay models to represent bright metal. Specify 0 or soft temper, one side bright finish, 0.001", 0.0008", or 0.0015" gauge or thickness and 1100 or 1145 aluminum alloy.

A. J. Oster Foils Inc.
2081 McCrea Street
Alliance, Ohio 44601
Phone (800) 321-9750

Artists' Materials and Supplies

There are many artists' supply stores that furnish the supplies needed for design development. These materials include: black photographic tape and other tapes; all types of pens, pencils, markers, paints, and brushes; all types of papers, pads, poster-board, and copy papers; many drafting supplies and design studio furniture. Listed below are companies in the Detroit area that sell to individuals and have commercial accounts. They deliver in the Metropolitan Detroit area and ship via UPS or Allied to other locations. Dick Blick and DMI have stores in other cities.

Dick Blick
14339 Michigan Avenue
Dearborn, Michigan 48126
Phone (800) 447-8192

Northwest Blue Print & Supply Company
13450 Farmington Road
Livonia, Michigan 48150
Phone (734) 525-1990

DMI
43215 Grand River
Novi, Michigna 48375
Phone (248) 374-9300

Clay Extrusion Machines

There are two companies that market clay extrusion machines. Lamerson, U.S.A. manufacture a machine of their own design. Russ Simpson Co. sells a machine manufactured to their specifications.

Lamerson, U.S.A.
21844 Wyoming Place
Oak Park, Michigan 48237
Phone (248) 548-0676

Russ Simpson Co.
21906 Schoenherr Road
Warren, Michigan 48089
Phone (810) 771-2768

Clay Modeling Tools

Tools made specifically for styling clay sculpturing use are marketed by:

Chavant, Inc.
42 West Street
Red Bank, New Jersey 07701
Phone (800) Chavant
Fax (732) 842-3621

Clay Modeling Tools - Other

Some tools used by sculptors in plaster and ceramic clay work may be available in artists' supply stores. A full line of sculpturing tools are available from Sculpture House, Inc.

American Art Clay Co., Inc.
4717 W. Sixteenth St.
Indianapolis, Indiana 46222
Phone (800) 374-1600

Sculpture House, Inc.
National Arts Complex
100 Campmeeting Avenue
Skillman, New Jersey 08558
Phone (609) 466-2986

Clay Ovens

Especially constructed large drawer type ovens that require a 220V AC electrical outlet are manufactured by:

MOCO Thermal Industries
One Oven Place
Romulus, Michigan 48174
Phone (734) 728-6800

Hot food servers sold by restaurant supply companies are also used as styling clay ovens. These units are sometimes called bun warmers or food warmers and may be found at restaurant supply houses. The ovens are available in sizes from one to four drawer and 120V AC. They have a stainless steel finish and can be furnished with legs and casters.

These units may be purchased from:

These units are manufactured and marketed by:

Goldstar Products
21680 Coolidge
Oak Park, MI 48237
(248) 548-9840

Star Manufacturing International, Inc.
10 Sunnen Drive
P.O. Box 430129
St. Louis, MO 63143

Wittco Foodservice Equipment, Inc.
7737 N 81st Street
Milwaukee, WI. 53223
(800) 367-8413

Clay Ovens (Cont.)

Electric convection ovens made for kitchen use can heat small amounts of styling clay. It is important to use ovens that have a temperature control indicating 110° F to 160°F.

Some styling clays need only to be heated to 110°+F while other clays require heating to higher temperatures, some as high as 155°F. Each type of styling clay has a critical working temperature range. Above that temperature, styling clay will begin to break down and become ruined. Therefore, temperature control is essential.

Microwave ovens for heating food will not heat styling clays. However, industrial thermal electronic ovens are used to heat large quantities of styling clay. This type of oven can heat 30 pounds of hard styling clay in 90 seconds in repeated cycles.

Also available is the Bulldog machine. This is a mixer type oven sometimes used in heating American Art Clay.

Bulldog Factory Service, Inc.
425 S. Campbell
Detroit, Michigan 48209
Phone (313) 842-5060

Plans for constructing your own styling clay oven are available for two size ovens. The smaller unit has six warming shelves. The larger unit is a walk-in oven with a large capacity for heating styling clay. Either oven may be heated with an appropriate space heater engineered to maintaining a temperature up to 160°F.

Plans for constructing your own oven can be obtained from:

TAH Productions
P. O. Box 2583
Dearborn, Michigan 48123
www.TAHProductions.Com

Computer Software Systems

Several companies supply computer aided modeling systems for rapid development of 3-D free formed mathematical modeling. These include the companies listed below:

Alias|wavefront - Headquarters
110 Richmond Street East
Toronto, Ontario
Canada, M5C 1P1
Phone (416) 362-9181

Paraform, Inc.
795 San Antonio Road
Palo Alto, CA 94303
Phone (650) 846 -2100

Control Data Systems, Inc.
4201 Lexington Avenue North
Arden Hills, Minnesota 55126
FAX (612) 482-4876

Steinbichler Optical Technologies U.S. A.
40000 Grand River Ave.
Suite 101
Novi, MI. 48375

Coordinate Measuring Machines

Several companies supply machines to scan styling clay models. Some of these machines also mill points, lines, and surface into clay models. Listed below are two companies that market machines having these capabilities:

Digital Electronic Automation
Brown & Sharp Manufacturing Co.
51170 Grand River Avenue
Wixom, Michigan 48393-3327
Phone (248) 449-9400

Tarus Products
38100 Commerce
Sterling Heights, Michigan 48312
Phone (810) 977-1400

Dinoc Material

Dinoc is available in rolls from the 3-M Company or it can be purchased by the foot from Russ Simpson Co.

The product is : Series 9 Model Maker Film 9-7521-1, Grey 75346710959

3-M Center
Attention: Shirley Cherry
Bldg. 223-1 South-02
St. Paul, MN 55144
Phone (651) 733-1867
Fax (651) 736-5313

Russ Simpson Co.
21906 Schoenherr Road
Warren, Michigan 48089
Phone (810) 771-2768

Drafting Supplies

One of the drafting supply specialists for the automobile industry is Du-All Instrument Service Company. Special tools available for design development include: true sweeps or radius sweeps, ship curves, railroad curves, and all other curves; beam compasses; rules, scales, and gauges; straight edges; papers and vellums; furniture, and many other supplies.

Du-All Instrument Service
31431 John R
Madison Heights, Michigan 48071
Phone (248) 583-9158
Fax (248)583-4714

Modeling Equipment

There are two companies that have supplied most of the special equipment for dimensional control of automotive design models. These companies are Lamerson, U.S.A. and Norton Equipment Corporation. Listed with their addresses is the equipment for which they are noted. Both companies also build equipment on special order, and supply industry world wide.

An additional company, Item Products, Inc., supplies an unique modular "industrial erector set" of precision aluminum profiles. These are used to construct typical interior buck fixtures and other frame work for display purposes. However, they will not provide the stability nor accuracy required for precision modeling.

Item Products, Inc.
6703 Theall Road
Houston, Texas 77066
Phone (800 333-4932

Item Products, Inc.
12874 Westmore St
Livonia, Michigan 48150
Phone: (734) 522-9100

Specializing in:

Aluminum Profiles and Basic Hardware Components, Fasteners, Panels, Bearings, Shafts and Drives, Tools, Fixtures, Support Software, Work Stations, and Material Handling Equipment.

Lamerson, U.S.A.

P.O. Box 1139
Oak Park, Michigan 40868-1139

Phone(248)548-0676
Fax (248) 548-1105

Specializing in:

Modeling Bridges in various sizes to accommodate table size models to full size recreational vehicle models. Bridges are built to be operated manually, or they can be equipped for any degree of automated scanning and milling operations, as in coordinate measuring machines.

Clay Extrusion Machines that are portable, plug into any 120V AC outlet, store and heat the clay billets, heat the extrusion die and are breech loaded.

Cast or Fabricated Steel Floor Platens are able to accommodate full size bridges. Platens can be mounted flush with the floor or supported above the floor.

Aluminum Angle Plates in various sizes come equipped with counterbalanced adjustable platforms. The larger angle plates may be purchased with a cross bar and cursors for a bridge set up.

Modeling Platens that are highly accurate portable work surfaces. They are equipped with height adjustable casters and leveling pads, and can be set up anywhere on any floor. They are available in various sizes and are only 2-3/4" high.

Modeling Tables that range from a width of 35" to a length of 140". They are finished to a surface flatness within .003 of an inch. They are available in either English or metric sizes. Table Options include:

Grid lines
Straight Edges
Table locators
Quick change leg attachments
Recessed table mounted caster attachments
Dual Wheel Casters
Dual Wheel Sprung Casters

Bench Type Precision Fixtures that provide height adjustment for mounting a variety of design models. Models can be mounted from either side of these fixtures.

Low Profile Height Adjustable Casters that mount inside the floor platens and other equipment and provide a height adjustment from 0" to 2".

Bridge Pointers for pointing off clay surface.

Especially developed clay milling cutters for both line milling and surface milling operations.

Mouse Scribers in various types and sizes.

Special Scales and Verniers for all measuring equipment.

Hard Aluminum Splines, 18", 24", and 30".

Norton Equipment Corporation

P. O. Box 68
203 East Adrian Street
Blissfield, Michigan 49228

Phone (517) 486-2630
NewBldg. (517) 486-2113
Fax (517) 486-2444

Specializing in:

Starrett granite surface plates

Cast iron base plates or bridge rails

Cast iron surface plates of all sizes

Magnesium angle plates of many types and sizes

Magnesium box parallels and height blocks

Magnesium bridge set up that includes:

Pattern Makers' angle plates with:
Sliding platform
Parallel bar with or without rotating ends
Butterfly or sliding angle
Universal angle unit
Satin chrome finished scales
Magnesium Straight Edges
Magnesium Mouse Scribers.

All magnesium equipment is also available in aluminum and Meehanite castings.

Equipment is available in either English or metric sizes. Hand scraped finish to plus or minus 0.0004 in 12" is available.

Modeling and Industrial Supplies

Thomas Quintal, Vice President of Russ Simpson Co., has a wealth of knowledge in the use of the various casting materials and tooling plastics sold by his company. He supplies both the materials and the "know how" to the automobile model and development industry in the Detroit area and automotive and allied firms throughout the U.S.A. and Canada.

Russ Simpson Company
21906 Schoenherr Road
Warren, Michigan 48089
Phone (810) 771-2768

Specializing in:

Styling Clays.

Dinoc Material.

Coat "N" Strip - Moisture Barrier, strippable protective vinyl coating.

All materials, supplies, and equipment required for making molds and casts from plaster, polyester, epoxy and epoxy clays.

Many supplies, materials, and equipment for wood working and metal working and many other industrial supplies.

Clay Extrusion Machines that are portable and plug into any 120V AC electrical outlet.

Many other modeling supplies and tools.

Other companies supplying the Detroit industrial model, pattern, and tooling industry are:

Freeman Manufacturing & Supply Co.
27655 Groesbeck Highway
Roseville, Michigan 48066
Phone (810) 774-1210 or (800) 345-9259

Tool Chemical Company, Inc.
31200 Stephenson Highway
Madison Heights, Michigan 48071
Phone (248) 588-2270

Precision and Machinist Tools and Supplies

These tools and supplies can be found in specialty hardware stores and in firms selling precision tools and machines. An exceptional hardware company in the Detroit area is:

Production Tool Supply Company- Main Office
8655 E. Eight Mile Road
Warren, Michigan 48089-4030
Phone (810) 755-7770
Fax (810) 755-2151

Production Tool Supply Company
12161 N. Telegraph Road
Redford, Michigan 48239
Phone (313) 358-8150
Fax: (313) 538-4009

The world's largest manufacturer of precision instruments is Mitutoyo Corporation. In the U.S.A. and Canada, MTI Corporation represents Mitutoyo. There are offices and warehouses in Detroit, Chicago, Los Angeles, Dallas, and Toronto. The main office and warehouse is in New Jersey:

MTI Corporation
18 Essex Road
Paramus, New Jersey 07652
Phone (201) 368-0525

MTI Corporation
45001 5 Mile Road
Plymouth, Michigan. 48170
Phone (734) 459-2810

Styling Clays

Special clays for sculpturing design models may be purchased directly from the manufacturers. There are two firms that develop, process, and market styling clays in the U.S.A.; however, Chavant styling clays are used by most design and model development studios not only in the United States but Europe, Japan and other parts of the world.

American Art Clay Co., Inc.
4717 W. Sixteenth St.
Indianapolis, Indiana 46222
Phone (800) 374-1600

Chavant, Inc.
42 West Street
Red Bank, New Jersey 07701
Phone (800) Chavant
Phone (732) 842-6272
Fax: (732) 842-3621

You may contact these companies for the location of a distributor of styling clays in your area.

Supplies and Equipment - West Coast, Los Angeles Area
Epoxy Resin Supply

Pattern Supply Co.
17117 Roseton Ave,
Artesia, CA 90701
Phone (562) 402-6993

United Resin Corporation
1305 E. St. Gertrude,Suite B
Santa Ana, California 92705
Phone (714) 662-2404

Fiberglass Cloth and Supplies

A-1 Foam and Fabrics
1812 South Main Street
Santa Ana, California 92707
Phone (714) 835-1181

South Bay Plastics
20820 So. Normandie
Torrance, California 90502
Phone (310) 320-8180

Foamcore and Gatorboard

Superior Studio Specialities
3013 Gilroy Street
Los Angeles, California 90039
Phone (213) 662-3031

Plaster

Central Valley Builders Supply
7030 Canby Avenue
Reseda, California 91335
Phone (818) 343-4614

Polyurethanes

Fiber-Resin Corporation
20701 Nordhoff Street
Chatsworth, California 91311
Phone (800) 624-9487

B.J.B. Enterprise
14791 Franklin Ave.
Tustin, CA. 92780
Phone (714) 734-8450

Finish Master
6071 Beach Boulevard
Buena Park, California 90621
Phone (714) 521-3344

Tooling Foam

Ad-Tech
1651 E. Edinger Ave., Suite 204
Santa Ana, California 92705
Phone (714) 953-5822

United Resin Corporation
1305 East St. Gertude Place Unit B
Santa Ana, California 92705
Phone (714) 662-2404

Addendum

Credits and Recognitions

In an unusually creative ten years that started in the late 1960's, tremendous technical advancements were made in Ford Design. Commencing in 1968, for interior and 1970 for exterior, all new modeling equipment was ordered to coincide with the beginning of each new model program. After a period of approximately three years, all models were built-up on stable welded aluminum armatures, bucks, and frames, and they were precisely located on steel surface tables or surface plates. All models were portable; all armature, buck and frame systems were modular. Styling clay modeling accuracy was improved to the tolerance levels of impreg master models.

This was no small task. To accomplish this we had the support of many individuals, both inside and outside of Ford Motor Company.

In 1969, the budgeted head count for the Design Modeling Department was 300 people. This included four section supervisors and thirteen unit supervisors. There were 50 separate work teams, each led by a Master Modeler. These teams developed all of the models for the four design offices. It was these work teams and their supervisors that had to be properly equipped to meet management timing requirements.

Starting in 1970, the budgeted head count for Design Modeling was reduced by approximately 8%. This reduction continued each year for several years. But the work load was not reduced. Actually during this time we maintained timing schedules and acccomplish tasks that were never possible previously. This included the development of a system to transport full size exterior styling clay models to market research clinics anywhere in the United States.

The study for this full size model transportation system was coordinated by James J.(Jim)Doyle, Design Modeling Department Section Supervisor. Doyle was responsible for all modeling work in the Lincoln-Mercury studios. Product Planning wanted to transport models of the new Mercury program to various cities for clinic surveys. Fortunately, these models were being built on the new stable frame and locator system, but it was necessary to test overland transportation of these models.

Jim Doyle worked with Ralph Rose of the Rose Moving and Storage Company, Inc. to come up with a satisfactory system. They determined that the criteria required a closed van with the ability to maintain a consistent normal interior temperature and have a soft ride. They chose a climate controlled van with air springs and Michelin tires. A tractor used for hauling moving vans was also equipped with Michelin tires.

A clay model was chosen and the surface was finished with Dinoc. Clay areas representing chrome parts, such as moldings and the grill, were finished with aluminum foil. The model was rolled into the van on its own tires and wheels except that tire pressure was reduced for a softer ride. Wheels were blocked in place and special tie downs were attached to the frame of the model. This took place during a cold snowy week in the middle of January 1971.

The truck driver was assigned a two day and two night trip through upper Michigan cities. When the van returned and the model was rolled out and set back down on its locators, there were no appearance changes to indicate that the model had been out of the studio. Following this test run, transporting finished styling clay models for market research clinics was established as a standard procedure for each new model program. Supporting these clinics became an additional Design Modeling Department service.

Also, of considerable importance was the development of a modular frame system for full size fiberglass cast models. These assemblies were simple in design concept and light weight compared to clay model frames. Lighter axle assemblies included tread and height adjustments and front axles provided steering control. The frames were constructed from modular square telescoping tubes having universal one inch pierced hole centers for easy assembly. Frame stock was stored on racks and assembled to fit any design configuration. When a cast model was no longer required, the frame was disassembled and parts were returned to the storage racks.

The many services and time and cost saving advances for model development didn't just happen, they were all planned and researched.

Under Nicholas Waskul, the Supervisor of Modeling Systems, the work was divided between interior and exterior modeling equipment. Interior was led by Roland McDonald and exterior by Robert Kirkpatrick. The Modeling Systems designers were: Herb Gaschler, Andrew Lesko, George Massie, Al Magewick, Glen Malmsten, Kenneth Rogman, and Edwin Williams.

I worked for Thomas J. Burns, Director, Administration and Planning Office, Design Center. Burns was very supportive of these studies and improvements, but before he would sign a purchase order he required a cost study to be conducted by the office of the Design Controller. The cost studies for the various modeling

Nicholas Waskul, Supervisor of Modeling Systems, checks drawings for modeling equipment. (Photograph: Author)

These tables also had precision locators attached to automatically position the table (and the model on the table) into a bridge or the CMM for scanning or milling.

There were other major suppliers for locators, axles, frames, fixtures and armatures in addition to Ganis, Trigon, and Lamerson. This support included Jerry and Doug Muldoon from Motorama Engineering, Inc., and Addison Getman and Bob Crinson from Jo Ad Industries.

One of the tools we developed was a clay milling cutter to be used on the DEA Alpha CMM. This CMM was to come online in early 1974. Anton (Tony) Vella did the initial study on this line milling cutter. Doug Muldoon from Motorama further developed the cutter design and made them in series for our use.

systems projects always showed a significant savings in a reasonable payout period. Tom Burns was a good friend and a decidedly strong supporter of this work.

Several one-eighth scale models were built to study interior buck and exterior frame designs. These scale models were constructed by a very talented Master Modeler, Larry Wilson. They were made from dimensioned plywood and rectangular hollow wood tube, channel, and H-beam stock. From these investigations and twist tests, designs were narrowed and engineering drawings were drafted.

Heinz Meier contributed some ideas concerning details for the design of the interior bucks. Ganis, Inc., Heinz Meier's company, fabricated the first series of aluminum interior bucks and exterior frames.

Roman Duda, from Trigon Engineering, turned, welded, heat treated and ground the first sets of Acme threaded locator pin and nut axle assemblies that were assembled to the exterior frames. He also fabricated the first series of locator stands.

Al and Ron Lamerson, Lamerson, Inc., had perfected hollow steel surface table construction. Tables so constructed were light weight compared to cast iron tables. These tables were heat treated and ground top and bottom and on all edges. We saw the advantages of this construction and Lamerson eventually fabricated over 200 various size tables for both interior and exterior models. Some of these tables had quick removable legs. These were equipped with casters that were attached directly to the bottom of the table.

Larry Wilson was an unusually skilled craftsman and modeler. He constructed several of the scale study models for Modeling Systems. (Photograph: Ford Design Center)

These were the first clay line milling tools that cut a clean line in clay surface. All other tools that had been tried plowed through the clay and then covered the line with clay chips.

The first models to have all sections, design lines, and the outer edge of the model milled were inner door trim panels. This was in the spring of 1974. The DEA Alpha was not yet available so we had these first models milled by Charles Bellestri at Visioneering, Inc.

The armatures for these door trim panels were

In the winter of 1977-78, I worked with Dan Ramsey from Numerical Control Systems Department, in establishing full size model surface milling techniques for both styling clay and foam model surface. In 1977, Dan accompanied me to Italy to the DEA factory and to Daimler Benz Design in Sindelfingen, Germany where DEA had installed an Alpha machine.

By the mid 1970s we were accurately scanning and milling styling clay models and doing so with a high degree of precision. Software was developed and data was

Al and Ron Lamerson inspecting one of the new point/scanning bridges. (Photograph: T. A. Hoadley)

welded aluminum structures with locator pins and pads so they were easily set up in Visioneering's 3-axis mill. Bellestri also aided us in some of our other studies.

From that time on, all models to be milled were processed by the Numerical Control Systems Department. I worked with John Zimmerly from that department to establish the Visioneering milling pattern for optimum scanning and milling efficiency. John accompanied me to France in 1978 to visit the Renault factory where VFW-Fokker had installed a CMM. Bezier's Unisurf system was being used on the CMM to mill prove out plastic models. Renault was also using this system and the patch mode to develop and draft all exterior surfaces and interior structures. At another location, an affiliate of Renault was using the Unisurf system, direct from the computer, to develop lines to mill prototype aircraft parts and develop a hull form for an unique sail boat to be used by Jacques Cousteau.

processed for the coordinate measuring machine and electronic plotter drafting machines to meet design and engineering requirements. This was a remarkable achievement. The credit for the Numerical Control Systems development must go to that Department's Manager, Abe Zold, and his supervisors and leaders Tom Stein, John Zimmerly, Dan Ramsey, Wilma Jackson, and Bill Sherman.

The Modeling Systems Unit developed the aerodynamic model test system. Test models, usually 3/8 or 4/10 scale, were built and finished by the modeling section that had completed the full size appearance models. The Numerical Control Systems Department scanned the appearance models and milled that data into the test models. Chassis for the test models were built-up by Mark E. Gleason under Charles 'Chuck' Haddad, Advanced Engineering Department.

Several new styling clay formulations were developed by Paul O'Neil at Chavant, Inc. Each sample was tested by several modelers using a standardized test evaluation form. Samples from each production run of styling clay shipments were tested by Richard Camen, Design Systems Department.

The DEA coordinate measuring machines and some parts and services were purchased from Jack Hicks at DEA here in the Detroit area. The special features, hardware and software that were required for automobile design were developed by Dr. Ing. Franco Sartorio at the Digital Electronic Automation company headquarters in Turin, Italy.

Gene Perry and Fred Norton, Norton Equipment Corporation provided us with standard angles and several other pieces of special equipment. This included the fabrication of a special tooling bridge angle plate set up for the development of the people movers that ran at Fairlane Town Center for many years.

During some of these studies we had assistance from Manufacturing Engineering Office individuals. This included A. E. (ED) DiGregorio, Norman Hopwood Jr., James E. Merkle, and Wally Stanley.

Paul O'Neil speaking at the Styling Clay Presentation for the May 4, 1985 Fiberglass Fabrication Association Seminar in South Bend, Indiana. (Photograph: T. A. Hoadley)

Gene Perry, Manager, Norton Equipment Corporation, Blissfield, Michigan. Gene was very helpful in providing many special pieces of equipment to Modeling Systems. Norton continues to supply equipment to Ford Design and many other design organizations world wide. (Photograph: Author)

Bibliography

Books

"Motor Body Engineering"
George J. Mercer, 1928
Ware Bros. Company
Philadelphia

"Motor Body Designing Problems"
George J. Mercer, 1935

"Motor Body Blueprint Technology"
George J. Mercer
Supplement to:
Motor Body Designing Problems

"The Elements of Dynamic Symmetry"
Jay Hambidge
Yale University Press

"Rolling Sculpture,
A Designer and his Work"
Gordon Buehrig with
William S. Jackson, 1975
Haessner Publishing, Inc.

"Industrial Design"
Harold VanDoren, 1940
McGraw Hill Book Company, Inc.

"Industrial Design"
John Heskett, 1980
Thames and Hudson

"A Century of Automobile Style:
100 Years of American Car Design"
Michael Lamm and Dave Holls, 1996
Lamm-Morada Publishing Company

"Perspective"
Jan Vredeman de Vries
Dover Publicatons, Inc, New York

"The Designers
Great Automobiles and the
Men Who Made Them"
L. J. K. Setright, 1976
Follett Publishing Company, Chicago

"Automobile Design
Twelve Great Designers and Their Work"
Roland Barker and Anthony Harding
SAE International

"Pinin Farina, Master Coachbuilder"
Michael Frostick
Dalton Watson Ltd., London

"The Art of American Car Design,
The Profession and Personalities"
C. Edson Armi
The Pennsylvania State University Press

"The Complete Guide to SCULPTURE,
MODELING and CERAMICS Techniques
and Materials"
Barry Midgley, John Calcutt, Trevor Crabtree,
Andrew Fyvie, Dave Harper
Chartwell Books 1982

"Model Shop Manual"
Joseph J. Farrer, 1990
Art Center College of Design

"Aerodynamix Des Kraftfahrzeugs"
Freiherr Reinhard Koenig-Fachsenfeld, 1951
Verlag der Motor - Rundschau
Umschau Verlag Frankfurt A.M.

"Aerodynamics of Road Vehicles"
Edited by Wolf-Heinrich Hucho, 1987
Butterworth & Co. Ltd. 1987

"Clay Modeling: Techniques for Giving Three
Dimensional Form to Idea"
Yasusato Yamada
 Car Styling

"Fiberglass Repairs"
Paul J. Petrick, 1976, 1986
Cornell Maritime Press

"The Artist's Friendly Legal Guide"
Floyd Conner, Roger Gilcrest, Peter Karlen,
Jean Persin, David Spatt
North Light Book, Cincinnati, 1988

Bibliography

Bulletins, Films, Papers, Periodicals

"The Trend of Automobile Body Design"
George J. Mercer
Metropolitan Section, S.A.E., 1920
Society of Automotive Engineers (S.A.E.)

"The Development of an Automobile
Design Model"
Gordon Buehrig, 1938-1939
Budd Body Company, 16mm Film
ACD Museum

"Master Modeling and Reconciliation
of Inner Models With Plastics"
Wallace A. Stanley, 1956
The Society of the Plastics Industry,
Incorporated

"Sealers and Parting Compounds"
USG Bulletin IG-515, for Gypsum Cements"
"Plasters Mixing Procedures"
USG Bulletin IG 503
"Drying Plaster Casts"
USG Bulletin IG 502
United States Gypsum Company
Industrial Gypsum Division
P. O. Box 803871
125 South Franklin Street
Chicago, Illinois 60680-3871

"Why Molds Stick"
Bob Lacovara
Fabrication News, February 1991

"Sandwich Construction"
Fabrication News, March 1991
Fabrication News, February 1996

"The Application of Jacques Kohn"
Andrew Kusnak
Composites Fabrication, November/
December 1997

"Understanding Composite Reinforcement"
Greg Kress
Composites Fabrication, March 1998

"Understanding Reinforcement Concepts
(Part II)"
Greg Kress
Composites Fabrication, April 1998

"Understanding Epoxies"
A. Brent Strong, Ph.D.
Composites Fabrication, November/
   December 1997

"Processing Breakthroughs of the Decade"
Joseph S. McDermott
Composites Fabrication, November/
December 1997

GLOSSARY - *Terms, Definitions, and Abbreviations*

ACCENT STRIPES - Fine, painted lines applied in contrasting colors to accent certain lines and contours.

APPLIQUE - A decorative panel applied to a surface. May be metal, plastic, or a combination with a bright, brushed, textured or painted finish.

ARGENT FINISH - A silvery, aluminum-pigmented paint with approximately the same color and luster as brushed or satin-finished chrome, aluminum or steel.

ARMATURE - A frame used as the base for a clay model.

BATTEN - A straight edged flat wood strip of varying widths, thicknesses, and lengths, which is used to clean up a clay surface prior to steeling. Sometimes identified as a wood spline.

BEAD MOLDING - A molding with a small cross-section of any length.

BEZEL - A frame, escutcheon, or rim, usually surrounding a lamp or opening. Either bright-finished or painted.

BLACKBOARD MODEL - Model of interior side of a vehicle.

BLADE - A thin, sharply defined ridge or an applique of a similar nature.

BLEEDING - Original paint finish discoloring or seeping through a new topcoat color.

BLEND - The flowing together of two or more surfaces.

BLIPS - Small ornamentation in series; i.e. several identical ports, bars, windsplits, etc., often aligned horizontally or vertically.

BLUE-LINE DRAWING - A print reproduced, usually on paper, by an ammonia developing process.

BLUSHING - A milky white haze that appears on lacquer finishes.

BOLSTER - The portion of the seat which rolls over or forms the uppermost part of the seatback or the leading edge of the seat itself.

BRIDGE - A moveable measuring instrument that straddles a model and is positioned by rails. Its use makes it possible for anypoint on the model to be transferred to paper or duplicated in three dimensions.

BRUSHED FINISH - Fine, directional, disruption of a smooth surface. Usually done on aluminum, stainless steel, or chrome plate but can be simulated in plastic.

BUTTERFLY - A sliding angle that works off the parallel bar of a Norton bridge setup.

CARRIAGE JOINT - The joining of two pieces of metal, one overlapping the other, and welded, bolted or riveted together.

CASING - A shell or jacket used to hold molds in their proper alignment.

CASTING - The positive shape formed by pouring, brushing, or spraying plaster or plastic into a mold and letting the material harden. Also used to describe the process itself.

CENTER LINE - The plane passing through the center of a form.

CHAMFER - The beveled edge of a surface.

CHARACTER LINE - A line on the basic shape, resulting in an intersection of planes and sometimes ornamented.

CHASSIS - In a vehicle, the under part consisting of the frame with axles, brakes, wheels, engine, transmission driveline and exhaust system. In equipment, the frame or structure on which parts and covers are attached.

CHEAT - To exaggerate an element in a drawing or rendering. A deliberate change from a package drawing to improve the appearance of a model.

CLAY BUCK - Same as armature, but usually for a full size exterior model.

CLAY SQUEEZE - An impression made by forcing soft clay on an object.

COACH JOINT - The joining of two pieces of metal, welded or bolted to right-angle flanges.

CORE - The portion of a mold that shapes the interior of a hollow or open backed casting; the portion that helps to fill the void of a surface cast tool.

CUBE - Three-dimensional representation of the allowable dimensions of a model under development. Also a grouping of exterior die models arranged in their proper position to check continuity of surfaces.

CURE OR CURING - The cross-linking polymerization of the molecules of a resin. The transformation of the resin from a liquid to solid state.

DAM - Shim stock or other materials used to separate or dam off a surface for constructing a mold.

DECAL (DECALCOMANIA) - A decorative or informative transfer sheet used for wood graining, labeling, etc.

DECK SEAM - Two pieces of material are sewn together, then both salvages are folded back and sewn together, making a seam that has a join line with a parallel stitch line on one side.

DIE CASTING - Injection of molten metal under pressure into a fully finished mold. Also the product of such a process. Greater detail and more intricate shapes can be obtained with die castings than with stamped parts.

DIE MODEL - A three-dimensional representation made of impreg, plastic, or hard wood from approved engineering drawings.

DINOC - Trade name for a decal material consisting of three layers: decal, glue and paper. The outer portion can be painted with a special elasticized paint.

DRAFT - The taper given to a form for casting or stamping purposes so that the work can be easily withdrawn; also a drawing or the act of drawing.

DRAW ANGLE - The deviation from the normal position or grid of a part relative to the direction of travel of the tool.

DRAW DEPTH - The vertical depth of the tool relative to the draw angle.

EGG-CRATE - A complex grille work made of intersecting planes, usually with more depth than can be obtained by stamping.

ELEVATION - A view of a form from front, side, or rear.

EMBLEM - A decorative part used for identification.

EPOXY - A thermosetting plastic resin containing reactive exoxide groups used in making fiber-reinforced plastic molds and casts.

ESCUTCHEON - An exposed panel or part used to retain, or to hide the retention of, another part; e.g. keyhole, door release, or window control

EXTRUSION - A part or component formed by forcing material (clay, plastic, metal) through a die by pressure, e.g. a molding.

EYE BALL - To establish or evaluate a surface or line by eye without the aid of tools, templates, etc.

FIBERGLASS - 1. A fibrous material made from glass. 2. Mold - the female taken from the original clay model, made from plastic reinforced with fiberglass. 3. Cast - the male reproduction from such female, made from plastic reinforced with fiberglass. 4. Model - a representation in plastic reinforced with fiberglass of a model made from clay or other materials.

FILLET - A concave-curved surface used to blend two intersecting planes.

FISH EYES - Small, crater-like openings in a paint finish after it has been applied.

FLANGE - A turned up or turned down edge of a part or a panel that provides strength, guidance, or a means of attachment.

FLO LINE - A surface layout term defining a line that lays on the surface in two views and may follow parallel to the grid lines in one view.

FLOP - The condition in which the color of a surface viewed at a direct or perpendicular angle is substantially different than that viewed at an oblique angle.

FLUSH - No offset between adjacent parts. A smooth continuous surface.

FRISKET KNIFE - Knife with a razor-sharp blade, used for detail work or to cut cardboard and paper. Originally designed to cut frisket (masking) paper.

GEL COAT - Polyester plastic resin brushed or sprayed on the surface of a model or mold.

GRID LINES - *A network of uniformly spaced horizontal and perpendicular lines for locating points on a drawing by means of coordinates. Major lines may be spaced 5" or 10" apart or 100 millimeters apart.*

GRILLE - *Ornamental grating or louvers designed to decorate and partially obscure an opening while allowing the passage of air or sound.*

HAND LAY-UP - *A process in which resin is brushed in and fiberglass cloth is applied by hand.*

HARDPOINTS - *Approved dimensions, or components that establish the limits around which a product is designed and built.*

HIGHLIGHT - *A reflected path of light described by the intersection of a curved surface and a line or plane becoming tangent to that surface at a constant angle, usually 45 degrees.*

HOB - *An engraved metal cavity, or female mold, from which plastic pressings are made.*

HOG OUT - *Rough cuts when forming from solid stock.*

IMPREG - *Multi-layer mahogany block impregnated with a plastic material.*

LAP JOINT - *An overlapping joint, recessed and solder-filled or covered by a molding.*

LOUVER - *A fin that controls the flow of air through an opening. May also be non-functional in a simulated opening.*

MACBETH LIGHT - *A lighting device for color match evaluation which closely simulates natural daylight and also provides standardized tungsten and fluorescent sources.*

MASTER MODEL - *A final model used for tooling purposes.*

METALLIC FINISH - *An appearance resulting from the use of metal flakes in paint pigment characterized by a sparkling appearance.*

METAMERISM - *The condition in which two objects are judged to be closely color matched under one set of lighting conditions, but which are mismatched in a second lighting condition.*

MOLD - *A negative reproduction of a model or form.*

MOLDING - *A strip of material or a form molded in, may be decorative or used for finishing an edge.*

MOTIF - *Main theme of a design or creative arrangement.*

MOTTLING - *Occurs on painted surface when the flakes form a spotty or blotched appearance.*

MOUSE - *A marking tool or scriber used by clay modelers. One end is beveled and pointed; the other end has a handle of various lengths.*

OGEE - *A long, S-shaped curve.*

OPALESCENT/OPALESCENCE - *Mica flake paint pigment giving a pearl type appearance.*

ORANGE PEEL - *Descriptive name of an uneven and undesirable paint finish resembling the surface of an orange. This is due to spray technique.*

OVERLAY - *A sheet of translucent paper or other material laid over an original drawing to sketch an alternate version or design. Technique used for comparing two or more designs.*

PACKAGE, PACKAGE DRAWING - *1. Package - dimensional hardpoints which together define the spacial constraints to be used in design. 2. Package Drawing - depicts hardpoint dimensions for use by engineering and design functions.*

PEAK LINE - *An intersection of two planes, or a sharply defined ridge in a surface.*

PILLAR - *A component connecting or supporting the upper with the lower portions of a structure.*

PLAN VIEW - *A view looking down on the subject.*

PLATEAU - *A surface extending above the normal surrounding surface.*

POD - *A streamlined compartment to house various mechanical implements; e.g. lights, dials, gauges, etc. It is usually round or elliptical.*

POINTS - *Exact locations on a model, usually derived from a drawing or from the model itself. May be used to duplicate the opposite side of the model or used for engineering purposes.*

POLYESTER - *A thermosetting plastic resin formed by*

the reaction between dibasic acid and a dihydroxy alcohol used in making fiber-reinforced plastic molds and casts.

POLYURETHANE - Various polymers used in flexible and rigid foams, elastomers, and resins.

PRE-PREG - Ready-to-mold material in sheet form which may be cloth, mat, or paper impregnated with resin and stored for use.

PRESSURE BAG MOLDING - A process for molding plastics utilizing fluid pressure against a flexible bag placed over the contact lay- up in the mold.

PROVEOUT MODEL - A clay model developed to verify data and/or surface draft conformation with the appearance of the model originally approved by management. A record cast subsequently may be made in fiberglass. (See record model).

RECORD MODEL - A fiberglass or plastic reproduction of the original clay model as approved.

RENDERING - A detailed illustration.

RESIN - Most resins are polymers used in reinforced products. The two most commonly used in fiber-reinforced plastic molds and casts are epoxy and polyester.

REVEAL MOLDING - A metal frame or molding outlining an opening or depression.

ROVING - Chopped Fiberglass.

SCRAPER - A clay modeling tool used to rough in the surface of a model. It is shaped like a short-handled rake with a straight or curved blade set crosswise to the handle.

SCRIM - A cotton fabric used for reinforcing plaster negatives and positives.

SECTION - View of any component at 90° to a plane cut through the component.

SHIM STOCK - Extremely thin metal pieces used for various purposes.

SHINGLE - Adjoining parts which are designed to overlap -- one over the other so that gaps or openings are minimized.

SILICONE - A plastic rubber like material used for

making molds of models.

SISAL - A fiber used for reinforcing plaster negatives and positives.

SLICK - A thin piece of plastic with the edges polished so they are free of all nicks and scratches. It is used to: 1. Smooth a clay surface. 2. To apply Dinoc, and 3. Smooth aluminum foil onto clay or fiberglass to simulate chrome trim on bumpers, moldings, etc.

SPECTROPHOTOMETRY - A means of analyzing the pigment or dye content of a colored material by measuring the light reflectance at various wave lengths of the visible spectrum.

SPLINE - A straight-edged piece of wood or metal of varying widths, thicknesses, and lengths, which is used to assist in smoothing low or high spots on the surface of a model. (See Batten)

SPRAY-UP - The application of resin and chopped fiberglass strand with a spray gun.

SPUD - A tool about 2 feet long with a flat steel chisel edge, used for heavy digging or clay removal.

STEEL - A tool made from spring steel and used to finish and smooth styling clay models.

SURFACE COAT - Epoxy plastic resin brushed or sprayed on the surface of a model or mold.

SURFACE PLATE - An accurate flat surface used as a base to take all dimensions. May be machined from cast metal, metal weldment, or granite. It is usually marked off in inch or metric grids.

SURFACE SCAN - Computerized record digitized from a surface.

SWEEP - A plastic, metal or wood guide used in drawing a line or developing a surface.

TAPE DRAWING - An outline of a design on tracing paper made with black, pressure-sensitive tape, which can be easily seen, removed, and changed. Most often depicts the side elevation.

TEMPLATE - An accurate surface profile taken from a drawing or portion of a model to be duplicated. Can be made of cardboard, plastic, Masonite, plywood or metal, depending on proposed use.

TEXTURE - The surface nature of a fabric or trim

material which imparts a three-dimensional surface appearance.

THEME SKETCH - A quick sketch to get an idea on paper; precedes a rendering.

TRICOT - A type of knitted fabric used basically for bodycloth and headlining applications.

VACUUM BAG MOLDING - A process for molding reinforced plastics utilizing a sealed bag. The entrapped air is removed by vacuum and the part is cured with temperature, pressure, and time.

VACUUM PLATING - The deposition of metal on basecoated objects by evaporation of a metal, usually aluminum, under high vacuum. Used to simulate chrome or other bright finishes in automotive design.

VALLEY -An area between two higher surfaces.

VELOUR - Fabric with vertical pile.

WASTE MOLD - A negative mold destroyed or wasted in freeing the positive cast.

WELT - A small, cord-like section usually with a lip, sometimes covered with upholstery material, that is sewn in a seam or border to enhance or strengthen a seam.

WRINKLING - Surface distortion or shriveling that occurs when lacquer is applied over an unbaked enamel surface.

ZERO LINE - Horizontal and vertical base lines from which all other dimensions are taken.

ABBREVIATIONS

ABS - Acrylonitrile-Butadiene-Styrene

AIS - Automated Inspection System

AWD - All Wheel Drive

BMC - Bulk Molding Compound

CAD - Computer Aided Design

CAE - Computer Aided Engineering

CAID - Computer Aided Industrial Design

CFD - Computational Fluid Dynamics

CLTE - Coefficient of Linear Thermal Expansion

CMM - Coordinate Measuring Machine

CNC - Computer Numerical Control

CSR - Cold Setting Rubber

DAP - Diallyl Phthalate

DCPD - Dicylopenta diene-resins

EMT - Elastomer-Modified Thermoplastics

EPR - Ethylene Propylene Rubber

EV - Electric Vehicle

FEA - Finite Element Analysis

FRP - Fiber-Reinforced Plastic

FWD - Front Wheel Drive

GMT - Glass Mat Thermoplastics

ISM - Inside of sheet metal

LCM - Liquid Composite Molding

LEV - Low-Emission Vehicle

LPA - Low-profile Additives

NC - Numerical Control

OSM - Outside of sheet metal

NGV - Partnership for a New Generation of Vehicles

NPG - Neophentyl Glycol-geo-coats

PVA - Polyvinyl Alcohol

PVC - Polyvinyl Chloride

RIM - Reaction Injection Molding

RTM - Resin Transfer Molding

RTP - Injection (reaction) Thermopastics - composites

RTV - Room Temperature Vulcanizing

SCRIMP ™ Seeman Composite Resin Infusion
                    Modeling Process

SCS - Systematic Computer Services

SL - Stereolithography

SLCM - Structural Liquid Composite Molding

SMC - Sheet Molding Compound

SPC - Statistical Process Control

SRIM - Structural Reaction Injection Molding

SRTM - Structural Reinforcement Transfer Molding

VR - Virtual Reality

2-D - Two Dimensional

3-D - Three-Dimensional

Index

GENTLEMEN'S BUSINESS COUPE

This design theme for the quarter scale model was illustrated by the author in April 1953.

Wheelbase	100 in. - 2,540mm
Overall Length	182 in. - 4,623mm
Overall Width	69 in. - 1,753mm
Overall Height	52in. - 1,321mm
Curb Weight (Estimate)	2,400lbd. - 1,225 kg
Tread-Front & Rear	57.5 in. - 1,460mm
Tires	195/65HR - 18
Rims	18 x 7J
Engine - Ford Zetec	2.0L DOHC 4
Optional Engine - Mazda Type KJ 2.3L DHOC V6 (Miller Cycle)	

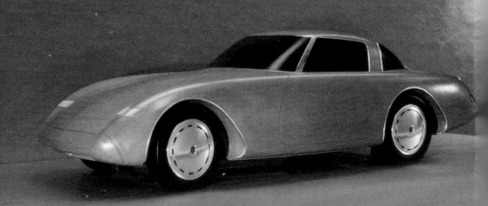